LION TAMER MEMOIR

HOW IT ALL TURNED OUT:

The Love that Healed Trauma

(Man in the Red Jacket

Mountain of Pride

Dolly with the Purple Gown)

Therese Marie Duncan

Copyright © 2022 Therese Marie Duncan
ThereseMarieDuncan.com

Published by 22nd Ave North Books

Published in 2022 in the United States

ISBN: 798-1-959765-00-4 Audio
ISBN: 798-1-959765-02-8 Paperback
ISBN: 798-1-959765-03-5 Hardback
ISBN: 798-1-959765-01-1 ebook

Cover Design by KMC Taylor
Cover Art: Painting by Therese Marie Duncan from photograph by
Andrew Deer.

This book is memoir. It reflects the author's present recollections of expe-
riences over time. Some names and characteristics have been changed,
some events have been compressed, and some dialogue has been recre-
ated.

Printed in the USA

ACKNOWLEDGMENTS

I want to thank everyone I've ever met, for helping shape my life, especially the clients at the Ventura County Oxnard DUI program, whose kindness I will never forget.

I want to thank my husband, Charles, who has endured for twelve years my disappearing into my other world, given me good advice, and kept me laughing; my parents who gave me so much, words cannot express my gratitude; my sisters and brothers: Joseph, Pauline, Anne, Mary, Billy, Sheila, Kay, Claudia and Susan (little kids rule!) who each gave me their blessing to write this series of books as well as much love and editorial assistance; the Ojai Writer's Workshop generously facilitated by Doc and Zoe Murdock, including Wendell Jones, Dana Huse, Dana Macy, Ilona Scott, Trina Emami, Joe Valderrama, Mary Vaynrynsoever, Sean Daley, Robin Gerber, Jodi Brandt, Vieva Kendig, Jan Correll, David Matzke, Jeff Guenther, John Meyer, Jeff Lawson, Gail Bellenger, Arthur Braverman, Sheila Brannigan, Susan Hart Hellman, Lis Grumette, Terry Tallent, and many more who allowed me into their worlds and who gave me twelve years of infinite patience and relentless feedback, without whom I would never have become a good enough writer nor finished the project; Pastor Derrick Temple, of Urban Publishing House, for his enthusiastic encouragement; Chuck Bartok, whose guidance helped me find my readers; Marylee MacDonald, whose selfless guidance as an author gave me confidence; my readers Anne Black, Lara Eisenhower, Marilyn Sweeney, Mary Burggraff, Cheryl Armstrong, and Cindy Mancini whose feedback and encouragement were priceless; all the people in my books, without whom I would have no tales to tell; Richard Wright, whose memoir *Black Boy* inspired me to write my own story; my recovery family, without whom I would never have gotten past a disintegrating life of random thoughts and painful feelings; Sister St. Matthew, my eighty-three year-old high school English teacher who never gave up on us, reminding us several times a day, remember your specific details, girls, your specific details; and Professor Marvin Mudrick who introduced me to Marcel Proust and taught me honesty in writing by lashing out against a pretentious story I had submitted, and by later reading with admiration my submission, "The Fast."

CONTENTS

To Mom and Dad

PREFACE

I was born the sixth of ten children, in the Pacific Northwest, in Seattle, Washington, into a Catholic family where we shared riotous fun and mortal dread. There was very little physical violence, but a lot of violation of physical, mental and emotional boundaries. Our dad made us laugh, taught us to think for ourselves, and sang opera while making pancakes. I loved when he quizzed us at the dinner table. But he also roared like a lion, even at two-year-olds, when he was upset. He exploded unexpectedly, so I was always anxious. He belittled my mom with sarcasm, which made me protective of her. And when I was twelve, he began fondling my breasts when we hugged. He did it to six of my seven sisters as well.

My mom was a big influence on me. She starched and ironed hankies and blouses, cooked, sewed our dresses and raised small children the best she could. ("I couldn't really relate with small children," she once told me.) When we were grown—meaning no one was still in diapers, Mom became a lion in her work to end the Vietnam War and in the Civil Rights Movement. Later, she championed the rights of nursing home residents. I learned a lot from my parents.

When I was nineteen, I didn't know the car-wash guy hired me to shove me into a big utility closet he called his office. What a jerk. He pushed me against a counter and forced kisses on me, and when I said, "No!" he said, "You should've known why I hired you!"

I had two thoughts at once: What—is he right? I should have known that? And: He's not going to ruin my work day.

He probably didn't know I would push my way out, wipe his slobber off my face and go back to work.

To this day I smile when I remember how, fuming with anger, not wanting to keep the boss's secret, I got up my nerve to tell my car wash co-workers, who were all former prisoners, about what our boss had done. What those guys did, I like to think about a lot, over and over. They took my side, shook their heads and muttered, "Prick." "Asshole." They would have done more, I'm sure, had they not been on parole.

Almost no one had ever been protective towards me before those men. Their concern planted a seed in me: I matter.

Someone asked why our cat Delilah is on my website. It's because she thinks she's fiercely independent as a loner, though she deeply needs affection and connection. She's the kitten who tames the lion. She's I.

I hope you enjoy LION TAMER.

Therapy
(1978)

A poem by Cheryl Armstrong

My friend Don Crain said
"How can I help you, Cheryl,
what do you want from me?"
(He sits in his chair facing me,
smiling, patient, waiting).
What I want from you, I said in my mind,
is a prescription.
Rx: A day of San Francisco
wind and mist, a ferry crossing
complete with fog and woolen hats
pulled low to cover ears and eyebrows,
beneath which my Zhivago eyes
will see stunning sunsets, silver-white sails
and never, never, orange paint instead of golden.

I take classes and read and
dance ballet,
my mind safe between my raised arms,
demi-plié.

What I said to Don Crain was,
"I'm not sure what I want from you."
I sit in a turquoise chair,
sweaty palms clutching the arms and
I return his smile.
In my mind I said,
How can I tell this man
I am searching for my Zhivago eyes?
Out the window I watch
silver dollar eucalyptus leaves
play with slender brown branches.

Their dancing shadows fall on my sunlit feet
and the red carpet. I lean forward
watching them expectantly.

I paint rooms and hang wallpaper
and carve pumpkins,
my mind safe within their
luminous orange skins.

CHAPTER 1
SO FAR AWAY INSIDE

April, 1993.

It's too bad it's sunny. Therapy day with a new therapist should be dark and moody. I'm forty-three years old—why do I need help? Hopefully a thick fogbank will roll into the Santa Barbara coast later, make it feel like Seattle drizzle in September. If it does, I'll go shopping for brown leather round-toe shoes—Oxfords—to tether the six-year-old within me, the way they did when dark fell at four o'clock in the Pacific Northwest. My inner six-year-old was held safe by a crisp white blouse, navy blue uniform and especially brown leather round-toe shoes. She walked in noisy rain toward the yellow lights in the windows at home. I haven't lived in Seattle since I was eleven, yet I'm always there.

It's not four o'clock, but dark's falling in my life.

My current uniform—cute jeans, big T-shirt, light blue flannel shirt, new white high-top sneakers—will have to do. I step out of my rusting white Corolla into sunlight so blinding I can hardly see the steps of a dazzling cream-colored building.

I shake my head at my unruly hair reflected in the big glass door I push open. I did brush it. Thankfully, the cold, sterile metallic lobby is empty. I can't bear to be seen. I'd be fine if no one ever looked at me. Unless I'm trying to catch a man.

I hate therapy. Someone looking at me wondering what's wrong. Why did I tell my sister Cecilia I'd try therapy again? I told her I would because though I'm responsible (forty-three years old, passed the Bar Exam, work as a law librarian) I can't stay away from Arnold.

I took the day off. I'll walk on the breakwater after therapy if I don't shop for brown round-toe shoes. Why don't they at least make their lobby warm? Don't they know they have scared clients who already feel bad?

Oh, God, look at the grin. He's handsome. Young. He said on the phone he was an intern. He may not know much. Why do therapists wear shiny pants? I don't like shiny pants on men.

"You're Marie?"

No, I'm Isadora Duncan. "Yes."

"Michael Andersen. Would you like to come with me?"

No, not really. "Okay."

At least he doesn't have a worried look like my first therapist had seven years ago. Well, that one did finally help me leave Isaac, my second husband, who I was with fourteen years. The therapist said I needed to honor my feelings. That was a brand-new idea for me.

That's not working with Arnold. It seems no one can help me now. What am I thinking coming here?

"Come on in. Have a seat."

The walls are gray. No windows. Good. I like everything gray, like Seattle. I wish we'd never moved. I didn't have a say. I was eleven. That little lamp should be on. Which chair is *he* sitting in? I can't stand it when nice people get close. They always want to touch you. I take the corner chair. Why is it so cold? They should turn the light on, make it cozy, make it feel like it's raining outside.

"Are you cold?"

"No, why?"

"You're shivering."

"Habit." Well, he's not blind.

Ah, shit. He pulled up a chair in front of me.

"What can I do for you?"

You can back up. "I don't know. I probably shouldn't have come. I need to figure things out, that's all."

"What things?"

He can't stop smiling.

"It's nothing, really."

"Tell me about nothing."

He won't give up. "Okay." Why not? "So, I'm having trouble … guy trouble … the usual, and…"

"What's the usual?"

"You know, can't live with him, can't live without him." I should have worn a parka.

"What's that about?"

I have to spell everything out for him. "Okay. So, he flutters his eyes, I fall in love, we're happy, he drops me, I want to die, he wants me back, he drops me, I want to die. That's the usual." I look away like I have somewhere else to be, press my brow for dramatic effect.

Why would someone hang giant abstract prints of pale pink and turquoise on the walls to the left and right? They're placed behind his field of vision. I'll drown in pink and turquoise if I don't look at him.

"That's not usual," he says. He's not smiling now.

It's not? I need to think about that. "For some people it is. Look, I don't really need help with that."

"You need help with relationships."

"No, I don't. I'm never having another relationship." I look away. My poor brain gets seared again by the pink and turquoise. The prints have no feeling in them, they could swallow me whole. They're sweet like my mother and her friends who care about everything with sweet pink caring. Everything except the truth.

"You already have relationships."

"No, I don't."

"You and I are in a relationship," he says.

Men always think they're the center of my world. "No, we're not."

"Actually, we are," he says.

He's not grinning now.

"Not an intimate relationship," he says. "We're in a therapist-client relationship. It's still a relationship. People can't live without relationships."

"I can."

"What makes you want to?"

"They don't work. You only get hurt. It's easier not to bother."

"All right. Why are you here?"

"My sister said I should come."

"Why?"

"I keep going back to Arnold, after we're done."

"Arnold's the guy who drops you."

"Yeah. I've only known him for seven months." What's with that amused smile? He's not very sympathetic. "He's a good guy, Arnold. Really kind and polite. Short, not especially good-looking, but he has a deep voice that mesmerizes me. We're both sober."

"Sober? That's great. How long have you been sober?"

"Two years. I would have four, but I took a pill for fun after one year, then again after another year. To be sober, I don't take anything that affects me neck up, unless it's prescribed. So, only two years for me. Yeah, I'm glad I'm sober. My brother Martin asked me one day outside my old waitress job, when I was still drinking, 'How are you doing?' I told him, 'Fine. I just feel like I'm losing my mind.' I'll never forget his sunlit smile as he handed me a book and suggested some meetings." I nod. "I'd be a wreck if I were still drinking. So, this guy I was with, Arnold, he has three years sober. But." I don't know if I should say it.

"But what?" He's kind now.

Here come tears. Nothing's wrong. Why do I cry whenever someone's kind to me? I hate it. "Nothing. It doesn't matter."

"You matter."

I frown to cover up trying not to cry. He's being nice, but I have to not matter. "Not really. I don't want to matter. Remember man, thou art dust. I like that." Funny. I'm calm and quiet inside now.

"All right. For now. We can come back to this. You said, he's got three years sober, but. What were you going to say?"

Tell him. "Sometimes he's mean."

"Tell me about that."

"He gets mad all of a sudden and I don't even know what I did."

"You think you cause his anger?"

"Yes."

He leans forward, his arms on his knees. "Does he hit you?"

"No," I shake my head, "nothing like that. Once he pushed me down on the bed." That doesn't count. "He never hit me. No, he yells. Rages at me, especially when he drives. He talks crazy, yelling stuff like … let's see. Like, *You don't like how things are? Maybe I can fix that – huh? Huh? Would you like me to fix that? Let's fix that for good!* He'll rage, you know? With a green-handled hammer on the seat. I don't know why he keeps a hammer on the seat. I'm scared to look at it, like looking at it will give him the idea to use it on me. I can see the green handle out of the corner of my eye. It's just a hammer, I tell myself. He's not saying he's going to kill me. I think, what's the hammer for? It's insane, but … I'm scared he'll *kill* me. He wouldn't, of course, but I lock up inside. I want to die. Then, I leave him … then, he's sweet … I go back, thinking I can tame him."

"Hm," he says, looks down. He nods, looks at me. "I wonder, did you ever lock up inside and want to die before?"

That's a good question. Did I? Yes, come to think of it. This guy's good. Wow. I never connected it. "My Dad—"

No, I can't tell him that. It's too embarrassing. He won't understand why it's such a big deal. I don't even understand, nothing happened. But I want to die when I remember what Dad did. Tell the therapist something different.

"My dad's a handful, but now that I think of it, when I was little, these third-grade boys threw rocks at me. I was terrified. I was only in first grade. I froze. Locked up. Then suddenly, Eddie appeared out of nowhere. I was really surprised to see him. He was a nice fifth grader. Most kids were mean to him because he was mixed-race, so he hadn't been around much. He got between me and the third-grade boys throwing rocks and told me, 'Don't you worry. You go on home now. I won't let them bother you.' He was so kind." I choke up. Therapy's good. "Anyway, this guy with the hammer, who keeps dropping me, scares me like those boys with rocks did. But everybody at our sobriety meetings loves Arnold. Why are you grinning?" I can't believe he's grinning at me. "What's funny?"

"You almost got that one by me."

He's good, and tough. It's good he's tough. "What one?" I know what one.

He's not laughing now. "The one you started to tell me about your father."

Fuck therapy.

"Yeah. Well, that's a long story. You should turn the lamp on so it doesn't feel cold in here. Lamps make things cozy. I strung Christmas lights in Isaac's and my studio apartment one July, so when I hung blankets on the windows I could have it cozy like winter and Christmas in Seattle inside."

"Who's Isaac?"

"My second husband. He's Jewish. My dad said he'd never marry me, but he did. Isaac's kind. He didn't complain about Christmas lights in July. It was hard to leave him."

"How did you and Isaac meet?"

"Well, he was the tall, lean, librarian with a shock of dark hair over one eye who I saw one day at the library in the music room. I had to win him when I saw him burst into laughter with a very old man. I had headphones on so I didn't hear them laugh, but I saw Isaac's sweet smile. After being with him for fourteen years, I didn't want to leave him. I had to. I should have left after the first year when he said he didn't like to talk about life. I didn't understand. How could anyone not like talking about life? So, I'd bring up questions. One night, walking home from dinner, I said that I thought people must exist for some reason. You know, life must mean something. I asked what he thought. He got angry, yelled he didn't like to talk about life.

"Fourteen years of not talking, I felt lonely, wanted to die. And he didn't want children, which was the deal breaker. After our first year, I got pregnant. I was so happy. But he said he'd leave if I had the baby. I didn't want to be abandoned with a baby. I'd seen how hard it was for my sister Jean, a year younger than I am, being a single mom. So, I had an abortion." Tears come. "I can't think about it without crying. I gave up even wanting kids. Helped with other peoples' children. But the last couple of years, wanting kids came back strong."

"Why did you stay with Isaac?"

"I kept thinking of how I'd already left my first husband after three years when he wouldn't quit heroin. I thought, you can't leave *two* husbands. It didn't seem right. I thought I was supposed to live with my choices."

"So, what happened?"

"One day, fourteen years in, when Isaac couldn't be at marriage counseling for some reason, the counselor told me I needed to honor my feelings. I said, 'Some feelings can't be honored.' He said, 'You say that a lot—I can't.'"

I take a deep breath, let it out, look the new therapist in the eye. There, I've told you something big.

"That was it." I smile with pride. "It took six more months of trying to make the fourteen-year marriage work. The day came when I took a walk, hit the crest of the Garden Street hill, dreamed of living in a small community of celibate women. Suddenly I felt it, knew it—I had given the marriage my all. I was free to go. I never needed a man again. Well, I guess that part wasn't true. Anyway, I honored my feelings and left."

"You're shivering again," he says. "I'm sorry you're so cold. I don't have a blanket or anything for you."

Maybe I'm shivering from emotions. He didn't listen. That was a good story. I'm glad he doesn't have a blanket. He'd find a way to come on to me. Men always do. "It's dark in here."

"You can *turn* the light on." His tone says I should have known that already.

I short out feeling ashamed being told I should know I can turn the light on. Fuck him. I go away within, where it's peaceful and quiet, out of his reach.

You know what, Michael Andersen? I *do* know that already. I don't need you to tell me I can turn the light on. I don't need you at all. I will turn the light on. I'm in charge. Watch.

I reach over, turn the light switch, let the cozy glow bathe my face before I turn back to face him, not shivering anymore. He'll never see me shiver again.

"Where did you go?" he asks.

"Some place quiet."

"Do you want to tell me about when you locked up with your dad now?"

He looks at me with his dewy brown eyes that can flash and make him handsome. Right now, they're indifferent enough for me to tell him about my dad. Anyway, he can't hurt me where I've gone. Nobody can.

"Okay. About seven years ago, my parents went to the Holy Land for a few weeks, their dream trip of a lifetime. While they were gone, my two brothers, six of my seven sisters and I had a meeting at their house." It's like someone hypnotized me. I'm not afraid now. "My sister Cecilia and my brother Martin had each been in therapy. They told us their therapists had said when our dad had fondled us it was molestation. I realized for the first time that Dad's touching … you know, my …" I hate to say the word out loud, "breasts … was molesting. He'd done it since I was twelve. He's quick when he does it. I've never gotten used to it."

I just disappear down into my own deep Crater Lake whenever he does it. "But I never thought it was molesting."

I don't believe my ears. I'm saying out loud what happened.

Michael Andersen nods.

"Once, when I was twelve, I woke in the night to my dad's hands pressing on my … breasts. My dad saw me open my eyes and close them."

I'm so far away. It feels like a quiet drizzling day in the woods at Schmidt's Park in Seattle, where everything's dark green, except for bright green moss here and there.

"What did you do?"

"I didn't move. I just lay there. Waited for him to go away. I saw a woman near me, in a smokey bar, wearing lipstick and a forties evening dress, the way Lana Turner did in old movies. She told me in a deep voice, 'You just endure, dear.' Then I felt and saw a large, shiny steel cylinder grow inside my chest. It sealed in my heart."

"Did you say anything?"

Is he crazy? "No. I was terrified. My Dad roars like a lion if you contradict him. God knows what he would have done if I had told him to go away. I couldn't bear his hands resting on me. After a long time, maybe two minutes, or three, I rolled away from him. I'll never forget his warm hands sliding off me as I turned. He never did that again."

Wow. I actually told the therapist.

"He only grazes our breasts with his hands, my sisters and me, when he hugs us, or sits by us on the couch. My brother's and sister's therapists both said it was molesting, and because there were grandchildren, our dad needed to be confronted. I thought, fuck, I'd rather die. I'm scared of him. He's roared like a lion since we were toddlers. I'm sure that's why I startle at ordinary sounds." I chuckle. "My co-workers are always telling me not to be so jumpy. I can't help it. It's imprinted in my DNA from growing up with Dad.

"He's roared my whole life. He'll be going along fine, then, suddenly, he's angry. He still scares me. But the therapists said he could get help. He needs help. I wish I could help him, because I don't think he wants to be the way he is, and he's not a bad guy, when he's in a good mood. He's hysterically funny when he's joking about his customers, or talking about chocolate cake for dessert." I'm telling him everything. Why not?

"The therapists said there should be an intervention. I thought, bad idea. I went along since I didn't have a better idea. We all agreed to confront Dad at a therapist's office. We weren't going to tell Dad what the meeting with the therapist was really for."

I've been going on and on. "Is this story too long?"

"No."

"Okay. Well, *I* thought we should tell Dad the truth about the purpose of the meeting. Not telling Dad the truth would be too big of a shock for him. I was out-voted. Others thought he wouldn't show up if he knew the purpose was to confront him. We made up a story. Told Dad the session was to support our brother, Martin, who was newly sober at the time. I wasn't sober yet.

"I'm going on too long."

"Not at all."

Shoot. I have to tell him. I can hardly bear to think about it let alone say it out loud. "All right. About a week after our secret meeting at their house, Mom and Dad flew in from the Holy Land. My brother Martin and I picked them up at the airport. No one else wanted to welcome them back. I thought Mom and Dad would be in a great mood, coming back from their dream trip, but they were quiet. It felt as though they knew our plan, somehow, though I thought no one could have told them.

"What we didn't know was Dad's business associate, who lives with them, might have overheard our meeting and warned Dad, because Dad could have called home from the Holy Land to check on things at the house."

I don't know why we can't let sleeping dogs lie. Michael Andersen won't understand what happened. He's staring at me, waiting.

"It wasn't even anything bad. But I needed to die."

I look down, go far away beyond the floor between us. "It was January, cold outside. Martin carried the luggage inside, said goodnight and left. I love my parents. I felt bad because this was their big trip of a lifetime and nobody had welcomed them home except Martin and I. Everyone else was mad at Dad. I think we were all unnerved by the plan to confront him. But I didn't want to run off right after we'd brought them home from the airport.

"Mom and Dad and I stood there by the dining room table. I tried to visit for a bit. Mom and Dad still seemed uneasy. I thought maybe they'd had a fight. I finally said, 'I'd better get home to Isaac,' and hugged and kissed my mom. My dad thanked me for picking them up. He gave me a big hug with my mom standing nearby."

I catch my breath, choke back a sob. Dang. "But then…"

I can't hold back. Hard quiet sobs come for a whole minute. Take a deep breath. It's nothing. Just say it. "He wouldn't let me go."

I'm far, far away. It's silent. I don't talk for a minute, maybe two minutes.

"Come back," Michael says quietly.

I'm not ready.

"Okay." I hear myself say. I'm here. But I'm not. He can hear me. No one can touch me. "I pushed," I say, "like you do, when you're done hugging. He wouldn't let me go." Tears, hot tiny bowling balls roll down. "I told him, nicely, so I wouldn't make him mad, 'I need to go.' He held on tighter. I pushed again."

Funny, tears are spilling down but I'm not crying. I'm calm. "He still wouldn't let me go."

So, this is therapy. All right. It's not killing me.

"Is that when you needed to die?"

"No. I pushed harder to get away. That only made him hold tighter."

The old wave of shame that the memory of that moment always brings fills me. A feeling of being disgusting and worthless. "I understood then he wouldn't let me go until I gave up. I didn't want to. I had to. I quit pushing, let him be locked onto me, felt his body against mine." I take a deep breath. "That was the feeling that made me need to die—subjugation." I push the tears back towards my hair. I want to die now.

"You know, I love my dad. It couldn't happen, him forcing my body against his. I needed to die so it would stop."

"Are you okay?" he asks.

I'm no trouble. "I'm fine." I'm back. "It was just a hug. I don't get what the big deal was. Maybe I'm too sensitive. I don't know how long he held me. I think five minutes. But maybe only three."

"Your mom didn't say anything?"

I shake my head. "Mom probably thought he'd kill her if she stood up to him. I mentioned it a few years later to see if she'd noticed. She remembered. I was glad. She said she'd thought it was strange. She couldn't say more. What could she have done? I have to go now."

"We have time. When your boyfriend has the hammer on the car seat and you need to die, do you feel trapped?"

"Yes. It's the same feeling. Dying's the only way out. That makes sense now. But why do I keep going back to Arnold?"

"Well, it's just a thought, there could be an unconscious connection. A neurotic attachment to your boyfriend."

"A what?"

"A pathological connection."

The words splash cool water onto the fever in my nerves. The room, the light, the shiny crease of the therapist's trousers, all suddenly appear crystal clear.

He nods. He understands.

"Can you say those words again?" I ask.

"A neurotic attachment. A pathological connection involving your dad. Could be why you have a hard time breaking away from Arnold."

It's true. It's neurotic, pathological, connected to Dad, I can tell. I just don't know exactly how it's connected. Still, for the first time I feel hope.

"Can you write those words down?"

"Sure. Neurotic attachment, pathological connection," he says, writing on a new page of his steno pad.

"What do they mean?"

"Well, to be honest, I'm not exactly sure I could explain it without," he says, tearing off the note and handing it to me, "looking them up."

He doesn't know?

Don't forget, he's an intern.

Never mind. I'll figure it out. "I've always had that, starting in third grade, staring across the playground at a sixth grader for three years. Neurotic attachment." I have to go so I can look it up. "Even Isaac. I fell for his smile when an old man made him laugh in the library music room. That's a neurotic attachment. And Randy when I was twenty-two. Seeing his face glow that night when he lit a cigarette with a match in the cup of his hands. Adam before him. Adam had a twinkle in his glistening steel eyes. Wow. It's not a relationship, it's a neurotic attachment I have with my hammer guy with the deep, resonant voice." I take a deep breath and give a big sigh.

"You could see it that way."

How else would I see it? Michael Andersen's not as bright as I hoped, but he's still pretty good. He gave me the words I need.

"How are things with you and your dad now?"

"Oh, not bad, not good. After the intervention, he called us sluts and whores for even thinking he would be inappropriate. He doesn't try to hug us anymore, since the intervention. Though if you're not careful, he'll still get you, if you get close enough. We shake hands with him. Sometimes, I want to hug him—he's my dad—but I don't." I shrug, harden within. "It's no big deal."

"How did the intervention go?"

"Badly. The therapist had asked everyone to write a page about what Dad had done, how it affected us. Jean couldn't be there. She was in Oregon. Our brothers were hugely supportive, wrote how Dad's behavior affected them because they care about their sisters. I forget who went first. Dad interrupted. The therapist asked Dad to wait until we had all shared. He was quiet then. Mom sat beside him, sad with big watery eyes. It was awful. Finally, after everyone had read their message, Dad, angry, pointed to each of us, one at a time. He said, 'You're a liar! You're a liar! You're a liar!' all the way around the room.

"After that, the therapist broke the silence. Said something like, 'This was a great start, let's end with the Serenity Prayer.' I thought, is she crazy? This isn't a good plan. She's not going to talk to Dad? I had forgotten a therapy session with two other therapists, who were a couple, had been scheduled as a follow-up.

"After the prayer, people seemed relieved and happy. I didn't know why. I was nervous about what Dad might do. I thought he might get one of his rifles he keeps in his office at home and kill us or kill himself. I watched him edge toward the door and slip out, unnoticed. I said, 'He's gone, you guys.' No one else seemed worried.

"He didn't kill anyone. That afternoon we called Child Protective Services to report him. God, that was hard. Except, when the clerk asked how old are the children, we said most of us are in our thirties and forties. We lost it, laughing so hard we could barely talk. Yeah. That was in January, seven years ago. A few weeks later Dad told one of our nieces that his daughters were all sluts and whores. Then, Easter time, he called people and said there'd been a miracle and that he had good news. I didn't think he'd apologize, but who knows, I thought. With a miracle, maybe he would. It turned out the good news was he had decided to forgive us all." I smile. Shrug.

Michael Andersen smiles. He understands that part.

"He's not allowed to see his grandchildren," I say. "That's a heavy hit. He's not invited to most family gatherings. Mom comes without him, sometimes. She's always sad about it. I'm careful around him. He gets me with his hand now and then when he reaches in front of me to open a door, something like that. He's quick.

"I never want to confront him again. He felt so betrayed, it killed me to hurt him.

"It's not rational, but now I feel he'll kill me if I confront him. Roar for sure.

Maybe shoot me with one of his rifles. I don't know where I got that idea. Bad guys on TV when I was little, probably, roaring like Dad, shooting people who made them mad. Visits are hard. Mom wants us to all get along. She's pretty sad. She wants apricot-picking day."

"What's apricot-picking day?"

"The mythical day we all get along and pick apricots at their house. They're getting older. Mom'll be eighty soon. I feel for her." That's an understatement.

"All right. Good work. Our time's up. Next week?" he asks, like it's a fun date.

Why? "I think I got the answer to my problem. I can figure the rest out. I don't *have* to go back to my boyfriend again. It's not a real relationship, just a… neurotic attachment. Yes. And the other word."

"Pathological connection."

"Yes. Thank you."

"Well, you might want to follow up with another session."

I don't know about that. "Okay, sure. It's just ten dollars."

"Yeah. Can't hurt," he says with a wry smile.

He means the work. But it does hurt to be seen. He doesn't understand my shame.

We stand up. His arms go out to hug me. He's insane to think I want to hug him. I shake my head no. Everybody likes to hug these days. I don't like to be touched. Unless it's sex … with Arnold.

I pay Michael Andersen and leave. I feel lighter walking out of the cream-colored building. He said I matter. What could go wrong if I let myself matter? I'm so worn-down feeling crazy with Arnold, with my life in general, I need to learn to matter to myself.

For starters, stay away from Arnold.

A quiet fear murmurs something inaudible.

I dismiss it. I can't pay attention to every little sparkler of nerves.

Definitely never get another neurotic attachment. Only a real relationship for me. I don't know how to get a real relationship, but I'll figure it out.

I don't get how my neurotic attachments, like the one with Arnold, are connected to Dad, though. I'm not neurotic with Dad. I'm in reality. My anxiety makes sense: he's my dad, who's not safe.

I get in the car and sit. I watch big clouds slowly move in from the ocean. I long to be covered by clouds, the way clouds covered our house in Seattle when I was small, when Dad carried me up to bed with the other little kids, held me safe and warm. In those days, even though he scared me, I had a real connection with Dad.

And when he molested me, it probably got severed. Of course. Now, I have an empty place inside where a safe connection with Dad should be. That's why I neurotically attach to guys like Arnold, Isaac, Randy, Adam. I'm trying to make a connection. I watch the clouds above and sink deep down inside to feel for the truth: I want connection. The adrenaline of my neurotic attachments is so strong, it feels like connection. It's not.

I drive toward the harbor.

I thought Dad and I had a strong connection, but it's more of a nervous cat-and-mouse relationship with a childlike longing for him to change. It's not a real connection.

As I drive, a wave of sadness builds inside me. My connection with Dad isn't real, it's adrenaline. Now I understand. When a guy smiles, I'm hooked by the adrenaline, because I'm driven by my angst for connection. Even when we have sex, there's only the fantasy of connection.

I've never had a real relationship, the kind where you talk, make plans, do things, then, after weeks, or months, after a real connection grows, have sex. No. I never have. Now I know why.

I park at the harbor, get out of the car. Cold wind gusts against me. Crazy. It was warm in town. Hopefully, the ocean waves will crash over the breakwater and help me feel the truth more deeply, that I matter, that I can't fill my emptiness with adrenaline. I watch huge dark clouds push in from the sea toward the sunny mountains. I feel alive and scared.

I need to get things right. Stop having neurotic attachments. Tears well up. Even if I do, I can probably never have a real relationship. For sure not one with Dad. Unless he changes.

Right. I zip my jacket all the way up, let the tears flow. I miss having a relationship with him. It never occurred to me I missed having one. That's what this is all about. He and I can never go deeper than joking about dessert. I knew I was scared of Dad, repulsed by him. Now I know I miss a connection with him.

If he changed, we could connect. I've wanted him to change, so he can see his grandchildren. But he could also have a relationship with me. Him changing isn't likely.

I pass fishing shops, tall masts of small docked boats in the harbor. It all feels placid here. It doesn't match the storm brewing within as the realization comes: I can no longer have what it seems I'll die without—the neurotic attachments that have always seemed to give me connection. They made me feel alive. But feeling alive was only nervous excitement and fear.

I'm going to miss the electricity those guys gave me.

Not the devastation. I have broken emotional bones everywhere from those relationships. Broken emotional bones that healed crooked. They make me off balance so I've stumbled through life the best I can, one blunder following another. No wonder I can't get anything right. No wonder things are so painful. Now, losing Arnold, my emotional bones are getting broken again, but this time I'll let them heal straight.

I look to the ocean. High tide. Foamy water rushes up the brown sand near the Yacht Club. Farther out, waves crash on the giant boulders holding the breakwater's concrete walk, now and then spraying over the top. I can dodge the spray. I walk on out, collar up in the stiff wet wind, hands stuffed in my pockets, in agony thinking of letting go of Arnold. I'm nothing without him.

Why haven't I mattered to myself?

Because I'm nothing.

That thought cuts and burns its way into the vault of my fear: Who would ever want me for a real relationship?

Silence.

No one.

A loud crack startles me out of my misery. It was a big wave hitting the boulders. Water shoots skyward and pours onto my head, cascades down my back. I gasp from the icy cold and catch my breath. I stand in the deep flow of wave water pouring over my hi-tops, across the concrete walk into the harbor, and chuckle. So much for a moody walk. I'm soaked head to toe. There could be another wave coming. I'd better turn back.

I didn't see that wave coming. I wasn't paying attention. That's a lesson to remember. The next time some guy flutters his eyes at me the way Arnold did, I'll pay attention and walk the other way.

I've had enough therapy for one day.

The thought of bundling up at home in warm dry clothes like I matter, like I'm not nothing, exhilarates me.

Below the wall, smaller waves slosh against the rocks. I look out and see another set coming. I dare them as I hurry back in my wet clothes. I feel good. No more neurotic attachments for me. And maybe I can connect with Dad, somehow. What if I can help him? I'm sure he doesn't want to be the way he is. So what if a revulsion rises in me? I can handle that. There must be a way to help him fix things so he'll be safe to be close to.

Therapy. It helped me in one session. It might help him. I feel light-headed with excitement thinking about that as I hurry toward the car in the cold wind, my wet jeans scraping the pavement. I've wanted to be a therapist since I was nineteen. I flunked out of college. I never had confidence anyone would hire me as a therapist and was sure I wouldn't know what clothes to wear. But now, I'm forty-three. I can become a therapist, or a counselor if that doesn't take as long, so I'll know how to help Dad. Probably no one else could.

Not that it's ethical to counsel a family member. But how else will it get done? Dad needs to be ready to change. I'll help him get ready. I'll talk to him, ask about his childhood, let him know he matters. It'll be great, because, if he changes, he'll see me for who I am. And I'll see him for who he is. If he lets down his guard, he'll see himself.

I don't know. It seems he's so far away inside himself, he may not know he's in there. His problem has to be in his childhood. Mine is.

CHAPTER 2
YOU'VE GOT MAIL

April, 1993. The next morning.

At 6 a.m., I sit at my sobriety meeting in a great chilly hall with wooden plank floors. The several lights of large windows let in the blue dawn. Though the hall is big, it feels cozy with the wood and the windows, the lamps hanging from the ceiling. About fifteen of us sit in folding chairs around four long folding tables placed to make a rectangle.

I like the topic—acceptance. Just *thinking* about accepting that I'm letting go of my neurotic attachment to Arnold makes me feel alive and happy. He's not here yet. Sometimes he's late. Who cares if he shows up or not? I try on the new feeling of freedom from Arnold. I'll never end up in his truck with the green-handled hammer again. Thank goodness I'm dealing with all this sober.

Here he comes, with his shiny brown hair, looking sharp in a pressed long-sleeve plaid button-down collar shirt, blue jeans with a crease, black shoes. He doesn't see me. He sits at the other end of the tables, on the opposite side from me. I don't feel anything, except exhilarated with my new freedom from the neurotic attachment. It's a miracle.

Through the entire one-hour meeting I'm not even nervous or excited to know Arnold's in the room. I'm free. At last.

The meeting wraps up with a prayer. I get up to leave. There's no reason to say hello to him. We're done. I walk toward the door.

"Marie," Arnold says behind me, in that deep, warm, genuine voice of his.

Damn. With Adam, it was his eyes. With Arnold, it's his voice. There goes my feeling of freedom.

"You've got mail," he says warmly.

A jolt of fear hits my head.

I'm fine. It doesn't mean anything. I turn towards him.

I hate this fear.

But here's something new—sadness, which flows underneath the fear. Sadness for feeling so helpless. I matter to myself! I can feel it. "You have my mail here with you?" I finally say.

"Well, I don't have it *with* me. Did you want to pick it up? Or, I could bring it here."

My mind goes blank. "Sure. No," I say. Trembling begins in my arms.

I didn't make sense. See this trembling, Marie? It means run.

Running would look stupid.

He laughs softly at my blunder.

Which makes me mad, so now I can think better. "I'll come by when I'm in the neighborhood," I say, smile, wave, and walk away so rattled it's a wonder my legs work.

As I go, I watch my new white high-top sneakers. They tether me to myself all the way to the car. I'm so glad I bought these white high-top shoes, before I had to cut up my credit cards. I didn't know why I obsessed on them, though now I do. They make me feel safe, in a speechless way. Obviously, they're white baby shoes. They soothe me as an infant with invisible parents who are ready to scoop her up if danger comes.

At home, in my small second-story studio, I'm no calmer. I hurry into the miniature alcove kitchen with its handy sunny roof outside one of the kitchen's three windows. Whenever I want, I step right out onto the roof and sit there a while.

I take a head of romaine from the miniature upright fridge, tear off four large dark-green leaves, rinse and roll them up and eat them like a hotdog. It's normal to panic when you have a neurotic attachment that you're afraid of going back to. Someone once said romaine has B vitamins and calms you down. Four leaves usually work. I look around as I chew. I love this little doll house kitchen. It even has a tiny four-burner stove with an oven just big enough to hold my roaster. Child-size. The way I feel.

I chew the greens and gaze at the small colorful striped lamp shade on my pole lamp. I loved the shade when I bought it, but right now I can't stand its stripes. Quit looking at it.

Chew. I wish I could sit down in a lawn chair with a blanket on my lap today. When I was small, I wished I could have TB so I could go to a sanitarium. I thought it was a place to get sane, which I thought meant to get calm. It looked so inviting in movies to be sitting peacefully on a large sloping lawn with a blanket on your lap. And you would be there for months, maybe a year, or two. I knew what insanity was from old movies I saw on TV when I was seven, eight, nine. "Spellbound," "Picture of Dorian Gray", "Lust for Life." I related to the anxiety in the characters' faces.

I bite off more of my big roll of romaine. I'd put dressing on it, but it might dilute its calming effect. I sit on my little bed to chew, curl my fingers into Grandma's maroon wool blanket to soothe myself. The blanket's been with me since Mom took it with a brown one down from her closet shelf one night when I was drunk and about to head east into winter with Randy in a three-hundred-dollar Ford Galaxie convertible. I was twenty-three. Mom's eyes danced as she handed me the blankets. "You'll need these," she said with unbridled happiness. Anyone could see my plan was bad, even I could. I wondered about her lack of concern—what are you thinking, Mom? Then I understood: she wished she were going. That made sense. When I left Randy, I gave him the brown blanket. I'm glad the maroon blanket made it through all my travels. Mom's mom was always kind to us kids. Maybe she can help me now from heaven.

I look at the black phone. I don't want to go back to Arnold.

I'm afraid I will.

I need more than romaine to calm me down.

Arnold has a good side and a lot of friends. I treated him badly this morning. No hello, how are you, from me.

Dang. I panicked. "You have my mail here with you?" I asked politely like a volt of terror hadn't just smashed the inside of my skull.

It is terror. Something's wrong with me to feel that scared of talking to Arnold.

It isn't talking to him, it's fear of going back to him. I finish the romaine.

I sit, stare at the glossy black telephone like it's a magic wand. I could call Arnold right now, apologize for being stand-offish this morning, and feel … electric.

"You're insane," I say aloud, trembling all over again. Even if he won't kill you, he'll always drop you, out of the blue. Get a clue.

It would be good to pray.

I don't want to, now.

Running up and down the stairs a few times will calm me down.

I skip down the two flights of stairs, pretending to imaginary onlookers I need something from my car. You have to be rich to sit under a blanket on a lawn and be cared for by nurses. I'm not rich. I'm paying off my nine-thousand-dollar law-school debt plus a few thousand dollars of twenty-five-dollar little purchases. I didn't know the credit card balance gets up so high that the interest is more than your extra income. So, no sloping lawn to calm me down. No. It's running up and down stairs for me.

Outside, I skip down the porch steps into the bright sunlight, go up the street, touch my car, pretend I forgot something upstairs, trot back toward the house.

I have an appointment in a week at an agency where I cut the credit cards up, which stops the interest, and they tell me how much I have to pay each month. So that part of my life is fixed.

I start back up the stairs. No, there's no sloping lawn on my horizon. Still, there are other good things. I passed the Bar Exam on the first try. That makes me feel good. Though, if men can do it, anyone can do it.

I reach the kitchen, touch the stove and turn around to go back out.

I still have a resentment towards men, don't I? I need to let it go, if I'm going to stay sober, because resentments really are poison. Just because a lot of men have talked over me, dismissed me, hurt me, doesn't mean it's good to keep that resentment towards all of them. It's not for me to judge others. Recovery says people who hurt me are sick people. I need to see some men as sick people.

Down the stairs I go. Stairs make good exercise. I jog over, touch my car, turn around.

That attorney at the rent control gathering a few years ago was the last straw when he started talking over me like I wasn't even there speaking in the middle of a conversation. You know what? I thought, if an idiot like you can become an attorney, anyone can, you arrogant jerk. That's how I passed the Bar Exam. A resentment. Am I hard on Arnold, because I have a problem with men?

I hurry back up the stairs, into my studio, touch the stove, turn around, go back down. No. I'm wary of Arnold for good reason.

I leap down the porch stairs into the sunshine.

Still, when my poor body needed a break after twenty-five years of labor jobs and I wanted an office job without being some man's secretary, it was good I got through law school on a resentment.

I tap the car, turn around.

Because now I'm a law librarian where I get vacation and holiday pay and I don't need permission to use the restroom the way I did at minimum wage jobs with those bosses always hovering over me.

I run up the stairs.

I handled a few cases as an attorney. Mostly hoped my phone wouldn't ring. That was the biggest clue. Practicing law wasn't for me. Yep, anyone can pass the Bar. You need average intelligence, hard work and a calm disposition. I am calm with school work.

Not with men.

Back in my room, I pause to catch my breath, stare at the shiny black phone. Will it to ring. If Arnold calls, I can at least apologize for being abrupt this morning. I'm calmer. The stairs are working. I won't call him, though he doesn't scare me now.

I go in the kitchen, touch the stove, turn around, go back down.

When the sunlight hits my face, suddenly the memory of Mom and Dad coming to my swearing-in as an attorney lodges like a splinter in my mind. Darn it. I was just feeling good. Now my most painful memory ever, almost, has to walk in without knocking. It happened six months ago. Why did it come up now?

They were pleasant, with pained faces. They drove seventy miles from Santa Maria! Not my fault Dad moved them there, he was so angry after the intervention. Mom said she was proud of me, but not surprised, she knew I could do it. You're right, it's no big deal, Mom, I thought, irritated, knowing that's not what she meant. Even though I brag it's not a big deal, I wanted her to say with awe, how did you do it? So, how's the weather up there, I asked. I didn't give her a chance. I was angry. Miserable in my cap and gown for needing them there after I had planned to not invite them. Someone had said of course I should invite them. I felt guilty for showing off, putting them to shame, somehow. Why was it so painful? I couldn't ask them what was wrong. They appeared so uncomfortable. I was trying to be normal, asking them to come, but I couldn't be normal with them. Were they awkward because they didn't go to college? Because my siblings and I confronted Dad seven years ago? They needed me to show them how to find a seat in the small court room, and I was embarrassed, because they were like children. I had put them there, by asking them to come. I had to ask them. I love them. It hurts so much remembering that day. I didn't want Dad to touch me.

I touch my car, my breathing slow but loud now, and turn to go back up, walking slowly.

I think I wanted a nice connection. They weren't glad to see me. I felt like a fraud.

I didn't want *anyone* at the swearing-in, except Arnold. When he didn't show up, I was frantic, worrying it was over with him, again. As I stood waiting my turn to shake hands with the judge, I was finally a little relieved, because my panic from Arnold not showing up had changed to anger. And I thought: Arnold, you'd better be in the hospital.

I smile as I slowly walk back upstairs. Arnold was in the hospital. He had fallen off a ladder that morning and shattered a leg. Poor guy, he was so nice to me, with his leg in a sling after the surgery, sorry to have missed the swearing-in. That's the real him, who everyone loves. That's why it's so hard to know what to do. Go get my mail from him? I said I would, but something tells me it's not a good idea. I drink some water in the kitchen.

Okay. Run down the stairs one more time. I go. The air's warming up. I catch my breath at my car. It's not hard to know what to do. Because it's not about Arnold! It's about needing a connection with Dad. It's so painful to touch Dad's hand to shake. Why can't Dad see what he does, and change? His hands are so quick, and his temper's so quick too, to object when he gets me with his hands would make a scene. I couldn't bear being publicly roared at. He would sever the connection we do have. Barbed as it is, it's something.

Is that pathetic?

Is it better to stop trying with Dad? To cut ties?

I touch the Corolla, shake my head no. The thought of cutting ties with Dad rips me up inside. He's my dad. Our relationship is twisted wreckage. Still, I won't cut ties, because I know there's a reason for the wreck, I just don't know what it is. And I love him.

I trot back up to my studio, short of breath, calm, coming to a new understanding. My sense of self is also a twisted wreck, partly because reality doesn't match who I grew up believing I was. I was brought up the opposite of men. I was taught to believe men know better than I do, are better than I am, and will protect me. But none of it's true. I never saw it all so clearly before now. I was brought up seeing Dad belittle and dismiss Mom, as though she didn't matter.

Though I've experienced over and over again on the job, in jokes that I hear, in my relationships, the message that I'm disposable while men matter, the truth is, men aren't better than I am, smarter than I am, and they don't protect me. Not so far. Except Eddie, who stood between me and those boys throwing rocks, and the former prisoners at the car wash, where I washed the inside back windows. When I told them how the boss had pushed me into the closet-office and forced a wet kiss on me, they took my side. "Prick. Asshole," they said. They made me feel I matter.

In my kitchen, panting from the stairs, I feel glad for the clarity. As Martin Luther King said, the truth will set you free. And the truth is: I'm just as good and smart as men. It's crazy how ingrained that childhood conditioning to believe otherwise is. I'll fight it. Tear it out of me.

I feel good. Romaine, a few trips up and down stairs, a reality check. Magic. I look out the window to hazy clouds beyond the sunny roof, look down to my white high-top shoes which give me bliss of mythic proportions. *Why do they do that?* Maybe I was wearing white baby shoes the last time I felt safe in my life!

I laugh. That explanation's too easy.

I see the phone and nervousness returns.

I'm glad I don't drink, because this would be the time. Well, every day was the time. But with Arnold glad to see me this morning, I would take charge of my feelings with a bottle right now, if I weren't sober.

The thing is, my body feels better, but a dark cloud gathers in my soul. Deep inside, I feel worse, not better. Something within mocks me—I can run, eat romaine, go to meetings, but I can't hide from the thing that mocks me. I'm not scared, I'm terrified. Hypnotized. Arnold has power over me. I'll walk back to him, suddenly, impulsively. I'll call him, drop by, unable to hear myself screaming, don't go back!

It's the same as those times that come where I want Mom and I feel paralyzed, terrified, and softly wail in pain of missing her. It doesn't matter if it's the middle of the day or at night. I get the feeling she's a block away, on a rainy night, and she can't hear me yelling to her, so she doesn't come no matter how long I scream. Of course, I'm not really screaming, it just feels like I am. Until it passes. But the fear of returning to Arnold doesn't pass. And I can't help getting angry at that colorful lamp shade. It's the stripes—vertical stripes. It doesn't matter that they're colorful like candy, which I liked when I bought the lamp shade. They're stripes. I can't bear the feeling they give me. It doesn't make sense that I can't stand stripes. I look away but I feel them, like a brand on my forehead.

Stripes have always been a problem. I usually snap myself out of the fear of stripes by telling myself I'm just a wannabe neurotic like Gregory Peck in Spellbound. I didn't impale my sibling on a wrought iron fence, the way Gregory Peck did, pushing his little brother in fun so he could slide down the snowy porch banister. *He* was scared of stripes. But I don't want that lamp shade. I can't have it anymore.

I'll put the shade on the sidewalk in case someone wants it. No, it could still be there when I leave. Well, I don't have to look at it. No, but I'll just— here—I pull it off the bulb, set it on the floor. It's okay, it was only seven dollars. I made a mistake buying it. I don't have to keep it.

I step on it. It crushes easily.

Good. I feel better. I pick up the flattened shade and take it in the kitchen. I can breathe better now. It's okay. There it goes, into the garbage bag. Good thing it's small. I stuff it down the side of the bag, cover it up with trash. Yep.

Whew. I didn't like it.

Arnold isn't like that lamp shade. He's warm and kind. When he sneezes, he sounds just like Dad, it's uncanny. When Arnold's arms squeeze me, a warm buzzing runs through my spine into the back of my head and I feel *nothing* could ever go wrong. I feel I'll die without that feeling. Why can't I have that? Why?

Because he rages with a hammer between us. And he drops me!

That's right. I forget that. How do I get him to not do that?

I'll talk to my sister Cecilia. She'll have a suggestion.

The next day at lunchtime I wait for Cecilia in a little public garden spot about halfway between the two law firms where we work, she as a paralegal, I as a law librarian. The dappled shade soothes me while I sit on a concrete bench planning how to explain my mail dilemma with Arnold. Cecilia always listens to me. She's smart. She goes to therapy. She knows how hard it is to love him because he has trouble with commitment. I know I'm good for him, and I think he does love me or I wouldn't feel this way about him.

Here she comes. "Hey. Thanks for meeting me!" I wish my hair were long and silky like hers. She didn't bring her lunch.

She gives me a big hug. I'm still not used to her hugs. Hugs are a new thing these days, it seems, mostly with people in therapy. Still, I don't mind. She's so nice to me. Only three years older, but like a mom.

"How *are* you?" she says with a concerned smile.

"I'm fine, really." I don't want her to worry about me, only to listen about Arnold, as usual, and give me some good advice to calm him down so he won't rage anymore when I go back. "How are you?"

"Oh, I'm all right. It's the usual at the office. The attorneys are swamped so I'm swamped. You didn't say what you needed to talk about."

"You didn't bring your lunch."

"No, I'll need to get back to the office and eat at my desk."

"Oh. Okay." I hoped we would have a whole hour to figure out my problem. "Well, here's my problem. Arnold and I broke up, you know."

"That's right. I remember. Two weeks ago?"

"Yes. For the fourth time," I say.

"Right." She checks her watch.

Darn it. I begin eating my sandwich. I'd better get to it. "I had moved in. And I gave Arnold's address to a few places—my bank, my doctor. So, I've been doing good, not going back to Arnold, not calling him, but this feeling that we're *supposed* to be together keeps coming up. Okay. So, fine. I know better than to go back. But I keep thinking maybe I can calm him, somehow. It's risky, but life's risky, right? If we don't take risks, what's the use of being alive? I'd rather die, frankly, than not risk going back. Not really … but sort of."

"I don't have much time today, Marie."

"Okay, I'll get to the point. Yesterday, Arnold was at the morning meeting. I was about to leave, when he said he has mail for me. I froze, not knowing what to do. I told you he pushed me down on the bed once." Don't tell her about him raging with the hammer between us. "I was scared I'd go back to him. He said I could drop by when I'm in the neighborhood, or he could bring the mail to a meeting. He was really nice. What do you think I should do? I mean …"

She raises her hand to stop me. "Marie, don't take this wrong …"

Oh dear. She's never said that before.

"… but I have to say …"

No. She's never said anything like this before.

She looks into my eyes. "The answers are within you."

The words punch me in the gut. She doesn't want to hear about Arnold anymore. I've used her up.

Now what?

The answers are within me. "Okay."

It's so dark inside me, I can't see answers. Still, if she's right, then there's hope, an answer to my problem. I need to find it. "Did you want to talk about something yourself?"

"No, I've got to go, sweetie. Except," she brightens with a cheerful smile, "you might want to buy a rubber duck, or two, or three. In my inner-child group, we all agreed to buy rubber ducks, to take bubble baths and nurture our inner child. It really works. That might help you."

She's crazy. "Okay. Sounds good." She doesn't understand I need to solve my problem first.

We say good-bye. I walk slowly back to work, still shaken by having been shut down, and intrigued. What if the answers are within me? It rings true. I'm going to act as if it's true.

I rack my brain for hours. The urge to see Arnold grows. After work, at home, it occurs to me I could call and ask Mom what she thinks I should do about getting my mail from Arnold. The problem is, it hurts when Mom's too busy to talk, which is all the time. And even if she has a minute, if I tell her I'm scared I'll go back to Arnold, she'll say how smart I am, and that I'll figure it out, which is usually true, but this time I don't think I *can* figure it out.

I'm being pulled back to Arnold, and no one can hear me call out. What can I do?

Chapter 3
Baby Steps

May, 1993. Two weeks later.

At four o'clock in the morning, I start my day. I hop on my kitchen stool to write on my computer, as usual. Writing's the only thing that connects me to myself. Well, painting, does too. But my place is too small to set up oil paints. I love the wee hours, writing on my computer, white print on a green screen. Still in pajamas, cozy green jacket, cold air around me, hot cup of coffee beside me. You can't buy this.

Arnold hasn't been at the morning meetings. Someone said he goes to the five o'clock ones now. He still has my mail. I drink some coffee. Look down, to the left, wonder if I should go pick up my mail. Outside the window, on the gently sloping roof, sits the big blue roaster pan with the stuck-on remains of four chicken quarters I baked for my lunches last night. The roaster pulls me to it for some deep meaning.

I write:

> When I was a child, a dirty roaster was a monster you never wanted to have in your life. What do you do with a dirty roaster? Soak it. For weeks if necessary. As children, we filled it to the brim. Soaked it until no one knew what lurked beneath the hard white grease layer. No one recalled whose job it was to clean it. I did as I was told, sank my skinny arms into the greasy pond and scrubbed, sloshed water onto the counter and the floor. It never occurred to anyone to soak the roaster in only an inch of water, as I did last night.

I pull up my jacket collar. My childhood—cold, deep, greasy water. I need a lesson, some deeper truth about life that can save me from my current murky dilemma: get my mail; or have Arnold bring it to a meeting. I write some more:

> Being little was hard. Not only the dirty roaster. Never knowing when Dad would roar like a lion, or when he'd ever come home from his months' long trips. Never knowing when Mom would cringe with a half-smile to appease

him because he'd belittled her with some cutting complaint, or whether they'd kiss and be happy making everything seem good. What answers lie there in those nervous years?

I feel a certain sweetness. I didn't know any better as a child. I did my best despite deep, gray, cold, scary water. I didn't know how to skim off the grease, wasn't strong enough to pour out the water, never thought to make hot sudsy water. Or to soak the roaster in only an inch of water to begin with. It wasn't my fault. I didn't know any better.

No, I didn't.

Wow. The truth appears like a great archeological find: I needed help.

I laugh, drink my coffee.

That's my answer, my deep meaning from the roaster: I need help. I needed help back then and I need help now dealing with Arnold.

Damn. Can dealing with Arnold be that bad?

I see him raging at me with the hammer between us, recall his warm tender voice. I run my hands through my long hair, untangle some strands. I hate asking for help. My eldest sister Sarah said when I was little Mom never had time for me, pushed me away. The big kids got angry when I told them Mom said to ask them for help. No wonder I'd rather die than ask for help.

That was childhood, Marie.

I don't care. I'll figure it out on my own.

No. It's been two weeks. I haven't figured it out.

Fine. I'll ask someone. The therapist came up with a good insight about neurotic attachments, but I told him I was afraid of going back to Arnold and he didn't say anything about that. He can't help. My sister Jean's as tired of hearing about Arnold as Cecilia is. My sobriety sponsor, Jill? Maybe she can help.

It's getting light. That's poetic. I'll go to my sobriety meeting. Then I'll come back and call my sponsor. Then I'll bring the roaster in, climb out the window with a pillow and a blanket, and lie on the roof in the warm sun. It'll be like sitting on a lawn in the sun to get sane.

After I get back from my meeting, I dial the phone. Everything feels in slow motion, with me far away from here. Why's my heart pounding so hard? What can go wrong? She won't care? I'll look like a fool? I can hardly bear the anxiety of asking for help.

"Hello," Jill, says.

She's a good sponsor, never judges me. I'll be all right. "Hi Jill." Don't waste her time. "I have a question."

"Shoot."

"I'm scared of Arnold. He got mad and pushed me so hard I fell on the bed. Maybe I'm sensitive. He rages at me when he drives. With a hammer between us. I've seen too many movies. I'm scared I'll go back to him. He's got my mail." There. It's out.

"Yeah. I remember you told me about the guy on the ranch who beat you up."

What made her think of that? "I guess. It was just black eyes…and an egg on my forehead."

"Yeah."

"But that was twenty years ago," I say, watching a breeze rustle leaves in the trees outside my window.

"Uh huh."

"Everyone likes Arnold," I say.

"I notice that."

Why doesn't she say what she's thinking? "I don't want to go back to him. I'm scared I will. He's got mail at his house for me. My mind's at work, showing me the good times. He's really kind and funny. I can feel the pull."

"There's a group you should go to," she says.

Shit.

"Dixie, the woman who runs it, is wonderful. You need to go. It's for battered women."

I stare at clouds beyond the trees and feel far, far away from here. "I'm not battered."

"It doesn't matter. You were beat up before. Arnold pushed you." Jill sounds so far away.

"Big deal," I say. I know she's right, because I'm scared I'll die if I don't go to this group.

"Do what you want. But I think you should go."

I'd rather die than ask for help. We're quiet. My move.

"How do I find it?" I finally ask.

"It's at the community services office. Seven p.m. Tuesdays. You know, this is a sacred step, Marie. If it were I, I'd take my God with me."

"Okay," I say. My eyes warm with tears. She was beaten and molested as a child, believes God never left her alone. I want that connection. But my God's always mad at me. "How do you pray?" I ask.

"Oh," she says. Her mood brightens. "I tell my God my problems, and then I have my God say, 'My precious, precious child, I love you more than words can say. There's nothing you can do to lose my love.' Then, my God says something like, 'Now, I notice you've been worrying a lot lately. Don't worry so much.' Or something like that."

Don't worry so much. I want that so bad. Tears make it hard to talk. I ask her to say the prayer again so I can write it down. The calm I want floods in as I write. Maybe I can learn to trust God too. Not to save me. To love me.

"All right. Thanks. I'll go," I say. "Why do you suppose I always have to have a man in my life? Without a man I feel as though I don't matter."

"Oh. That's easy. Somebody lied to you when you were little," Jill says.

"How?"

"Did they treat you like you matter?"

"Not really. Dad left to his library when he was upset. Mom was too busy to talk to or notice me. She still is."

"They lied to you. You did matter. They told you by their actions that you didn't. We have to find our own worth," she says. "Getting a man seems like a short-cut."

"It's not."

"No. The good news is since you've been traumatized, your spirit's been carved out deep, which means more love can flow through you when you clean out all the gunk inside. But you have to go down into the yuk."

"Why? I'm tired of doing that. It seems never-ending."

Jill laughs. "It seems like it. It's not. You're going to go down into the yuk until you hit bedrock. Then, on that solid foundation, you build up from there your sense of self no one can ever take away."

"That sounds wonderful. It makes sense. You're really wise. I'll do that."

"Good girl."

We say good-bye.

Through the window, the tree tops shimmer in the breeze. I put the roaster on the stove. Get a pillow and blanket, climb out the window and lie down on the roof, watch the cotton clouds change. Feels good lying here. Someone lied to me when I was little. What a relief. There's a reason I'm messed up. I'm going down through the yuk. Telling Jill already helped a lot.

I probably don't need that group now.

Tuesday evening, I clean out my fridge. I'm not going to the battered women's group. I feel good.

Except, I said I'd go.

Shoot.

When it's time, I rinse out my rag without emotion.

As I walk to the car, my legs go weak.

Why're good things so hard to do? I think of Jill's prayer. I like the part about there's nothing I can do to lose God's love. I've been saying it every night.

At the community services office, the lobby is a bare-bones tiny space. Nothing like the spacious therapist's lobby with its expensive decor.

A young woman with fluffy dark hair, black darts of eyeliner and pale lips smiles. "Can I help you?"

I don't know the name of the group. Are you supposed to say the word battered woman here? Shoot. Say it. "I'm here for the battered women's group?"

She smiles, nods, hands me a questionnaire.

I'm forty-three, too old to be here. I want to go home.

"Thanks," I say, and take a seat. A quiet, hidden engine, one that I'm not used to, pushes me forward against my resistance. I don't like it. I'm used to fun excitement to get myself to do things. Stop complaining. Fill out the form.

When I'm done, the young woman takes me into a small windowless room where I take a seat with four other women who sit in a circle on folding chairs. I look around. Now only one chair's empty. How come no one talks? The other women are young with lots of makeup and cute clothes. Their hair's done up. They've probably been stalked and strangled. I don't belong here. Well, the questionnaire said, "Have you *ever* been hit, pushed," etc. So. Okay. I qualify. Barely.

Here comes someone. She's old, cute with long white strands falling from her pinned up hair. She wears lots of makeup, a pink T shirt and baby blue coveralls.

"I'm Dixie. I'm the facilitator," she says with a southern accent as she takes the last chair in our little huddle.

I want to look just like her.

"How about everybody say your first name," Dixie says.

"Rose."

"Jennifer."

"Donna."

"Tiny."

"Marie."

"Marie, you're new, would you like to tell us about yourself?" Dixie asks.

Her tone's not as gentle as she looks. Can't she see I'm emotionally fragile? I don't want to talk if she's going to bark at me. Well, she didn't bark. I thought she'd be more sympathetic, though. They're all looking at me. Wow. I'm mad at Dixie. I feel lost. Humiliated. They can see I don't belong here. I squeezed in. A wannabe. Shit. I'm not a battered woman. Tears well up. I don't know what to do. No one can help. If I go back to Arnold and die, it's meant to be. We all die.

I can leave here.

Calmness settles in. Words come out on their own. "I don't know why I'm crying. Nothing's happened," I say.

"Your questionnaire said you're scared," Dixie says, nicer now.

I nod. Here I go. Just because someone's nice, tears flood out. It always happens. I look down, cover my face. I'm embarrassed. I breathe all the way out, look Dixie in the eye. "I don't know why I'm so scared."

I tell them everything as fast as I can, so the people who really need help can talk. I tell them how a long time ago Randy beat me up once, but we were drunk so it doesn't count. And how recently Arnold pushed me down on the bed. He raged at me in his truck with a hammer between us. Now he has my mail.

"He pushed you. That's just the start," says Rose.

I love her eyeliner, it's black swords.

"You know it's true," she goes on, "because you've been beat up. The one who beat you up, did he push you first?"

I think about that. "He did. He cracked my head on the ground, in a little park, come to think of it." I forgot all about that. How could I forget?

"See? It don't matter it was a long time ago," Rose says.

She doesn't even know me but she talks like she does.

Rose nods. "You're in denial. You need to look at the truth."

Dang, she's good. Rose tells the truth, but I look to Dixie for authority. Dixie raises her eyebrows at me. Shoot. I nod. Not mad. Confused. They're right. But I had thought there'd be some complicated psychological explanation to help me. I only have to be honest?

They're quiet, looking at me. "I have to be honest. That's all?" I ask.

"This one's dangerous," Rose goes on, "and that's the truth."

That's the truth. Hold on to that. I nod.

"I don't have to worry, mine's in prison," says Donna, a smooth-skinned girl with fine shiny brown hair. She looks so young, not more than eighteen.

"But he's getting out in nine months," says the small girl with big black hair who called herself Tiny.

"And I'll be long gone," says Donna.

"She's moving home to Texas," says Rose.

Everyone applauds. Their friendliness lifts a weight off me. I join in. I worry about Donna being around her dad at home, though. "Is your dad safe?" I ask. "Mine isn't." I can't believe I said that.

"Oh yeah. He's the best."

"Oh, good." I feel ashamed for suggesting her dad might not be safe, and saying that my dad's not safe. I wish I hadn't said anything. This is crazy. I'm so used to Dad, I thought I was immune to being embarrassed about him. It makes me sad for him, his own daughter's embarrassed.

The others take turns reporting positive things they're doing to nurture themselves. Rose got a manicure and took all the time she wanted to pick the color. How great. Jennifer got a library card and brought home a stack of books. I don't even know her. I still feel proud of her. Donna did the dishes and cleaned the whole kitchen.

"Doing dishes doesn't count for self-nurture, even though it's good to do them," Dixie says. "Think of something else for this week, Donna."

"Alright," Donna says.

We brainstorm what Donna could do.

"I'll make a cup of tea and read a magazine," Donna says.

Everyone applauds.

"And I'll do that inner child handwriting exercise," she adds.

"Explain it to Marie, Donna."

"Sure. It's where you write with your dominant hand, the one you write with, and ask your inner child how she's doing. Then, with your non-dominant hand, you write what your inner child has to say. It's just yourself when you were four or five. You picture where you would be standing or sitting, what you'd be wearing. You go back and forth with the pen, having a conversation. It's a good way to connect with your true self."

"Thanks," I say. "I'll try it someday." First, I need to deal with Arnold.

The hour's up.

"This was a good group. Any questions?" Dixie asks, as chipper as when she came in.

"What should I do?" I ask, confident of their helpful friendship now. Nobody told me what to do about my problem.

"Take care of yourself," says Dixie. "Most of us have to work at that. By treating ourselves with love and kindness, we grow a stronger sense of self so we're able to make healthier choices. What's some small thing you can do tonight to nurture yourself?"

That's not what I meant. "I mean should I call him and explain anything? Or should I just go get my mail?"

"That's up to you," Dixie says.

That's no help.

"What works for us, Marie, is taking self-nurturing baby steps. What's something you'd like to do for yourself?" Dixie asks.

Baby steps. Dixie looks like candy, but she's tough.

"Make hot chocolate?" That'll be easy. Maybe next week they'll help me figure it out, if I get this assignment right.

"Is that what you're willing to do?" Dixie asks.

"Yes," I say. Everyone applauds. Up come my tears, again. These people are so nice.

We say good-bye.

I get in my car, drive away, swell with pride. I did it. Went to a battered women's group. I'll go home and make hot chocolate for myself. I feel like a new person. I guess they did help. The hard part of the night is over. Making hot chocolate will be a breeze. And then I'll know how to make healthy choices.

I bound up the stairs, into my studio, lock the door, go straight to the dim kitchen, which feels moody as night falls. It's just right. I have cocoa powder from the frosting I made for Dad's birthday cake last October, which I had the brilliant idea to bake in my roaster, since I don't have a cake pan. I had to use two cake mixes. I love that roaster. People looked at the cake concerned. But, because it was still hot when I frosted it, the frosting melted and was the most delicious frosting anyone had ever tasted. I am resourceful. If I can make the most beautiful cake in a roaster, I can figure out how to stay away from Arnold.

I have milk. Sugar. I'm going to nurture myself. Dixie will be proud of me.

I put my sauce pan on the stove.

Something feels wrong.

I look around, scared.

Nothing's wrong. My mind's playing a trick.

I get the cocoa powder from the shelf, scoop a tablespoonful into the pan.

Something doesn't feel right. Nobody's here but me. Still, I'll look under the bed to calm down. Just boxes. There's only one small room, plus the kitchen area. No closet. It's not an intruder feeling, anyway. It's a sick, disgusted feeling that I'm doing something really wrong. I'm not doing anything wrong. I'm making hot chocolate, nurturing myself.

I pour white sugar into the pan, stir it and the cocoa powder together in slow motion, and slowly fill up with dread I don't understand. I'm nurturing myself, but I'm getting warnings, forebodings, as if I'm loading a gun to point at my head.

To cheer myself up, I think brightly I'm going to get a pink T-shirt like Dixie's and pin my hair up like the other girls do.

Gloom moves back in. I can hardly move. I'm fighting to walk to the refrigerator for the milk. A big chunk of me feels frozen.

A vicious wave of self-recrimination wells up, pure venom. *Hot fucking chocolate? Of all the fucking stupid ideas! What do you think you're doing?*

What? It's a cold, merciless voice I don't recognize.

Wow. I can barely move my arm as I reach for the refrigerator handle. This has never happened before. I'm only nurturing myself. This is supposed to be fun. I was excited. Now this?

Hot chocolate doesn't help anything! Don't do it! the angry part of me yells.

I'm stunned. Something's wrong with me. I can't do this.

Seriously? I can't make hot chocolate? Can't nurture myself?

I'm ready to fight to nurture myself, but a painful emptiness blows in on a sad wind.

You're nothing! You don't exist!

It's excruciating. This can't be happening.

The over-powering urge to give up making hot chocolate drains me to exhaustion. I want to give up, try again tomorrow.

Through a haze of thirty years, I see Mom fight for Civil Rights. Hear Dad say sometimes you have to fight for what you want.

Fight.

I fight to open the refrigerator. "Leave me alone," I say, a quiet, strong engine now. "I'm *not* nothing." It's a fight to even murmur the words. I fight to lift the milk carton from the shelf.

The gale of anger blows normal thoughts away. *It won't fucking help! You're stupid to try! Stop!*

The milk carton weighs a ton with the frozen feeling in my arms, but I lift it, carry it. "I'm…making …hot …chocolate," I mutter under my breath.

I pour milk into the pan.

Stop! Don't do it! It's insane! comes the rage.

I tuck my head down over the pan. "I'm *doing* it. I *won't* stop," I softly growl.

I turn the burner on, stare into the blue flames, stare at the cocoa, sugar and milk. Stunned by the rage, I stir. I won't stop.

The chocolate gets hot.

The storm subsides.

So, this is why Dixie said baby steps.

I pour the hot chocolate into a mug, set it on the floor beside my bed. I collapse onto the little oval rug by my bed, drink the hot chocolate, exhausted. I need sleep so badly. I sip. It tastes like ordinary hot chocolate. It's not. I sip some more.

I set my empty cup aside, get on my knees. "You know my troubles," I say. "Your turn, God, if you're there."

"My precious, precious child, I love you more than words can say. There's nothing you can do to lose my love. Now, I notice you had a hard time making hot chocolate tonight. Put on your PJ's, crawl into bed and get some sleep. I'm proud of you."

Everything's so quiet. I put on PJ's, crawl under the covers, lie mute like a baby, watch billowy moonlit clouds outside my bedside window. Warm tears cool my ears, make me smile. I feel safe, solid, held, nurtured. The silence is full of love. This must be God.

Nothing can go wrong now.

CHAPTER 4
CIGARETTE-EMBER CAMPFIRE

May, 1993. The following morning.

Daylight wakes me. Seven o'clock. I slept ten hours. 1 feel great. What happened last night? A part of me I didn't recognize didn't want me to nurture myself. Who was it? I have no idea.

I feel strong. Refreshed. It doesn't matter if I get my mail from Arnold, or if he brings it to a meeting, because I'm not worried anymore. And I don't want to wear those little black heels to work anymore, either. I've worked as their law librarian five years. What, they're going to fire me for wearing flats? Who would have thought one battered women's meeting and a cup of hot chocolate would work so well?

I drive to work feeling so good I feel high. I'm buying a rubber duck at Woolworth's on my lunch today. I know something about an inner child. I just forgot to nurture her. I need to tell my inner child I won't abandon her, she's not bad, she makes mistakes.

I wonder where my little pink book of inner child affirmations is. Cecilia gave me it four years ago when I was bitter in my marriage to Isaac, starved for connection. I read one affirmation, thought, this is sick, slammed the book shut, buried it on a shelf. Inner fucking child, I thought.

But two years later, it struck me how often I thought of ways to kill myself. I thought the problem could be my marriage. A year after that, Isaac and I split up. When I packed to leave Isaac, I found Cecilia's pink affirmations book and read a random affirmation. I thought, God, I need this so bad! I packed the book around with me and read eight entries a day, for months.

I laugh. I could use that book now. I don't know where it is.

Lunch time comes. I pick up my sack lunch. The secretaries and paralegals have already left, except Marsha, who's agonizingly shy. "Bye Marsha!" I say with a smile and a wave, like she's somebody. Nobody talks to her.

She smiles down at her desk, waves, says, "Bye."

I don't think she knows what to make of my being friendly. I used to be that shy. I sure would like to know her story. I bet I could help her. She might need a copy of my inner child affirmations book. It helped me a lot.

I bound down eight flights of stairs, exhilarated, open the street door. I feel high, like the best drug I ever had. "Leash me to the planet!" I say. I walk to Woolworth's, sort through rubber ducks and test their squeaks. I buy two.

After work, I drive home, ducks in my purse. I still feel great. Must be all this self-nurture. Taking myself to that battered women's group. The girls there were so nice to me. And then I was nice to myself, making the hot chocolate, nurturing myself. Taking care of myself matters.

I climb the stairs to my studio. I'm not afraid of Arnold anymore. I'll get a bite and drive to Arnold's, get my mail from him and we'll be done with each other. It's a good plan, because I don't feel neurotically attached anymore. Then I'll come home, take a nice bath, add dish soap for bubbles, and add my ducks! Then I'll think about the weekend.

I'm not anxious at all. Is this how people normally feel? That would be so great to not be anxious all the time.

Call him first, make sure he's there.

I dial.

Arnold picks up the phone on the third ring. I hear is smooth baritone voice say, "Hello."

I feel the pull. Damn it! I'm not fixed! "Hey, it's me," I say, filling with adrenaline.

"Hello, Me."

I'm fine. "Just thought I'd get my mail if you're home."

His warm chuckle is electric. "Don't know where else I'd be."

That tells me he's not with someone else. It'd be easier if he were. Why am I so hooked on him? Oh, yeah. No connection with Dad.

Neurotic attachments are strong. But I'll be all right. Use an aloof voice. "Okay. I'll be over in ten minutes."

"Take your time. I'm not going anywhere."

He's got all night for me. Shoot.

I could go over, watch a movie the way we used to when we decided to be sibling roommates, which worked, oddly, until the night he had phone sex in the next room with someone in Florida. I felt awful, lying in my little bed in Arnold's living room, trying to hear everything he was saying. God, it was awful. Good thing I remembered the first therapist told me I needed to honor my feelings. My stomach churned a long time as I lay there listening to him on the phone. Then it struck me—my stomach's talking to me! It's telling me my feelings! "Get out!" it was saying. I left in the night. God, it was an awful night. I'll never do that again, live with an ex I'm in love with. I know better.

No. No movie. I'll say hello, get my mail, come home, take a bath with my rubber ducks. I feel tired. I need to get this done, forget him, and get on with my life.

My life. The scan of my life shows me on my own, Mom and Dad waiting for me to visit. Not much more. No future. No past that I care about. Except childhood. I need to go see Mom and Dad. It's been more than two months. They're over an hour away, now. At least Mom didn't let Dad uproot them all the way to Seattle, the way he wanted to after the intervention. She told him she wouldn't go farther north than Santa Maria. Good for you, Mom. Some of the family thought she should leave him. It'll never happen. She's in love with him.

A few weeks after the intervention, Mom came to my house. I heard her light steps on the old wooden porch outside our studio apartment. I opened the door. I'll never forget the terrified look in her bright blue eyes, her white hair back-lit by the sun. She was afraid he'd leave her.

I'll go see them this weekend. Two months is too long.

I drive to Arnold's. A solid adult feeling fills me up. I'm the Lana Turner character I saw in my vision when Dad's hands woke me when I was twelve. I'm not in a smokey bar. I don't drink or smoke any more. Still, I'm calm and mature like Lana Turner, not the impulsive child-like woman I've been, for years getting myself into one emotional scrape after another. I'm quiet, composed. I've been hurt a lot. Time to end getting hurt.

I knock on the screen door. I can see through it. Arnold sits lengthwise on the couch in his PJ's. I can't believe how in charge of myself I feel. He's not the lion I needed to tame. The lion's within me. I met her when I made my hot chocolate. Warm tears come up remembering how I stood up to that inner rage and calmed it. Don't let tears out in front of Arnold.

"Come on in. It's open," he calls warmly.

I'm walking into a lion's den, don't deny it. "Hey. How are you?" I say, composed.

"Good! Have a seat. Can I get you a cup of coffee?"

Why not? "Sure." I'm Lana Turner, smooth, self-assured. Is it an act? No. It's my real self.

We gossip. He's fun. Feels like an hour's gone by. It's great. We're old friends laughing at opposite ends of the couch. Except we've only known each other seven months. He's irreverent. Honest. It feels good to laugh with him. We might as well at least get along. We see each other at meetings.

"Feels good to have a friend," he says, looking me in the eye from under his long lashes.

"Yeah," I say, "one who won't drop me again!" I grin.

"Wait a minute!" He laughs, a deep doubtful laugh. "As I recall you dropped me!"

"You were having phone sex in the bedroom!"

"Oh, yeah, that." He smiles at his feet. "Sorry."

"You should be!" My toes push his foot.

Shouldn't have done that.

But why not? I'm myself, an adult, not a needy neurotically attached lost little girl empty inside. How could I be? I'm too calm. Other people have casual sex. Why can't I? I'm not Catholic anymore. Sorry God. I don't believe everything Catholics believe.

His toe pushes back.

Oh dear. Do I want to do this?

Yes. I'm mature, at last. It's just sex, between friends. What could go wrong?

The more we look at each other, the more I calmly want him.

"You sure you want to do this?" he asks tenderly.

I don't *need* him. I want him. Pure sex. Nothing more.

I nod.

"We can't be a couple," he says.

"That's for sure!" I say.

We laugh.

I'm invincible, grown up. We're adults. We can do this if we want.

As we get up from the couch, a quiet commentator mentions that this is the same bravado I used to get when I wanted to get drunk. I'm too distracted by his hand taking mine to pay much attention.

I don't care.

The next morning, in his dim yellow kitchen we sit in facing chairs, knees inches apart, the glowing orange ember of his cigarette our campfire. We warm our hands on coffee mugs, speechless. The campfire glows bright as he takes a puff. What was I thinking? I'd have fun, waltz away with a feeling of accomplishment for being an adult.

The connection in the night, so magical and pure, is gone. There's nothing between us and that fact is so painful it's hard to breathe, hard to make sense of anything. I was myself last night, it seemed. Now I'm gone, and I can hardly bear the pain. I think about Dixie's group. I'm not going back there. I'd be too embarrassed to say I went back to Arnold.

For five days, when I think about how I slept with Arnold, I shake my head in painful disbelief. That much pain doesn't make sense. I hardly know him.

Ironing my work blouse one day, a realization chills my soul. The only way to ensure I never again feel the pain I felt, when I watched his cigarette ember glow in the kitchen, is to kill myself.

No, I'm not going to kill myself over someone I barely know. I better not even think about that.

Do other people feel this way when they slip with an ex?

I can't trust myself to stay away. What if I do kill myself the next time I go back to him? Could this insanity be connected to Dad molesting me? It doesn't feel like it. And making hot chocolate didn't feel like nurture. What else could it be? I could be a sex addict. I need to talk to Cecilia. Arnold's not the first guy I've been with since I left Isaac. He'd better be the last until I get my head screwed on straight.

At work, I shelve books in the law library. An odd feeling that I don't exist comes over me. I haven't felt this for years. I hope no one comes in. I don't think I can act normal. Don't say anything to Cecilia about it. I worry her enough. Tap the reading shelf. It's real. Count. That'll help. Feel the heft of the books.

Thankfully, twenty minutes later, the spell has passed. No one saw me. I'd hate for the attorneys to notice me tapping and counting. They already think I'm strange—who goes around announcing to each one of them and the rest of the staff I'm in a sobriety fellowship now, the way I did a few years ago? Thankfully they only smiled politely and congratulated me. What was I thinking? I don't think sometimes.

I meet Cecilia for lunch at our little garden area. A cold wind picks up, helps me feel alive, though I wish I were dressed for the cold. "It's freezing," I say. "I won't take long. Don't worry, it's not about Arnold." I turn up the collar of my light jacket.

She smiles. "Good."

"You took me to a meeting a couple of years ago where people talked about incest."

"Yes. A survivor's group," she says brightly.

How is she so relaxed about it? "I couldn't believe people said out loud what others did to them."

"Right. If memory serves me, you didn't think what Dad did was bad enough to talk about."

"Something like that."

It's hard to talk about what he did, even to her, and she's my sister.

"Is this what's coming up for you?" She asks like it's easy to talk about.

I nod. "Maybe."

"It's a big one, Dad's hands grazing our breasts, for years and years, like it's nothing. Believe me, Marie, it's not nothing. I'll tell you something, you can do with it what you like. This kind of invasion, by a father, who's supposed to be a protector, can cause a person to lose their whole sense of self and not even know it. To become someone else, in a sense."

"Yeah, but." I lost myself, but …

"I know. He didn't rape us."

"Right. It was awful what he did, but was it? Really? My mind keeps asking that."

"Look at it another way. This is from my therapist. Suppose you come home, find your windows broken, your door's open, your things are missing." She leans in close. "You know a burglar's been there. You didn't see the burglar. But you know a burglar's been there."

I think about the wreckage of my life. I nod. "I know a burglar's been here … and took away things I need."

She watches me figure it out.

I can't speak. I see slow-motion emotional explosions, one after another: cutting my hands and running headlong into a wall as a teenager, obsessing on one guy after another: David, Adam, Joe, Randy, Isaac, the French guy, now Arnold. My life, never finding connection. Blackouts, black eyes. Thrown against a car by a guy I should have known not to approach. Where was my sense of self? Surrounded by three guys after skinny-dipping alone at midnight. A miracle saved me. Carving my first husband's name in my stomach with a razor. Where was my sense of self?

"How's Arnold?" she asks.

Tears well up. I shake my head. "I don't know what's wrong with me. I slept with him again. It felt magical at night. In the morning, I wanted to die. I need the incest survivors' group again. And another therapy session."

"You didn't go back to the therapist?"

"Not yet. I wanted to figure it out on my own."

We exchange smiles. She knows I don't like to ask for help.

"In the morning, after casual sex, I was shattered feeling disconnected."

She nods. "I'll call you, give you an address for an incest survivors' meeting."

"Thanks."

On the way back to work, cold wind slides across my face into my hair. It exhilarates me while my guts churn. I'll check out the incest survivors' group— jump off a cliff, tell strangers what I don't want to tell.

CHAPTER 5
RAW, TWISTED, PAINFUL BUT AUTHENTIC

June, 1993. A week later.

Cecilia gave me the incest survivors' meeting information, but I'm going to wait a few weeks to go. I need to feel ready.

At work, in the file room, a couple of secretaries ask my opinion about whether a certain paralegal's paying too much attention to the cute new runner everyone likes to claim.

"Sorry, I don't really pay attention to those things." That was a lie. Why shouldn't the paralegal go for the runner? I take my files and slide away from the conversation with an irritated feeling. It's none of my business what people choose to do. So, why do I judge the gossipers? It's what they choose to do.

Why am I at odds with the world? Maybe because Jean and I are going to see Mom and Dad on the weekend. Seeing them always makes me nervous. And I'm still smarting from Arnold.

I need a nice one-on-one visit with someone whom I can draw out. It gets me out of myself. I like getting people to show me their true selves. I validate them. People need that. I'm good at doing it.

What about Marsha? She's possibly the most introverted person I've ever met. She won't want to talk to me. I'd love to hear her story. No one ever visits with her. She wears plain long sleeve blouses with long skirts and little black heels. Her gray hair sits on her head like a cap. She's still cute. She's only about ten years older than I am. My heart goes out to her whenever I see her eat lunch alone. Why not ask her to eat lunch at the fish pond? I'm too shy.

But what if I could help her?

"Hi, Marsha."

What are you doing, Marie? She barely knows you. "I know we haven't ever hardly talked, but I was wondering, because we both bring our lunch," good way to make a connection, "if you'd want to eat together at the fish pond today. It's in a small park a block away."

"Oh." She smiles, looks away with a little laugh. She looks back and forth across the floor at her feet. "I guess so." She looks up at me. "I know that pond."

"Oh, good. Let's meet at the elevator at noon."

"Sure," she says to her lap. "That'll be all right."

She won't show up.

At noon, she's at the elevator! We smile awkwardly, ride down in silence, walk out to the street.

"Beautiful weather," she says.

"Yes. Not too hot," I say, surprised she spoke first.

"Exactly. Don't you just love the breeze!" she says. Her eyes close for a few seconds while she smiles into the light wind.

She's come alive before my eyes. What makes her so shy? There must be some childhood experience, or self-talk, that holds her back. I bet I can find out what it is.

At the fish pond, we find a stone bench in the sun and sit.

"Aren't they beautiful?" I indicate the foot-long gold and silver carp. They slowly move like spies in the deep pond water.

"Yes! I guess it's good they have the black net to protect them from the raccoons, but the net spoils the view," she says with a sad laugh.

"It does."

We fall silent. What should I say?

I open my sandwich. I take in the warm sun on my arms and the intricate patterns of light and shadow among the shrubs and small trees, some emerald green, some deep forest green. The plant life runs along twisting paths where kidnappers could hide. Life is just like this park—complicated, stunning, dangerous. Don't say that out loud. Be more normal.

"Strange," I say, "that more people don't come here to eat."

"You'd think they would."

"What did you make for lunch?" I ask.

"Oh, just some pasta with ham and vegetables."

"It looks delicious. Tuna sandwich here."

"Tuna's nice."

We eat in silence. I'm a bit of an introvert too, when I'm not on a mission. It's nice to eat and not talk, to exist.

Several minutes pass. I look at her. She smiles and looks away, seeming embarrassed.

If only I could see inside her, without digging. I want to tell her she's a wonderful person and doesn't need to be embarrassed for who she is.

I know—I'll draw her out without asking point blank what went wrong in her life to make her so withdrawn. Part of inner child work is knowing what you wish for. Ask what she'd wish for if she could have anything. That's such a great idea.

I'm already feeling better about seeing Mom and Dad. They don't seem to loom so big in my psyche, neither does Arnold, come to think of it, now that I'm focused on Marsha.

"Marsha, if you could have any wish, what would you wish for?"

She smiles into her lap and nods, then smiles out to her vison. "I wish that my husband would get hit by a bus."

We look at each other.

I burst out laughing.

She smiles at me and laughs.

I didn't see that coming. "You're not joking," I say.

"No."

Quiet Marsha has a spirit that's been carved out deep.

"All right. Good for you!" I say.

"Thank you." She nods a few times, smiling.

I want to ask her why, but I'm not a counselor. I'm just glad she said it out loud and I got to be her witness. "Can I ask you another question?"

"Sure," she says good-naturedly.

"What do you dream of?" We're supposed to let our inner child dream.

"Oh. That's easy. Buying a yellow convertible and driving it with the top down, with the wind and sun on my face!"

"Oh my gosh. What a great dream."

She grins, nods, eats her lunch.

Marsha's fine. She's intact. She doesn't need me. "Thanks for telling me those things. I feel honored."

"You're welcome. You asked. No one's ever asked me."

Tears come up. People are so brave living hard lives with private dreams. This is why I love visiting one on one, drawing people out. She seems so glad. It's good for her and for me.

"What do you wish for?" she asks.

"A good mate. Someone who'll roll up his sleeves and do life with me."

She nods approvingly. "What do you dream of?"

"Writing a book about my life."

"And publishing it," she adds.

"Yes. Thanks for saying that. It's hard to say that part. And publishing it."

We eat. I tell her a few things I'm planning to put in my book. "I ended up with two black eyes and an egg on my forehead. Of course, when we got out of jail in the morning, I apologized to Randy for making him so angry. I didn't know any better back then."

Marsha smiles and nods. She gets that part. Could be why she wishes her husband would get hit by a bus.

"Luckily, the rancher who hired us to clean the stalls of his prize quarter horses only saw Randy. If he'd seen me, he would have turned us away. Instead, he gave us lodging in the studio in the barn and forty dollars a week. Then the owner and I ran into each other one night in the barn. He told me he didn't approve of black eyes, as if I'd done it to myself."

Marsha shakes her head.

"I grew another little layer of steel, looked him in the eye, said it wouldn't happen again."

We laugh.

I won't tell her about layers of steel from what Dad does, touching me and my sisters. I don't want her to have to hear that. Though that'll be in the book, for sure.

"Your book sounds fascinating."

"You really think so?"

"I do."

"Thanks. It's just my life."

We eat.

"A yellow convertible?" I say smiling.

She chuckles. "Yes!"

When the hot sunlight makes little beads of sweat on our brows, we pack up our things.

"Well, this has been very enjoyable," she says.

"Yes, it has." I feel renewed. And ready for the weekend.

On Saturday, Jean drives us in her fire-engine-red Capri. We fly up San Marcos Pass, speed toward Mom and Dad's in Santa Maria. Jean doesn't like her fluffy blonde hair but I think it makes her look beautiful. Mine's straggly brown. It's hard to believe I'm a year older than she is. She always seems more mature. She probably is, from the discipline of raising twin boys who are young men now.

"I haven't seen Mom and Dad in two months," I say.

"I haven't seen them since before Christmas. I guess that's six months."

"I feel guilty."

"Not me," she says.

How can she be so calm? "It's just that they're old," I say.

"Not that old."

"Mom's seventy-nine." I look to see if she's joking saying they're not that old.

"Eighty's old," she says with a smirk and a smile.

"Are you sure you want to go see them?" I ask.

"Uh uh. I don't," she says.

"Me neither. Not really. It's awkward."

"Everyone has to pretend everything's all right. It's not. My kids don't get to see their grandparents. That's sad."

"I forget about that. It is sad."

We crest the hill of San Marcos Pass and begin the descent. Suddenly the complex folds and patterns of majestic blue mountains looming in the distance come into view. They're size is so compelling they should be able to change the way things are, somehow, make things better than they seem, but the stunning view can't touch my life. The beauty makes the pain of needing to go to see Mom and Dad more real, by contrast. But I remind myself of that day on the break-water, after therapy, when I understood I can help Dad, shortly before the wave doused me. Why not start the plan today? See if I can help Dad talk about his childhood and see if I can help him understand why he does what he does. These thoughts ease my normal resistance to seeing him. I won't mention my plan to Jean. She'll say I'm crazy to try to counsel him, which I'm not.

We ride in silence over the long, high arch bridge many have jumped from. The bridge spans a canyon. I try to imagine jumping, but can't get past standing there, feeling the wind of the cars. "It must be a loss of holding on to life, the way most of us hold onto life, all day every day, that makes it possible to jump," I say.

"What are you talking about?"

"People jump from this bridge. I tried to imagine jumping just now. I couldn't jump in my imagination. I think they have to lose the urge to hold on to life."

"Oh. I don't know that we hold on to life. We just live."

We talk about whether we hold on or just live all the way to Santa Maria.

"I hold on to life. Or else I'd drift away, back to drugs and alcohol." The thought of drinking gives me a cold bloodless feeling.

"I just live my life. Hey, do you believe in reincarnation?" Jean asks.

"Like coming back as a dog?"

"Well, possibly. But more like coming back as a person. I've been reading about Edgar Cayce."

"He sees the future, right?"

"Not exactly," she says.

"I don't think Mom likes him," I say.

"Well, just listen for a minute. He wasn't a crack pot. And he never promoted himself. He was actually a devout Christian. Read the whole Bible every year. But when he'd go into these trances to help diagnose people—he was good at that—he saw that this wasn't their first life-time. He urged people to study and learn all they can, because he saw that people take with them everything they learn in life."

"You really think we come back?"

"I hope so. I sure want a better life than this one."

"You don't like your life?"

She gives me a look. Looks back at the road. "I would have liked a better childhood. Better self-esteem. I feel so screwed-up, I can't believe my kids have turned out okay. You know, Michael and I ate at a little place downtown a while ago. They didn't have a restroom. Michael said he needed one and drove off to find a restroom. My first instinct was to figure out how I would get home if he didn't come back. It made sense to me. He'd never left me stranded. It was just how I reacted, to take care of myself. That's not normal, expecting to be left for no reason. We weren't arguing. So, yeah. I'd like to come back, have a better life."

"I get the same feelings, no matter who I'm with." I notice the street looks unfamiliar. "Jean."

"What."

"You passed the turn that goes to their street. Way back there."

"What?"

"Neither of us noticed. Guess we really don't want to go see Mom and Dad!" I say.

We burst out laughing.

She pulls into a small parking lot. "Part of us *really* doesn't want to go." We laugh some more. She turns around and heads back.

"See?" she says. "It's our unconscious doing for us what we won't do for ourselves. Edgar Cayce would say pay attention to this message."

"I think you're right. We really don't want to go see them. My stomach's stirred up thinking about it." A small pain tells me my ulcer may be coming back.

"Why are we going?" she asks.

"I told Mom we were coming and she was really glad."

"It's so awkward," Jean says. "Acting polite. Hearing Dad grumble."

"Hearing her talk about newspaper articles to avoid talking about anything real. If I hear about one more newspaper article, I'll scream," I say.

"I like her newspaper articles. She has interesting ideas. At least she's interested in the world."

"Jean. We did it again."

"What?"

"Passed the turn," I say.

We howl.

"I didn't see it," she says, laughing so hard she can hardly talk. She turns us around. "Never gave it a thought."

"It's not like we don't know the turn!" I say, laughing.

"No!"

We laugh some more.

"I'm turning now." Her face is red holding back a laugh.

"Good. Because come hell or highwater, we are going to visit Mom and Dad!"

We laugh.

"Yes, we are and it'll probably be both hell and high water! At least our unconscious thinks so," she says.

She's so smart.

"'Go home!' our unconscious is saying! It's not too late to go home!'" she says.

We laugh.

We stop at a traffic light. Look at each other. We're a block past the turn onto Mom and Dad's street. We scream.

"I don't think we're going to make it!" she howls. She sobs, laughing so hard she sounds drunk.

"We're trying, Mom, we really are!" I call out. I weep, wipe tears from my eyes, hold my sides, unable to stop convulsing with laughter.

We laugh so hard we gasp for air for another wave of howls and silent wails as Jean turns the car around in another parking lot. She slowly drives back.

"I'm turning here," she says, looking at me to make sure I see.

I nod, still laughing.

She makes the turn down their street.

I point at their house.

She nods. Parks.

We catch our breath for several minutes, sober up from our howling, wipe our eyes. Sigh.

"Ready?" I ask.

"Ready."

We get out, go up the walk.

I knock on the door. Hear footsteps. The door opens.

Mom smiles wide in her light blue knit top, dark blue polyester pants, apron and slippers. "Well, don't just stand there, you two, come on in."

She hugs us each.

Jean says she's not old. She looks old. The last eight years have aged her. The stress of half the family at any given time not willing to visit them because of Dad. It's so fucking hard to imagine what Mom goes through.

"How was the drive?" Mom asks as she walks back to the stove.

Jean and I look at each other, clamp our hands on our mouths so we don't bust up again.

"The trip was good, Mom," Jean finally says. "What are you making?"

"Meatloaf. I hope you've got time to stay for dinner. It'll be ready in an hour."

Jean and I look at each other, nod. "Sure," Jean says. "Thanks, Mom. Can we help?"

"Well, one of you can go see if your father needs a glass of wine. Tell him dinner's in one hour."

Jean and I look at each other again. I don't want Jean to have to go. She's more fragile than I am. "I'll go," I say. Besides, this is a good time to begin to find out what went wrong in Dad's life to make him the way he is. Hopefully I won't be afraid to make a connection with him. I think that's the only way to avoid neurotic attachments. Being honest is the trick. Being myself. Don't lean over to kiss him, don't get close. Stand my ground. He'll respect that. Cecilia says the abuse took away my sense of self, so, as of now, I claim myself back, if you can do that with a missing self.

I go through the dining room into the living room. Dad snores in his recliner. I stop eight feet from him. His white hair's thin, still wavy on top. His skin's smooth. His tan arms are thin. He's lost weight. How can he be so stubborn, when most of his family won't be in his life because of his behavior?

He's a handful. Unpredictable, always has to be right, easily angered. Almost eighty years old. Could it do any good to talk to him?

My spirits fall. Get real, Marie. I'm dreaming if I think I can help him change. I wish he could have his family around him again, but I can't help him. No. It's too painful to interact. How can I claim and nurture myself *and* help him?

Don't wake the lion. I've always put on a façade, a smile, gauged his needs, absorbed his bitterness, laughed at his jokes. I'm *crazy* to think I can *connect* with him, help him sort out his childhood, find out why he molests us, so he can sort it out and change.

I quietly turn to go back to the kitchen.

"Marie? Is that you?" He sounds kind.

I turn back. "Yeah, Dad. I didn't want to wake you." That's the truth.

"Well, I've had enough sleep."

"Okay. Mom said to ask if you want a glass of wine. Dinner's in one hour. Meatloaf."

"Will you be having a glass of wine?"

"I don't drink, Dad. Two years sober."

"Oh, that's right. Well, I'll just have ice water, if you wouldn't mind."

"Sure. I'll go get it." He doesn't sound irritated, he sounds sad. This is a good time to talk to him.

I come back with ice water for us both.

"Pull up a chair," he says.

"Good idea." I pull a dining room chair in, leave a good six feet between us. "How are you?" Bad question. He doesn't trust that question.

"All right, I suppose. You?"

"I'm okay. I was wondering, Dad, about everything, you know, the stress between us ..."

He nods. He's honest.

Ask him straight out. "I was wondering what your childhood was like."

"My childhood."

"Yeah."

"Well, it was a happy childhood. Not a single unhappy day. My folks were loving. I bought them their house when I was twenty-seven years old. Cost five thousand dollars."

I've heard all this before. I thought now, after all the conflict, he'd have a different take on his childhood. "How about when you were selling newspapers at five years old to help put food on the table? Did anything go wrong when you were out there on the street that young?"

"No. I felt proud. Those were hard times. Everyone pitched in. Spike Davis gave me that corner. He'd gotten his own route. I was so proud. He taught me how to make change. That was the hard part. Being ready with the right change, because commuters were always in a hurry."

I can see him, five years old, quick with the money. He's sincere. Childhood was a happy time. There's something I'm not getting.

"Well," he says leaning forward, "I'd better get up. See a man about a horse. Give us a hand, Marie, will you?" He reaches out for my hand.

No. I can't take his hand. It's not safe for me.

But I can't tell him no.

Be true to yourself, Marie. Marsha was true to herself, opening up and telling me the truth about how she feels about her husband and a yellow convertible. Be your true self. Be your true self. "I better not."

You couldn't have said it a better way than that? No.

"What?" He says, irritated.

True self. This is hard! So, what if it's hard? "I better not."

"Suit yourself," he says, disgusted, and gets up, leaves the room.

He thinks I'm being petty.

I'm not. Thanks, Marsha. He could have touched me, grabbed me. Damn. My stomach hurts. So what? I was *myself*. It didn't feel good at the time. It does now. Plus, I didn't get touched or grabbed. I'm being myself. I can do this. I'm tough.

At dinner, Dad's moody.

"Your meatloaf all right, Honey?" Mom asks Dad.

"I suppose," he grumbles

"How was your nap?" she asks.

"Evelyn, my nap was fine!" he barks.

Mom sighs, tosses her sorrow away with a strong shake of her head.

"How's your ombudsman program going, Mom?" Jean asks.

Thanks, Jean. Mom brightens. Mom organized the ombudsman program for skilled nursing facilities when I was twenty-seven years old and went on strike with other aides protesting conditions at a nursing home. Mom and Jean chat.

I could join their conversation, but I watch Dad. He feels betrayed. I wouldn't take his hand.

Good. It hurt when he got mad, but an authentic interaction transpired between him and me. It was raw, twisted, painful but authentic. The beginning of a real connection. I feel its energy. I don't feel at odds with myself or the world anymore.

I'm ready for the incest survivors' meeting.

CHAPTER 6
FEAR OF BEING SEEN

June, 1993. A few days later.

I reluctantly return for a therapy session with Michael Andersen. I don't feel as desperate now. But I told Cecilia I would see him. I walk into Michael Andersen's cold office wearing a warm sweater this time.

"Good to see you. Have a seat," he says smiling. Interesting. He has a warm sweater on too.

"Thanks." I take my usual chair.

The same pink and turquoise prints look benign now, rather than ominous. What happened? They didn't change. I'm different. Hey, I'll turn the lamp on.

I'm getting a sense of self.

I don't want to talk about sleeping with Arnold, wanting to kill myself. It's too embarrassing. Not serious enough. It's not like I *tried* killing myself. And it's over with Arnold, I hope.

I should have figured out what to say before I got here.

I'll distract him with that amazing dream I had a few years back, so he won't ask about Arnold. "I had an amazing dream a few years ago. In the dream, I was a baby given away by my dad one night to a stranger. My house is across the street behind me. The street was dark. Branches of big shiny wet maple leaves surrounded us, lit up by lamplight in front of Holy Mystery Academy, which in real life was across the street from our house in Seattle, when I was small."

"When did you move to California?"

"When I was eleven. In the dream, I'm in my dad's arms. A man and a lady are there in the lamplight under the leaves. I don't know them. I want Mom. Dad holds me close, kisses me. I'm safe. He squeezes me. I'm safe. But then his hands lift me away from him. 'Be good, now, little Marie,' he says, looking me in the eye. I panic being lifted away from him. He lowers me into the hands of the man I don't know.

"In the dream, I startle, gasp, scream. I scream and scream so Mom will come. She seems just up the street. I can see her, almost, trying to find me. She's looking everywhere while I'm screaming. She doesn't see or hear me. I wail, like a saxophone. And that's all I remember."

Michael Andersen nods. "Interesting dream. What do you make of it?"

He's supposed to tell me, isn't he? "It was awful. My Dad never gave me away in real life. It doesn't make any sense."

"I'm sorry, but dreams aren't really my specialty."

Darn. That was a good dream.

"That's okay." What else can I say? What comes is a fleeting urge to hit my head on something the way I used to. Tell him about that. "I used to hit my head, you know, on a door jamb, or with a small piece of two-by-four, to kill emotional pain. But I don't think that's connected to the dream, except it could be, because the urge just came up."

"You say you used to. How long did you do it?"

"I started when I was about fifteen. I used the brick post, which was part of our porch. And the edge of a swimming pool worked. And I ran into a wall once. That hugely helped. But usually just the door jamb, or a piece of two-by-four. Only when everything was too overwhelming. Maybe a few times a year. I didn't want to do it too much and give myself brain damage. I stopped about a year ago. It didn't seem right, being sober, in recovery, and banging my head. I called my brother Martin after the last time I did it, to ask his advice. He's sober. He said, 'You can do that if you want,' meaning bang my head to kill emotional pain, 'but you might be missing an opportunity for spiritual growth.' Boy, that went in. I haven't done it since. He was right."

"What do you do instead?"

"I cope. Use spiritual solutions, like acceptance. I pray. Eat sweets. Trust God. I have no idea who God is. I act as if God's some loving spirit who doesn't judge us. I eat romaine." Or wail. I need to stop getting into neurotic attachments.

"I'm glad to hear that. So, you don't do any self-harm now?"

"Nope." Well, too much candy.

"Good for you. How are you doing with that relationship you didn't want to go back to? Arnold, was it?"

Shoot. He remembered. "Fine. I think I'm really done this time. I went back for one night. It was bad the next few days, wanting to die, you know, the usual. I'm okay now. I've cried every night since then. I'm feeling better." The therapist can't help me. He can't heal the gaping hole inside me.

"Do you want to kill yourself?"

"No, not at all. You know, it was just wanting to die. To be done."

I wish I had more to say to the therapist. The silence is awkward. "I'm sorry,

I don't have much to talk about this week. I think I'm going to try an incest survivors' self-help group. Oh, and I went to a battered women's group. They said to nurture myself, so I made hot chocolate. That wasn't easy."

He looks confused.

"Part of me thought it was stupid to make hot chocolate. That part raged that I shouldn't do it."

He nods. "That's interesting. I haven't heard of that before."

Really? "Maybe it was an angry inner child." Or inner lion, more like it. Dad's not the only lion in my life.

"Yeah, I'm not sure about the inner child movement," he says. "I'm not saying it does any harm, but it doesn't have a scientific basis."

"Oh." That doesn't make sense. "It's pretty simple. For example, when I want to say no to everything good for me, that's my inner two-year-old acting out. And she needs me, the Marie who's the responsible adult, to give her healthy choices and to nurture her. Or if I'm desperate to hit on guys, that's my inner thirteen-year-old acting out, needing sexual control, from having been molested when I was twelve."

"Okay. Well, that makes some sense, in a way, but it's a fiction. As I said, the inner child paradigm won't hurt you."

"It's saving me."

"It does seem to be useful to you."

We chit chat about the inner child movement, as he calls it, and therapists who specialize in dream analysis and therapy. I'm bored. Is it rude to leave before the hour's up?

"Who recommended the incest survivors' self-help group?" he asks.

"My sister, Cecilia. She used to go a lot. They helped her."

"Well, let me know how it goes."

He can't help me. "Okay. So, I think I'm okay now." I don't have anything else to say.

I must not be cut out for therapy. Cecilia gets a lot out of it. I don't get it. I tried.

I stand up. I'll wait till I have a real problem before I go back to therapy. Well, I do have a real problem, but he can't help.

Michael Andersen stands up. "Okay. We're almost out of time."

"I'll call you if I get another problem." I shake his hand.

"I'll be here."

"Thanks." I pay him.

Yeah. I'm ready. The incest survivors' meeting's this week. Hopefully that'll somehow straighten me out so I'll never go back to Arnold.

The night of the incest survivors' meeting, I walk up the steps of a house where the meeting's held, afraid as usual of being seen by people.

Inside the house, old-fashioned comfortable furniture, wall paper, and a beautiful mirror on a credenza in the entry hall comfort me. Cecilia said the person who lives here only lives in the upstairs part, and donates the entire first floor for different kinds of recovery meetings. Doesn't she worry about being robbed? There're meetings each night of the week, and some during the day. Tonight, it's incest survivors.

I feel embarrassed to be here, but also solid inside. Here comes a guy with a short military haircut, white T-shirt, strong looking arms, O.D. green pants, white teeth in his big smile. I didn't think there'd be men. I'm glad there are. He's not tall enough for me.

Do all women automatically think this way? It's not why I'm here.

"Hello," he says, putting out his hand.

"Hello."

We shake hands. Who abused him?

"Haven't seen you here before," he says.

"No. First time. That is, to this meeting. I went to a different meeting a few years ago."

"Okay. Well, great. Glad you're here." He laughs. "Well, not really, it's probably better none of us were here, but since we are, you know what I mean."

He has a sense of humor. "Yeah." So far, so good.

"Come on in, grab a seat. We're about to begin."

Circled around the living room are an empty couch, a few stuffed chairs, a few straight-back chairs. I pick a straight-back chair. Someone probably has dibs on the stuffed chairs.

Six other people, men and women all talking to each other, take cups of coffee to their seats. Most wear black outfits, edgy styles. A few in leather jackets. One cute guy with blue green eyes and long dark chestnut hair wears a big army jacket. It's a militant group. I like that. I feel out of place in my blue jeans, giant T-shirt and big green jacket. I don't care.

I might not fit in with these people, but I'm comfortable with myself. They're all friends with each other. I'm a loner. I write at four a.m. Work. Shop. Go home alone. It's okay. I don't need people actually in my life, I only need them here at a meeting.

"Sorry, I didn't get your name," says the friendly guy who greeted me.

"Marie."

"Marie, I'm Mark. Everybody, let's welcome Marie. It's her first meeting, in a long time."

People say hi. I make a little wave. I don't like being here with strangers, but I need them.

A pale thin girl with dull wispy hair, younger than I am, opens a binder and reads about why we're here, how <u>we're survivors, not victims.</u> "<u>Healing comes,</u>" she reads, "by <u>bringing to light the truth of what happened, because the disease</u> thrives on <u>keeping the secret, and we thrive on speaking up and reclaiming our</u> <u>true selves.</u>"

The words are so beautiful I choke back tears. I'm in, though I won't share tonight.

The same girl starts the sharing. "I'm Dinah, incest survivor. I don't know what to do with my son. He's twelve. When he's with his dad, he goes to school, does his homework. But when he's with me, he won't do anything. I think I messed him up. For a few years, I couldn't function, my depression was so bad. My son had to raise himself. Now, since coming here, I finally have a voice, a life, a sense of humor. I'll never be normal, but life's worth living now. I just wish I could find a way to make things up to my son. We're not supposed to cross-talk, but ..." She looks at me.

"Then why are you going to cross-talk, Dinah?" a lively guy in a black leather jacket interrupts. He laughs.

Everyone laughs.

"Because I can, Scott!" Dinah says, smiling back at him. She looks at me. "Don't let whoever hurt you take your life away twice, once when they abused you, and again when you try to deal with life on your own. Don't do it alone. This is a good group. Keep coming back."

I nod. "Thanks." She's nice. The group's fun. I'm not edgy, so I don't fit in, but I'll come back. I never want to go back to Arnold, or get into another neurotic attachment trying to fill the hole within me where a connection with Dad should be.

"All right," says the lively handsome guy named Scott. "I'm Scott. I'm a survivor!" He grins. "And my life is *fucked up* beyond repair, that I can see. I live in a corner of a shop where I work, never see my family, it ain't safe—for them." He laughs. "The fucked-up bullshit of the past can stay there as far as I'm concerned. I don't like to talk about it. But I'm glad I'm here with all you nice people. Thank you for letting me share."

I can't help wondering what happened to him. I guess the details don't matter. He's angry, but he's not bitter. He has a sense of humor.

"All right, Ella, let's hear from you," Scott adds warmly.

A young woman with thick black hair grins, shakes her head no.

"I'll share," says the long-haired guy in the army jacket. He folds his arms. "Baker. Survivor."

I wonder if Baker is his first or last name.

"Longtime friend of the earth, interstellar traveler and survivor of incest," Baker says. "Molested ongoing from eleven to thirteen by a guy on my paper route, survivor of nightly whoopins with a belt on the bare ass—that's sexual abuse, by the way—and we'll just throw in the ice water treatment—five years old, naked, arms held, five-gallon bucket of water and ice dumped on me in front of twelve adults and kids."

Oh my God. My eyes grow hot with tears seeing the little five-year-old held.

"That counts," Baker says. "Yeah, so, if I had a dollar for every time I stood tongue-tied, unable to speak up for myself, unable to collect for papers I delivered, unable to answer the phone or make a goddam phone call because of terror of being seen, I'd be a goddam wealthy man."

I know that fear of being seen. I'm like he is. I uncross my arms, fold my hands in my lap. A warm feeling of connection with these people flows in. I can relate to their feelings.

"So," he continues, "I'm taking a step toward my recovery from phone phobia. I will be making one phone call a week. To somebody. Anybody."

Everyone cheers.

I want to share after all.

When the others have shared, Dinah looks at me. "Marie, would you like to share?"

"Sure." Tears come up. "It's not that bad what my dad does." I look down. "Touched my breasts whenever he hugged me, until my sisters and brothers and I confronted him. Now my dad and I just shake hands. But he gets me when he can." I look back up. "I'm glad I came to the meeting. I relate to what you just said." I nod at Baker. "I'm afraid of being seen. And I like the reading about reclaiming our true selves. That's all."

"Thanks, Marie. Well, the time's about up. We close the meeting with a silent meditation," Dinah says.

After the meeting, I'm too shy to try to talk to people. It seems I barely belong here my abuse was so mild. Still, I know I need the meeting badly, because if I don't get help, I'll either go back to Arnold or get someone else like him. It's still hard to imagine what Dad does messed me up so badly that I can't straighten myself out on my own. But I can't. I have a feeling these people can help. They already have. I'm not alone.

I slip out quietly. The cool fresh evening air hits my face and I feel alive. I'll come back next week. If they can talk about their problems and come to solutions, I can too. So that I'll never again marry someone only because I like their smile, without making sure we can talk. And I'll never get obsessed with a handsome guy like Randy who can't be faithful. Or one like Adam who never loved me. Or another like Arnold, who never loved me either. I'll have my true sense of self, Dinah said. That's what I need.

I get in my car, start the engine. Tears well up as I reflect on the hard times in my life. I've been too afraid to tell anyone. Now I have a place to share. My whole life I've been afraid of being seen, of being alone, of being abandoned, of being ridiculed, of hurting people I need to leave, of living my own life. I don't want to live that way anymore.

People from the meeting come out of the house.

I drive away.

Yep. I want to change. I also want a real partner, not a neurotic attachment. And, I might as well admit it, I want one who wants children. I'm forty-three. Too old to have kids. That's okay. We can adopt, or take care of foster children.

I join the stream of cars on State Street. None of these drivers know the big thoughts I'm having. I feel as though I've done something wrong, telling myself I want children. Why? How can I possibly ever be my authentic self if I can't even tell myself what I want?

CHAPTER 7
A DARK MENACING CLOUD

July, 1993. A month later.

Driving to an incest survivors' meeting, I happily roll my window down all the way and stick my arm out in the hot wind—it's summer! I drink in the pink evening light, sweet balmy air. Life is good, even with problems.

I've been thinking of Mom and Dad lately, feeling conflicted. At the incest survivor meetings, people talk about differentiating themselves from their families as part of recovery. It makes sense, though I don't really want to do that, which makes it something to look at. It feels like disconnecting, which, if there's no authentic connection, it probably is. Dad and I were starting an authentic connection last time I saw them when I told him I'd better not take his hand. He didn't like that, but we were authentic with each other. I'll go see Mom and Dad this weekend. It's been a while. I'm less vulnerable, more myself, so it should be easier to be around them. I'll differentiate myself *while* I visit them. What better test of being my own person?

I hurry into the survivors' meeting, almost late. After a month of showing up I'm finally a regular. I don't want to miss anything. The people are funny and kind, not as scary as I thought. I told them about my neurotic attachments, about trying to fill the empty place where a connection with Dad should be. I feel more myself because I trust them, even happy in my own skin sometimes. At the meetings, we validate each other in a way that doesn't happen anywhere else. Nobody else talks about shameful secrets and feelings. Validation's powerful medicine.

"Ella, survivor." She twists her long, glossy black hair, which I love, pins it up as she speaks. "I'm having a hard time. You know what? I'm really done with all this recovery bullshit and I ate two cream pies to prove it."

I laugh. I love cream pie too. I hope she's not really done with recovery. Hope she's just venting.

No one else laughs.

Two cream pies are bad. Shit. I'm shallow. "Sorry."

"No, it's good you laughed, Marie. Anything to shake me out of thinking I don't belong on earth anymore. Seems I never did, for that matter. My parents didn't see fit to look after me when I needed them. I told them my aunt was using me to keep her boyfriend happy."

She switches between friendly and aloof with me. Her erratic feelings make so much sense now.

"My parents didn't believe me," Ella says. "How can I believe myself? What kind of life can I have? A boyfriend would help. Someone supportive." She shakes her head. "Men … I've got plenty of those. But no one supportive." Tears fill her eyes. "I want a good man. Is that too much to ask?"

People nod. We get it.

I want a good man. Men here seem good. Especially Baker. If only his hair weren't long.

Ella wipes her tears, smiles. "And I want to *be* somebody!" She laughs, shrugs. "I want a life that matters. I'm a paralegal. Whoop de doo. Stuck in other peoples' doo-doo. I want to make a difference!"

Me too! But I could never leave my good paying law librarian job, with paid holidays, paid vacation and sick time—I never had a job with benefits before. Anyway, what would I do to make a difference?

Be a counselor. Or a teacher.

Those careers require school. Doing work and school at the same time is hard. I couldn't do it.

"Then comes the cloud, a dark menacing cloud that tells me, Ella, you're a piece of shit. Now live your shit life and be grateful! My mom talking, in so many words." She laughs, pulls her hair down, shakes it till it falls around her face. She looks away with cool detachment. "I'm done. Next."

I want to help her get out from under the dark menacing cloud. No crosstalk's aloud. I'll tell about the fight to make hot chocolate. She'll relate.

"Marie. Survivor. I went to a battered women's group not too long ago."

Baker looks at me. He's a good listener.

"I didn't think I belonged there." I tell the whole story. "They helped me see the truth. Getting pushed leads to getting beat up again. I had no sense of self. No real relationships, only neurotic attachments because I had no connection with my dad. I didn't tell the battered women's group about my dad molesting me, even though that's domestic violence. I was too embarrassed. The group said I needed to nurture myself. So, I said I'd make hot chocolate. Easy. Except when I went home and tried to make hot chocolate, part of me grew so enraged it took every bit of will to do it." I had my own dark menacing cloud. "Part of me didn't want me to nurture myself. I had to fight to finish making the hot chocolate. But

I did it!" I look at Ella. I want her to fight to nurture herself too.

She looks away. I think she doesn't like me for some reason. It hurts, but I can't worry about it.

"It felt like a hurricane inside," I go on, "with someone screaming, 'Don't fucking do it!' I was exhausted afterward. The next day, I felt great. More connected to myself. I'm done. Next."

Baker nods.

After the meeting, Scott says, "Everybody going to Hot Spots?"

I'm too shy to go socialize at a coffee shop. I told them a few weeks ago I need to go home to bed after meetings so I can get up at four in the morning to write.

"What about you, Marie?" Scott says. "And don't say you get up at four to write every goddam morning." He tosses his head and laughs.

"She's coming," Baker calls out. His look my way pulls me into the fold.

"Where is it?" I ask.

Scott laughs. "You don't know where Hot Spots is? There's a whole world out there, Marie. Follow us."

He's right. I need to get out more. I follow them.

Hot Spots is cozy, not too big. We get our own coffee in heated ceramic cups with old-fashioned saucers. We share a giant piece of carrot cake.

I'm on edge with nothing to say. I look for ways to connect to conversations. The others all seem at ease socializing.

"What do you mean, Scott? Men can*not* be trusted!" Ella laughs.

Ella and Scott have been arguing since we got here.

"No, it's women," Scott retorts. "Never trust a woman. Am I right, Baker? I don't care who the dame is, could be Mother Teresa for all I care, she'll get her grimy little hands on your wallet and swear it never happened, right, Marie?"

I don't want to get in the middle of this.

Sweet Mark looks over from his conversation with Dinah. His laugh shows his white teeth. "Mother Teresa, Scott?" He shakes his head.

"Yes, Father Mark, Mother Teresa!" Scott says and chuckles.

Okay, I'm in. "I'm with Ella," I say.

"Thank you, Marie," Ella says. "A voice of reason."

She does like me.

"Shit, that's not *reason!*" Scott cries. His neck turns red. "That proves my point. You women are thick as thieves because you are thieves!" Scott howls at his joke.

"You don't get anything out of the bargain?" Ella says with a gleam in her eye.

They carry on. Mark listens to Dinah talk about her son.

"Crazy story about making hot chocolate," Baker says to me.

"Yeah, huh. I still don't know what it was all about," I say.

Baker's sweet. And I'm not neurotically attached to him.

Ella stands, stretches her arms. "Marie, it was probably one of your alters who didn't want you to make the hot chocolate." She stands behind Baker, massages Baker's neck and shoulders.

Damn it. She's claiming him.

"What's an alter, Ella?" I ask. If he wants her, fine.

"Alters are your other selves," she says. "A lot of us have alters. They come out when they think they're needed. Not always a good thing, but they think they have a job. That's what it sounded like to me. You were making hot chocolate to nurture yourself, which pissed off one of your alters."

"That's so interesting," I say. I'll bet she's right. That would explain it.

"Interesting?" Ella scoffs. "It's *true!*" she cries. "Our alters won't have a place in a world of self-nurture!"

She's so passionate. "Why not?" I ask.

"They're the old guard. They think they protect us by keeping us down, suspicious, scared. They don't let us really get our hopes up!" She tosses her head. "I like my alters." She laughs. "They let me act out, have fun."

Scott and Ella howl at her joke. I get it.

Her long hair's so rich, it seems to move on its own. Why would Baker pay attention to me when Ella's fun and beautiful?

"Dinah's having a party this weekend," Mark says.

"You're all invited. I'll be three years sober," Dinah says with a shy smile.

We cheer. We're all sober, which feels good. I want to go to Dinah's party. I guess I won't see Mom and Dad this weekend after all. Next weekend, I'll go see them for sure.

Scott stands. "Come on, let's go outside and smoke."

"Go ahead," Baker says. "I don't smoke. Done with that shit."

"Let's go, Marie," Ella says. She taps Baker's shoulders, done massaging them, follows Scott and the others to the door.

"I don't smoke either. You guys go. Baker and I'll clear the table."

The others go out. The place is quieter.

We sit in silence for a moment.

I'm nervous having nothing to say. "I was wondering, is Baker your first name, or your last name?"

"First name. After my grandad."

"Oh. Okay."

We're quiet for another minute. He's shy too.

"Well," I say, "I guess we could clear the table. You take the cups. I'll take the saucers." I pick up the empty carrot cake plate, happy to be doing something with Baker.

Baker sits still, suddenly rigid. He stares into space. He seems to have a problem with what I said. Yeah. I gave him an order. It could never work with us if he's that touchy. Only one way to fix it. "Or, *I'll* take the cups, and *you* take the saucers?" I smile.

He looks at the table, relaxes and grins. "Well," he says, looking me in the eye, "as long as we're doing it together."

He's claiming me.

Ella can't have him.

Saturday comes and I feel nervous, like an imposter, but I make myself go anyway to Dinah's party. It seems I'll never be at home in the world.

"Welcome to my extra tiny abode!" Dinah says warmly and waves me into her small, old stucco cottage, romantic-looking outside, cramped with moldy walls within. She lives on relief checks. She's glad to see me. I'm glad I made myself come.

"It's all I can afford, to have a separate bedroom for my son. I sleep on the couch."

"It's cozy," I say. I look at paintings of animals, each skillfully rendered in a different color. "I like the artwork."

"You do? It's all mine."

"You're kidding." I study a blue horse, a pink otter, a green cat, a red rat. "You're good, Dinah."

"Thanks. Come get a soda. Mark's playing video games in the bedroom with the kids. Baker and Scott are on their way."

Ella comes from the kitchen. "Hi, Marie!"

She sounds happy to see me. I wouldn't blame Baker if he wants her. She's fun, beautiful and lively. "Hi Ella." Think of something to say. "I'm admiring Dinah's art work."

"She does it from memory," Ella says.

"You do?" I ask Dinah.

"I do," Dinah says.

"I have to have the person sit," I say.

"You do portraits?" Dinah asks.

"Mostly."

Men's voices come from down the walk.

"Your work's amazing," I say. I look around to the front door.

Baker walks in. I want to do his portrait with his twinkling eyes, rugged face.

Scott carries a homemade blue cake, with the number three drawn in darker blue frosting. He sings, "Happy birthday to you."

We all sing.

Throughout the afternoon, the slow swirl of people puts me at ease. They care deeply about each other, not about what each other has. Everyone barely gets by. I still don't know how to banter, though I'm not embarrassed for being quiet anymore. We eat cake and potato chips, drink soda, laugh at Scott and Baker's antics. In my heart, I sit on a green lawn of an old movie sanitarium with a blanket on my lap, safe.

"My co-worker is such a rat. He takes anything you have. My pen, scraps of photographic paper I salvage from the garbage, even my lunch!" Scott cries and laughs.

"Your lunch?" I ask.

"Marie spoke, you guys!" Scott teases. "Yeah, swear to God. He took my lunch the other day!"

Baker wrinkles his nose, "I'm a rat." He holds his hands up like paws, sniffs the air all around. "Hm. What's this? Bologna sandwich?" he says in a funny voice. His paw snatches the invisible bologna sandwich, slowly stuffs it all into his mouth.

I laugh.

"Apple." He shoves an invisible apple into his mouth. His cheeks bulge more. "I'm a rat. Paper. Mm. Good."

We laugh.

Baker the rat struggles to stuff invisible paper in his mouth. Baker's face contorts, stretches and bulges. He succeeds. Cheeks and eyes bulging, he picks up a stuffed bunny.

We howl.

"Mm. This yours?" he says to Dinah. "Too bad."

Baker could be on stage, he's so funny. I can't take my eyes off him. Now he talks for the bunny, "Please don't eat me!" and for a stuffed dog, "Bunny's a loser, man, eat him, Rat."

"God, here," Baker says in a deep voice. "What's everyone complaining about? Rat's taking everything for himself? Tell you what, here's a tsunami to take *all of you* out of here." Baker's mouth bulges slightly as he makes a quiet roaring sound, like a furnace. "Honey," he says, playing the part of a very anxious husband, "Better get the kids in the car." The quiet roar gets louder. He makes a noisy sound of an ignition turning over and over and over. More roaring sound of the approaching tsunami.

We howl.

"Baker!" I say.

"What?"

"God doesn't wipe them all out with a tsunami just because they complained about Rat."

"He doesn't? You don't know God," Baker says.

"It's exactly what God does," Scott says.

I frown and shake my head no.

"Oh, all right," Baker says. "No tsunami."

"Good," I say.

"A storm!" Baker says.

From within his mouth and chest comes a sound of crackling electricity, followed by booms of transformers, thunder, more lightening, more thunder, and a loud shhhh sound of a deluge of rain. "The river breaks its banks!" His arms brush the air as he makes a roar of the waves of a swollen river. "And everything washes out to sea!" He smiles at me and laughs.

He's a little dark. I make a sad face.

"Except bunny!" He picks up the bunny, tosses it in the air, catches it, sets it down. "Better?"

I scrunch my face into half a smile. "Not really."

Shoot. He's negative.

But so alive. And too irreverent to be conflicted. Compared to him, I feel I half-exist, under a menacing cloud no less. Where's the rest of me? With my parents. I always mentally run everything by what they taught me. I don't believe everything they taught me, but I'm still affected by it all. There has to be a God who loves us, somehow, who doesn't wipe us out with disasters. "Disasters just come. God doesn't cause them."

"Don't worry," Scott says laughing, "Bunny won't die. Not this time."

"Thanks, Scott."

I'm too serious. I could lighten up. Baker's a good performer, and a good influence.

After a while, Dinah opens a box of bead-making supplies, makes us all necklaces from beads we choose. She has almost nothing, and is so generous. She's not worried.

"I need to be more relaxed, like you are, Dinah," I say, watching her string my necklace of black, gray and turquoise beads.

"Do you like your job?" she asks me.

"No, not anymore. Why do you ask?"

"People who love what they do are usually pretty relaxed about life, in my experience."

She is really smart. "I agree."

"Here's how you get a job you love," she says. "Someone told me how to do it, and it worked. You write down five things you *love* to do, regardless of whether they'll make money. Set your intention to end up doing those things, then forget about it. Keep the list of five things with you, somewhere in your purse. You'll unconsciously aim at putting those things in your life. Try it. I had to quit the great job I got, which I loved, when I had a breakdown, but the method worked for me. I got the job. I went to chef's school, became a chef, and loved it."

"I'll do it. Write my list of five things I love." I can't wait.

When the sun goes down, the house gets cold. Others leave. Baker and I sit on the couch, while Dinah feeds the kids.

"Little Audrey's Café's closing," Baker says to me.

"No way! How sad," I say. "I love going in there to drink coffee and write. Little Audrey's has been there at least since I was eleven, when I moved here."

"We should go there before it closes. Say good-bye to the place," he says with a melancholy note.

He's sentimental, connected to meaning. I like that. "That's a great idea. Should we tell the others?"

"No. You and I'll go. How about this weekend?"

A date with Baker. "I'm planning to see my parents this weekend."

"You don't need to caretake your parents. He molests you, and your mom didn't protect you."

He's so abrupt and raw. "I know. I still love them."

"Do you *want* to see them? Be honest."

"Yes and no. That's a hard question. I'm split. Part of me feels my stomach turn at the thought. The other part wants to be with them. They're old."

"What, eighty? That's not *old*." He gets a sheepish smile.

I laugh. "Yes, it *is* old!"

"Love them from afar. From two weeks away. What about your own life? Go see them in two weeks."

Somewhere within, thunder claps in warning and lightning crackles—I'm choosing myself over my parents. Is that okay?

Baker's right. I need to live my life. Sorry Mom and Dad. See you in two weeks. "Alright. Little Audrey's it is."

The next day I wake from a dream that feels so real I'm startled to find it's not. I sit up in bed and reflect on the dream. I was in dazzling sunlight, standing waist deep in a beautiful aqua colored swimming pool with several other people, who were also standing waist deep in the pool. We were all listening to a Black woman who stood at the end of the pool, outside the water, on the ledge, speaking to us. She wore robes. It seemed she was a spirit—an angel maybe, or a saint. The sunlight behind her made her fluffy hair a dark silhouette. She looked straight at me and said, "The child isn't ready yet." Her words landed deep within me. I wanted her to say more. But that was it. I woke up. What did she mean?

Are Baker and I going to have a baby? No. We hardly know each other. The child I'm going to adopt or foster isn't ready yet? No. I'm not getting an Aha! feeling. Jean says when you're interpreting a dream, you know you've hit on the answer when you get an Aha! feeling. Jean also said a dream is the clearest message your unconscious can give you about a current problem in your life today. I have a problem. I want to raise children. But what message is the dream giving me? My parents are children, and I should go see them? No. She said the child isn't ready yet.

Chapter 8
Blue Streamers

July 1993. A week later.

Saturday morning, I shake my head as I get dressed. Why did I let Baker talk me out of seeing Mom and Dad? He and I are going to Little Audrey's this morning, but I'll bet we could have gone another time. I won't do that again, let him talk me out of what I want. Mom and Dad are old and lonely and I need to go see them. For sure I'll go see them next Saturday.

But right now, I need to set the course for the rest of my life—write Dinah's list of five things I like to do. I get comfortably situated on my bed with a scrap of paper, a book for a hard surface and a pen. What are five things I love to do, regardless of money, so that I can end up getting paid to do what I love? What do I love to do? Visit. Write it.

Visit.

I love visiting one on one. I laugh, because Dinah said don't think about money, so I'm not, but is someone seriously going to pay me to visit?

I don't have to think hard to know what else I love to do.

Paint
Write
Children
Theatre

There it is, the list Dinah said to write and forget about. Set my intention by it, then tuck it away and I'll end up doing what I love. Seems strange it could land me where I belong. No harm in trying. I read the list—Visit, Paint, Write, Children, Theatre—and swallow it with my heart. I fold it and tuck it inside my purse. Forget about it.

I get ready to meet Baker.

Downtown, outside Little Audrey's, Baker stands straight. He looks sharp in tan cotton pants and an ironed long sleeve shirt, which looks nice, especially because it's a deep teal blue, same as his eyes.

Our eyes meet. I feel calm. Sometimes it seems I've loved him for a thousand years.

"Good morning," he says, a twinkle in his eye.

"Good morning."

He opens the door for me. I like that.

We quietly make our way to a booth and take a seat. We're both quiet, shy without the other group members around.

"Could be the last time we sit here," he says. He looks around and nods at the soda fountain, the high ceiling, the juke box on the table. He makes our being here feel momentous. He's even more nostalgic than I am. I relate..

"It's so sad it's closing," I say. "My mom and I met here for grilled cheese sandwiches a few times during the Vietnam war. And I came here with rent control people during those campaigns. I'll miss this place. Sometimes I write here."

"You have some history here."

He's thoughtful. "I do."

The waitstaff pours coffee. We order English muffins.

"Were you born here in Santa Barbara?" I ask.

"Born in Johnson City, Tennessee. December, 1958."

He just told me how old he is, thirty-five, nine years younger than I am. Is that going to work?

"Seattle. April, 1950," I say. We'll see if nine years matters.

He nods approvingly. "My mom left my dad, the first time, when I was four," he goes on. "She hopped on a train with her three boys, the youngest in diapers, and came out here to Santa Barbara to be with her mother, my Granny. We stayed in Santa Barbara maybe six months, lived different places. Then Mom joined a cult whose leader got in trouble so we ran from the mob to Oregon, then to Hawaii."

"The mob?"

"Yeah. That's what I was told. I don't remember much. My dad joined us in Hawaii at some point. We'd left the cult. My folks had three more boys, raised their six boys on the windward side of O'ahu."

"What an adventure!"

"Yes, ma'am." He grins.

I love when he says that—yes ma'am.

"I always say," he sips his coffee, "if you're going to be abused, there's no better place than Kailua Beach, which was literally our front yard. It's a beach park now, but in those days, old houses were there. We lived in a few of them. I joined the army band at seventeen. Got out three years later. Came back to Santa Barbara, stayed with Granny awhile, then followed a gal to Sacramento. Ten years later, broke my foot, got kicked out—different gal—came back to look after Granny who was dying."

Kicked out with a broken foot? He must have really pissed her off. How?

But he came here to look after his granny. That's good. And he didn't have to tell me he got kicked out. Never mind why. We all mess up. "That's why you drive Granny's car."

"Yes, ma'am. Granny's also how I got my present place."

"How?"

"She'd been a church secretary. After she died, I returned her key to the church. The clerk thanked me. I told her I needed a job and a place to live. In case she heard of anything, could she let me know. The clerk turns around, picks up a card and says, 'This just came in.' It was a request for a live-in helper. So, I drive up on the Mesa, go down a long drive over-looking the ocean, and this old guy in a wheelchair greets me and takes me to the master bedroom. It has a view of the Pacific Ocean below. 'This would be your room,' he says.

"Can you believe it? That was the interview. All I do is pick up his mail at the top of the drive, and buy his groceries. He does his own personal care. I have another gig as a personal care attendant for a guy with cerebral palsy. The rest is history."

"What a great story!" And he has a nice place to live. And he's a personal care attendant. That shows he has a good heart.

Here come our English muffins. I slather mine in butter and jam.

He butters his.

"You don't like jam?" I ask.

"Not much of a sweets head. You have a good story?" he asks.

"Not as good as yours." My good stories are all sordid tales—the guy who threw me against his car *did* finally let go of my thumb, and I taught myself a psychological trick to take the scary memory away. That was good. And I *didn't* get gang-raped when I got surrounded by three guys after I went skinny-dipping, because Randy, upstairs, finally heard me yelling and came outside, made a disgusted look and the men left. Not telling that one.

Ergot. That's a good story.

"I didn't die of ergot poisoning in Paris when our host Gustav brought back from Germany his mom's rye bread in the hot trunk of his car." He's listening.

"Ergot's a fungus that grows on rye. Isaac, my second husband had planned this two-month trip to Europe. He had met Gustav in his other travels, which is why we were staying with Gustav and Gustav's girlfriend, April. It was a small studio apartment. I used the rye bread to fry grilled cheese sandwiches for the four of us on a little stove under the platform bunk our hosts slept on. The sandwiches were delicious.

We all bedded down, Isaac and I on the fold-out couch. I soon woke in a panic thinking something was wrong, like maybe there were burglars outside the windows. I talked myself down. But startled awake again, over and over." Why am I telling Baker this?

"This isn't the kind of good story you meant. We were saying how we ended up here, not how we almost didn't end up here," I say.

"No, no. This a good get-to-know-you story." He smiles.

"Okay. So, I finally decided to turn the light on to assure myself there was no need for panic. I scooted to the foot of the bed to get out. But when I stood up, I fell straight over like a board. I hit my head on the oak post of Gustav and April's bunk."

Baker winces. He's kind.

"I was so embarrassed for the loud noise I'd made, I scrambled to my feet. But as soon as I was upright, I keeled over in the other direction and cracked my head on an oak desk."

"Ouch!"

"Yeah." I laugh. "It was cramped quarters. I stayed down after that, wondering what was wrong. I rocked on my knees, alternating now between several minutes of convulsive shivers and then calm euphoria, like heroin." Heroin. That cat's out of the bag. "I realized I was dying and reflected how odd that I had always thought, if I were dying, I would want to be close to Isaac, but now that I was dying, being close to Isaac was the furthest thing from my mind. I wanted to talk to God. I was in a place of light. I saw that I had tried hard in my life, and saw that God seemed to know that too.

"I didn't die. We all got sick and threw up. Gustav tried to climb down from the bunk to use the bathroom. I scrambled away from the ladder just in time because he fell on Isaac who fell trying to help him down. We slept thirty-six hours.

"Later, Isaac figured it was ergot, which attacks the central nervous system, which would explain why we had no motor control. Ergot grows on rye bread and probably grew in the hot trunk and on the stove. It used to wipe out entire villages in medieval times."

Baker shakes his head. "Damn! You almost died. And you used to use heroin?"

He doesn't miss a thing. "Only for six months. Snorted it. Yeah. And the crazy thing was, when Isaac and I were finally able to eat saltines and to go for a walk outdoors, we saw from a bridge a body floating down the Seine. It was a guy in a tan jacket and brown pants, his chest arched upward so his feet and head were hidden by the murky water. The locals were saying, 'Un cadavre.' Crazy. Could have been us. Dead, I mean."

Baker shakes his head some more. "Crazy. You're here now. That's what counts."

He's glad I'm here.

"What are you doing this weekend?" he asks.

Is he asking me out again? "Going to see my folks Saturday. It's been a long time since I've seen them."

"Probably not long enough," he says with a wry smile.

He doesn't like my dad. I won't tell Baker my long-term plan is to rescue Dad. Baker won't approve. But I'm good at getting people to open up, and I think I can make it happen with Dad. It'll take time. It's worth trying, if it'll help him reconcile with the rest of the family. The rift between him and the family is painful.

We talk a little more, enjoy our coffee and English muffins.

"Well, I need to get going," he says.

So soon? Darn it. "Okay."

He pays.

Maybe he likes me. It's hard to tell.

Outside, we say good-by with regular hugs you would give anyone. Still, I feel good, which is strange, because in the past I've always felt anxious saying good-bye to someone I like.

The following Saturday, my stomach's riled because at last I'm going to see Mom and Dad. I don't care about my stomach being riled. The incest survivors' meetings make me more connected to myself, so I have strength to be with my parents, even if it's a challenge, which is good, because they need a visit. Everyone's life has challenges. This is mine.

I walk outside to my old white Corolla under big slow clouds, in warm summer air which makes me feel alive. I smile. Churning stomach, full heart. That's my life.

I get in the car.

Baker claimed me when we cleared the table at Hot Spots. *As long as we do it together.* Why didn't he put his arm around me or hold my hand at Little Audrey's?

I put the key in the ignition. My car's been making strange sounds lately. It has fumes. I hope it's still road worthy. I turn the ignition. The car's dead. Shoot. This hasn't happened before. Try again. Nothing. Again. Nothing.

I get out, open the hood. Nothing looks different than usual. I check the oil, water, get back in, try again. The car starts right up, lots of power. I'm good.

Except, cars *can* suddenly die on the freeway. Someone told me that. Or, what if it won't start when it's time to come home from Mom and Dad's? I don't want to have to spend the night with them. I need someone to look at my car before I make the seventy-mile drive. I should take it to my mechanic, Rod.

Except, Baker comes to mind. It'd be nice to see him. He seems to be a handy guy. He'll know if the car's safe to drive seventy miles, I think.

No, what am I thinking? I don't know him well enough to ask him to look at it. Go to Rod's.

Hey, I'm supposed to be learning to be friends with people. Friends ask each other for help. Call Baker as a friend. Yep.

I go back upstairs and, nervous, call.

"Hi, Baker. It's Marie," I say in a business tone. I don't want him to think I'm hitting on him.

"Yes, Marie."

He sounds so formal. "I hope I didn't interrupt you."

"I was just reading."

He reads. Good. "Well, my car wouldn't start, and then it did. But I'm afraid it might die on my way to my parents' house in Santa Maria." Why is this so hard?

"Okay."

"I wonder if I could come over and you could look under the hood. I looked, but it looks normal, but I don't know much about cars."

"All right. Not sure I can help. But, all right."

"Thank you. I'm sorry to bother you. I won't stay long." I really do need his help.

"Okay…" His voice sounds like he's smiling now. He thinks I'm hitting on him.

I am.

He gives me his address.

High up on the Mesa, I arrive at a mailbox with the house number. Long blue foil streamers attached to the mailbox wave in a strong breeze. He had a party without me. He's not interested.

I turn down a long, steep drive to a wide parking pad. Oh my gosh. I get out of the car and stare at a wide view of the Pacific Ocean. My parents' home Dad built on the Mesa had the same view from their balcony. A view they gave up when he insisted they move away, to an inland tract-house, to punish us for the intervention—Mom wouldn't go farther north than Santa Maria. Good job, Mom. I never thought of them giving up their view before. How sad.

I knock on the door.

Baker answers, stands there, shirtless in turquoise board shorts. One soft curl of hair in the middle of his chest swirls and trails downward over his lean stomach.

Don't stare.

I look up into his smiling eyes.

"Hi," he says. "So, your car wouldn't start."

"No."

"But you got here okay." He's smiling, amused.

"Yes. Because first it didn't start, then it did start."

"I see. Okay. Let's go look at it."

He opens the hood of my car.

I gaze at the ocean far below. "Quite a view. I see what you mean."

"Yes, indeed," he says, smiling up at me.

He takes a wire off something.

"What's that?" I ask.

"That's a spark plug wire."

"Is it okay?"

"It looks loose." He takes the spark plug wire off each plug, in turn. "They're all loose."

"They're not supposed to be?"

"No. One can be loose, can cause starting problems. But quite odd for them all to be loose. I've never seen this before. I'm surprised the car started at all."

I shake my head. "I don't know what happened." I feel like I'm lying. Dad never believed us when something went wrong that we couldn't explain. "Can you fix them?"

"Maybe." He walks into the garage. Comes back followed by an orange cat. Baker carries a tool. "It helps to have a spark plug wrench."

He really can fix it.

The cat sits near while he works.

"Your cat?"

"Yes. This is Seemore. S, E, E, M, O, R, E. Seemore, this is Marie."

"How do you do, Seemore. He likes you, Baker."

"He's pretty attached. Unlike his sister, Miss E. She's around somewhere."

Baker works for a few minutes under the hood. "Okay. That should do it."

"What did you do?"

"Tightened all the plugs." He hops in the car, starts it, gets out. "Hope that solves your problem. You should get it looked at. I smell fumes."

"Yeah, the fumes are bad. I keep the windows down."

He goes to the back of the car. "Here's part of the problem. Corrosion in the frame above the tail pipe."

"Yeah. Doubt that can be fixed."

"There's a product, Bondo, made for patching holes in cars. Shouldn't be too hard to do."

"Okay. I'll try it. Thanks. By the way, you have blue streamers on your mailbox."

He laughs. "Yeah. I keep meaning to get those. Had a gathering a few months back. Wait here."

I smile. I wasn't invited because he didn't know me then.

He effortlessly runs up the steep drive. Seemore follows halfway up. Baker walks back down with the blue metallic streamers flailing wildly in the breeze.

Seemore freezes when he sees the blue streamers, suddenly lunges at them, but twists in mid-air, touches down, and flies deep into the shrubs along the drive.

Baker bursts out laughing. "Did you see that? He didn't know whether to attack or run away!" He laughs so hard he holds his stomach, tosses his head back.

I smile. "Poor kitty," I say. "I can relate to feeling that scared. I just can't spin in mid-air."

"His eyes got big as saucers! Yeah. Poor guy. Couldn't handle blue streamers." Baker chuckles some more, goes back to the garage where he stashes the blue streamers, then he goes to the shrubs, calls, "Seemore, come here buddy!" He walks back to my car. "We won't be seeing him for a while." He cracks up some more. "Eyes big as saucers." Baker shakes his head.

I love his mirth. "Well, I hope poor Seemore comes back. I'd better get going. Thanks for your help." I get in the car.

"Have fun at your parents.'" Baker makes a terrified face with wide eyes.

I burst out laughing. "They're not really that bad." And I'm going to cure Dad.

He covers his mouth. "Denial," he says in a funny, high-pitched voice and cracks up.

He doesn't let a single thing go by. Is he right? Am I in denial? No. I'm not in denial, because I'm not acting like it's not stressful. I know how stressful it is. "Bye. Thanks again." I turn the car around. I wave before I climb the drive.

He doesn't understand. We all mess up. I sure have. My parents messed up big time. I got messed up by my parents' mistakes, but I'm getting better now.

I wave again at the top of the drive, but Baker's already gone inside. He doesn't know about waving good-bye until the person's out of sight.

Feels great knowing my spark plugs were loose and now they're tight.

It *seems* Baker likes me. I've never had anyone like me who didn't hit on me, though, so I can't tell. I think I like him. He's a handful. Opinionated. Dark. Kind.

What now?

Wait and see what happens.

Weird. I've never done that before. I've always needed to make something happen. That wouldn't work with Baker.

Most of the way, I play Etta James and sing sad songs at the top of my lungs for a good cry for no reason.

I turn off the music, roll down the windows, listen to the wind, think about my dream of standing waist deep in that beautiful pool. I replay the Black woman's words. The child isn't ready yet. Why the pool? I've heard water can signify a spiritual experience. Why a Black woman? Jean says pay attention to details that seem insignificant yet stand out. Her hair. Her black hair was a round ball with little spikes, come to think of it. Like Betty Boop's hair. Betty Boop's from my childhood.

I get it! The Aha! feeling. We had a nanny who was Black when I was small. The woman's talking about me in the dream. I'm the child who isn't ready yet! Oh my gosh. I can relax, not feel anxious about not having kids. I drive with a deep peaceful feeling the rest of the way.

I arrive at Mom and Dad's happy to have the answer to my dream and surprised to realize I didn't think about Baker the whole way. That never happened before when I liked someone. Strange. I'm really not obsessed with him.

I knock on the door.

Dad opens it, steps back. "Hi, Marie."

I look toward the sunny kitchen that opens off the dark hall for Mom.

"Hi Dad." I walk in.

Suddenly his arm hits my chest, blocks my way.

I freeze, go blank.

"Wait, just a minute. Lily's going by," he says, referring to the cat.

Lily walks past.

"You might have stepped on her." He lets his arm fall, grazing my chest.

Once again, I sink down into my own private Crater Lake, leave the world around me.

I would never have stepped on Lily. I walk in, hot with shame, feeling his arm grazing me as if it's still happening and won't ever end.

Tell him! Say, don't touch me, Dad!

I can't. He'll roar.

Roar at him! I'm an adult, my own person. Why not?

I can't do it. Someday, I'll stand up to him, I'll tame him. I can't now. I'm too far away inside.

I greet Mom, and help her in the kitchen, but I'm far away.

We all sit down to lunch. To calm down, I look at the wall with the sweet small lilac painting I remember from Grandma's house in Seattle, Mom's mom. I felt safe there. Grandma's mom committed suicide in an asylum. Grandma was kind. She's gone now.

Dad crumbles saltines into his tomato soup. "How's your job, Marie?"

Does he know what he did? Maybe he grew up with no boundaries, so he doesn't understand you don't throw your arm across your daughter's chest. "Job's fine. I'm beginning to get bored, though. I've been there seven years."

"Oh? Bored?" Dad says ironically. "I never thought of work as entertainment. Do they pay you well?"

"They do."

I am in denial. Baker's right. Dad knows exactly what he does. Why do I keep trying to protect him with excuses, like, he never learned boundaries?

"Then I'd think you'd be grateful to have that job. When I was a young man, you took anything you could get. Or you didn't eat."

He talks like a wooden form of a man. He's not interested in how I feel frustrated at work, only in being my teacher.

"Honey," Mom says to Dad, "I think what she means is possibly she's outgrown her position. I'm sure she's grateful."

"I am. How's Lily?" I change the subject, my stomach churning. They like telling stories about their cat.

"Oh, you should have seen her—Tuesday, was it, Mama?" Dad says to Mom.

I do want to know him. To do that, I have to be honest with him. I can't. Not yet. But someday I will be honest. The little gold relic on the mantle with a piece of bone and hair of Saint Therese catches my eye. It looks much smaller than it looked at bedtime when I was little and Dad blessed us all with it. His voice had such reverence for the relic. To this day it radiates meaning to me, that there's power of spirit, somehow, in it. I'm not religious anymore, but the relic gives me hope someday Dad and I will connect.

Baker's right. I deny exactly how stressful it is to come up here. It's not good for me. Trying to get Dad to understand his childhood will have to wait until I get better, somehow.

After lunch, Dad says, "I think I'll go close my eyes for a bit, Mama."

He sleeps in his chair. Mom and I clear the dishes. She updates me on her nursing home and peace activities.

I wish I could go home. I can't be open with either of them. I avoid telling her about my life, my new friends in the incest survivors' group, about being interested in Baker. She won't understand. The thing that's saving me, looking at my past, will make her sad. She can't help it, wishing we could all leave the past behind and be a normal family. We're not normal, Mom.

And the past isn't the past. It's still going on.

She sure wouldn't understand neurotic attachments, which I don't seem to have anymore, thank goodness. Probably because now, after going to the incest survivor meetings, I accept the damage caused by losing trust in Dad, the one who's supposed to protect me. I'm actually repairing the damage by being kind to myself. Why don't I be kind to myself and leave right now before Dad wakes up?

Eyes big as saucers.

It seems suddenly leaving now could kill Mom, and therefore me.

It's only blue streamers. I smile. It won't kill either of us. I am going home, before Dad wakes up. I don't have energy to talk to him anymore today. Or Mom, for that matter, though I hate to admit it.

I'll come back another time. "I think I'd better hit the road, Mom."

"So soon, honey?"

She must be lonely. I can't save her. "Yeah. The work week wears me out."

"I didn't get a chance to hear what you've been up to," she says regretfully.

"Well, not a lot. Which is a good thing, for me. I could use some peace and quiet in my life."

She laughs. "You certainly have had your ups and downs!"

She means Adam, Randy, Joe, Isaac, Dad. I never told her about Arnold. I love her when she smiles with watery eyes and shakes her head at me in wonder, the way she does now. She's surprised by me. I think she admires the scrapes I get into and get out of. She thinks I'm brave, when really, I'm blind.

"You always pull through," she says. "You have a good head on your shoulders and a good heart. But let's not waste more time. Come on, we'll get you out of here."

I have a good head on my shoulders and she's helping me escape. Thanks, Mom.

"Here." She pulls a frosty package of something from the freezer. "Meatloaf."

"Thanks, Mom." I love her and her frosty packages so much I can hardly bear to leave her now.

She wraps it in plastic, then newspaper, then foil, more newspaper, another layer of plastic. "It'll still be frozen when you get it home."

It will. "Thanks, Mom."

I take the bundle from her hands with a new longing.

We chipped away at a giant ball of frozen spaghetti one night on the road when I was twelve. Mom had stopped so we could camp at Castle Crags on our way to see relatives in Seattle. She had wrapped the spaghetti in newspaper, plastic and foil inside the roaster. It was still frozen solid. "I was sure it would have thawed by nightfall," she told us, sadly.

She tries so hard.

"I'll eat this tonight. Thanks again, Mom."

"You're so welcome," she says, her mouth agape in a big smile.

"Love you, Mom."

I want to save you from living with Dad, but I can't. Anyway, you're in love with him.

"And I love you, honey."

"Well, hope my car starts."

"Oh? Car trouble?"

"Hopefully it's fixed. It was just loose spark plugs. A friend fixed them."

"Good friend to have! Keep that one around!" She laughs, walks me to the door.

She's right about that. Baker's a good friend to have.

In the car, I start the engine. The car fires right up. "Bye Mom!"

Thanks Baker.

We both wave until I'm out of sight, the way her mom always waved at the car load of us ten kids after a Sunday dinner when I was little. I felt Grandma's love in that little relentless wave, as I feel Mom's love now.

As I hit the freeway in the early afternoon sun, I feel good about taking care of myself and loving Dad no matter what. Love does seem to be the only thing that matters in life. I'll never stop loving people, even Dad. The part I was missing was loving myself. It feels good to do that now.

Part of me wants to think I've done wrong leaving Mom and Dad now, earlier than usual. I haven't done wrong. I'm not bad. That's the truth. And someday, I won't be afraid of Dad's roar. I will stand up to him. That's the truth, too. The child isn't ready yet. I'm the child not ready to confront Dad. Dad's the child not ready to change.

Chapter 9
It was Easier to Hop in the Sack with a Magical Idea

August, 1993. A month later.

I cut small pieces of fabric and pack them in a grocery sack with a bag of popcorn kernels, a needle and thread and good scissors to make beanbags. I've used popcorn kernels before. They work. My project will save me from my embarrassing shyness at Dinah's party today. I love visiting with these people from the survivors' group, but only one-on-one. I can't do social banter.

Scott's bringing "The Endless Summer," a surfing movie, because he's a surfer and the party's a farewell to summer. I love the group's way of making a fun ritual good-bye to summer. They're passionate about everything because they know how to let their inner children out to play. We're even going to have a water fight. I pack a pair of jeans to change into afterwards.

Of course, I'm looking forward to seeing Baker, which is nice, because it's a peaceful feeling, not a neurotic neediness I get when I'm around him. He's interesting. That's all. He's not perfect. His sense of humor is often too crude for my tastes, but he's mirthful, fun, with a quicker wit than anyone I've ever seen. And I keep thinking of his tender tone when I told him to take the cups at Hot Spots. With a look of meaning in his eyes, he said, "As long as we do it together."

I pack the cookies I baked and my large stainless-steel bowl for the bean bag toss game and head over to Dinah's, a little nervous. The other group members have been to lots of parties and know each other well. I'm fairly reclusive. This is only my second one.

At Dinah's, near the ocean, when I get out of the car, oppressively hot humid air makes it hard to breathe.

"Hi," I say, carrying my things inside.

"Hey, Marie," Ella says.

"It's hot," I say.

"The way it should be!" Scott says, standing shirtless in shorts next to Dinah's TV. "We'll have no complaining!" He laughs. "I'm starting the video."

"The Endless Summer" in the VHS opens with credits against a silhouette of surfers and glassy ocean all in sepia tones. Soon, Bruce Brown, the film's maker, describes with understatement the basics of staying on a board and shows in full color the fun and thrill of the sport with wave after wave, naming the surfers who ride them. I'm hooked on the movie.

"I can't wait to meet the secret wife of Baker," Scott says.

Wife? I tear myself away from the TV. I haven't even set my sack of bean bag supplies down. Sunlight coming through the open front door catches my eye. It makes stark shadows in the rug's fibers. "Baker's married?"

"Apparently," Scott says, seriously. "And he's bringing her to the party."

Baker never said he wasn't married.

I never asked. How stupid not to ask him. Well, that settles that. We're not together.

"How come he never mentions her?" Ella asks.

"Not a real marriage. It's real, but they've been split up for two years," Scott says.

Oh. Two years. Still. He's married. Forget him.

"Apparently, she called out of the blue, said she's coming down from Sacramento to see him," Scott says.

Be your true self, Marie. Right. I'm fine without Baker.

And here they are. Baker parks Granny's blue VW fastback. He and a woman get out. His wife's got a fancy hair-do—hair-sprayed champagne-blonde fluffy style. Baker likes nice hair-do's? Of course, he does. I push my straggly hair back over my ears. Shoot. Be nice.

"I'd like you all to meet Barbara," Baker says warmly as they come in the door. He's awfully sweet to her, for not being with her.

He's a kind person, Marie. Be as kind as he is. She doesn't know anyone here.

"Nice to meet you, Barbara. I'm Marie," I say in a friendly tone.

We shake. She seems unhappy with me. Try again. "I'm going to make some bean bags for a bean bag toss game. Would you like to help me?"

Barbara gives me a long cool look. I wonder if Baker told her about me.

She takes a seat on the couch. "Baker," she says in a weary, irritated voice, "get me a drink."

Whoa. I'd never talk to him like that. She's no competition if she's bossy. He doesn't take orders.

What am I thinking? Who she is to Baker is none of my business. He never was mine. I like him, that's all.

"Water fight!" Scott yells standing on the bright green grass outside.

I drop my bean bag supplies on the dining room table.

Baker brings Barbara a glass of punch, runs outside, rips off his shirt, grabs water balloons from a big tub, throws fastballs at Dinah and Scott.

I join the water fight. Water balloons thrown by Baker and Scott pummel me before I can get to the tub full of water balloons. My bra shows through my wet white T-shirt. C'est la vie. These folks don't care.

The sun feels good now that I'm soaked head to toe. I forget about Barbara, run to the tub, get two water balloons, stalk my prey—Baker and Scott. They dance, bob and weave like prize fighters. My balloons miss. Ella gets me in the back. I shriek, grab more balloons, get Ella in the back. I haven't had this much fun since Jean and I over-shot Mom and Dad's three times. I sneak up on Baker, smash a balloon on the back of his neck. He wheels around. I scream, run for more balloons. Tub's empty. Scott's got the hose! I hurry inside for more balloons, pass Barbara on the couch. "You should come and join the water fight!"

"No, thank you," she says coolly.

There's a reason she and Baker didn't work out. I go in the kitchen. "Got more balloons, Dinah? We ran out."

She hands me a bag. Outside I call a truce to fill the balloons. The truce lasts ten seconds.

I find a large yogurt container, dip it in the soda-cooler ice water, get Scott square on the back.

He screams. I howl with laughter. It's war. It feels so grand to play with abandon like kids! I feel sorry for Barbara. She's too shy or too stuffy to play with us.

I turn around. Scott gets me in the face at close range. My glasses cut into my nose. I yelp. They fall off and hit the ground. Without them, I'm all but blind.

"Scott, settle down man," Baker says and retrieves my glasses. He's looking out for me.

"Sorry, Marie. Got too rambunctious," Scott says.

"Thanks. I'm okay."

Scott and Baker inspect my wound.

"A bruise," Scott says.

"She's good," they say in unison and run back to the game.

The guys lay off me. I fill balloons. Get back in the game.

But soon the sun goes behind tall eucalyptus, and instantly a chill comes on. How quickly things change. "I'm getting cold. Going in," I say.

"Don't go!" Baker yells. He quickly glances at me.

Shirtless, barefoot in boardshorts, he's got a water balloon in each hand. He faces off with Scott.

I'm glad. He wants me out here with him. He doesn't want to be with his wife. "Sorry! I'm cold!"

I go inside and change in the bathroom into my dry flannel shirt and jeans. Much better. Exhilarated, I go back in the living room, glance at Barbara who watches "Endless Summer" alone.

Time to sew.

When the others come in and dry off, the little house fills with quiet conversation. Baker stirs something on the stove. I sew at the dining room table, at peace. I always thought I needed connection with a partner to feel peace. But here I am, alone, peaceful. Come to think of it, whenever I had a partner, the opposite always happened. I became anxious when I got a boyfriend. Now, I'm alone, the guy I like is married, and I'm peaceful. I want to trap this feeling so I can have some of it whenever I want. I bend a small paper plate to funnel corn kernels into the small opening I left in my first bean bag. How much is enough?

"Marie," Baker says.

I join him at the stove.

"Tell me," he says in his slow formal tone which makes things seem epic, "is this white sauce thick enough? Salty enough? See what you think."

He's asking my opinion of his work. The man who won't be told to clear the cups. I take a spoon, slowly taste the sauce. "It's very good." I pause, give more consideration. "Good flavor. Enough salt. And good thickness, I'd say."

"It's good?"

"Yes. It's very good."

"Thank you."

"Of course." I go back to my sewing. That's a vulnerable thing to ask someone's opinion of your work. It's a gift of trust to ask for help. I've always done things on my own, without asking anyone's opinion or help.

I want to return the favor, ask him about my bean bag.

He's married.

Still, we're friends. If nothing comes of us, this is good practice.

I take my beanbag to Baker. "I have something to ask you. Do you think it has enough corn kernels?"

He looks at it. "Hm." He takes it from my palm. "Let's see." He lifts it, feels for its heft. "It's good, it's all right. You know, it might be packed a little too tight. I think I'd pour a few kernels out. So, you can really sling it, rather than toss it like a ball. You think so?"

He's honest. Not afraid of hurting my feelings. "I do. Especially when it's sewn up, it'll be even a little smaller, and so, tighter. So, yeah. Thanks." I take the bean bag back to the table, pour kernels out. I'm calm, contented.

Baker goes to Barbara who's still on the couch. I can't hear what they say. She stands up. They leave. I hear his car drive away. How strange. No good-bye. He'll probably drop her off and come back.

We watch "Endless Summer" again. Toss the bean bags for a while. People aren't into it. With evening coming on, a chill settles into the house. People retreat into themselves. Baker doesn't come back.

I'm disappointed, and strangely calm. Anyone I was ever interested in before made me anxious whenever they left. Tonight, I'm myself, not hooked into needing Baker. I drive home, quiet within, mutely watching tall blades of grass along the road.

The next day, rain clicks on the windows of my studio as a freak summer storm blows through. It'd be nice to sit here with Baker's arms around me. We've never so much as held hands. I wish Baker would call me. He has my number on the meeting phone list. I only want to know if something's possible between us.

Baker doesn't show up at the next few survivors' meetings. Did he go away with Barbara? I don't know him at all. I'm too embarrassed to ask the others if they've heard from him. He could call me if he wanted to. No one feels like going to Hot Spots lately where I might hear news without having to ask.

Weeks go by. In September, Baker comes back to meetings. I check his ring finger. No ring.

Why was he missing? He doesn't mention his wife in shares. Maybe she's staying with him. Forget him, Marie. He's a married friend. Be a friend. Forget about wanting more.

"Let's go to Hot Spots," Baker says one night after a meeting.

"Cannot," Scott says "Got to work, buddy."

"I don't want to go without Scott," Ella says.

People say good night, go to their cars.

Baker walks me to my car, stands there.

What does he want to say? I'm supposed to speak? "Thanks for walking me to my car."

"I was wondering if maybe you'd like to go to the Goleta Lemon Festival. It's this Saturday, always the last weekend in September."

He's asking me out. "Thanks. Maybe. What about your wife?"

"She went home."

I laugh. That doesn't tell me much. "And is she coming back?"

"I hope not." He smiles.

"So, you're married."

"Separated. Two years. Never got around to the divorce."

"Does she want a divorce?"

He looks me in the eye. "No. She wants to reconcile. When we left the party, a few weeks ago, I told her I was done. I took her to the airport the next day."

"It poured rain."

He laughs. "Downpour all the way to LAX with an angry ex. Poetic." His smile shines in the porch light.

"What's a lemon festival?"

"Probably things made with lemons. Music, crafts, Art. An excuse for a party?" He smiles.

"You look happy."

"Glad the interrogation's over."

I smile. I like him. Life doesn't come in perfect packages. "Sounds good."

"I'll pick you up at ten. My car's safer than yours," he says.

It's a real date. "I live on Bath. 1355. Upstairs. Number 4. It's an old house."

Saturday, I put on make-up and try on one combination of pants, jeans, shorts, and tops after another. Fuck it. Why do I have to dress up? I'm a T-shirt and jeans girl. He knows that.

It's a date. Wear something nice. I settle on shorts, a small T-shirt, my flannel shirt. I wait on the porch. Another stupid hot day, sweltering already at ten in the morning. I can't *wait* for winter.

He's on time!

I get in the car.

"Look at this. See what you think."

No hello, how are you? He sounds grumpy. He hands me a glossy yellow brochure as we drive away. He did go out of his way to get a Lemon Festival brochure. "Everything all right?" I ask.

"I need to eat."

"I have food at my place."

"I'll get something there."

We ride in silence.

We're not big talkers when it's only us, anyway. Do I really like him? He's moody.

I'm moody. I put on a better front than he does. At least with him, what you see is what you get.

"It says there's a shuttle to the festival," he says. "See if you can find where we get the shuttle."

"Can it be that big it needs a shuttle? I've never even heard of this festival."

"Just saying what it said."

I open the brochure. "Here it is. Shuttle. 'At Los Carneros, follow the signs.'"

"Okay."

We get on the freeway.

I gaze out the window at the passing ice plant. "They'll probably have lemon meringue pie. But I won't get my hopes up to have some. They'll run out, or the line will be too long, or the pie won't be ready yet. It's less painful to not hope for things. Do you like sweets?"

He smiles at me. "They'll probably have some pie. And no, I'm not crazy about sweets."

"You really don't like sweets?" I ask, incredulous.

"Not that much."

Darn.

"But you can bet I'll have some lemon meringue pie," he says happily. "Our mom raised six boys on food stamps. We hardly ever had lemon meringue pie."

My heart goes out to him. My family ate a lot of beans, but, on Sunday, we always had dessert. I'm glad he'll eat some pie. Get that blood sugar up. He's awfully skinny to skip a meal.

At Los Carneros we follow the shuttle signs, park in a vast dirt field quickly filling up with cars. We walk with others over dusty ground to the shuttle stop. I'm tired already. It's work to go to a festival.

A full-size bus comes. Baker beams at me. "Our carriage has arrived!"

He's full of fun now. We take a seat. The bus fills up. It slowly climbs the Los Carneros hill. We bounce around. I look to see Baker's face.

He's looking ahead, grinning. "Our first bus ride," he says.

I think I love him. I feel connected to him. I can deal with moodiness over not eating. We're connected. But he still hasn't held my hand. We haven't touched. He was molested by a man, friend of the family. Does he have a problem with touching? I'll have to wait and see.

At the festival, we head straight for the lemon meringue pie line. I'm afraid they'll run out before we get there. Soon, we get to the front of the line and get two big pieces of lemon meringue pie. From here I can see racks full of pies beside a truck full of more pies. I'm always worried something good won't come through. Tears come up.

"Are you all right?" Baker asks.

I nod. "I'm okay, thanks. Good things make me cry these days."

"I was a little nervous myself."

We laugh. He's easy to relax around.

"Food stamps didn't always go far enough," he says.

"Yeah. Ten kids in our house. Pies didn't go far. Plus, our mom took in people who were having problems. We had food. Not a big piece of pie like this!"

I get anxious thinking good things won't happen.

I relax more as we stroll around just like a couple eating their pie, looking at crafts, listening to musicians. He would be nice to be with.

I look around at the hills and trees. "I like being out here, sort of in the country," I say. "I'd like living in the country someday. Not way out in the country, but where there're horses around, open spaces."

He listens, nods. "I agree. The country's nice."

We have that in common.

"Let's go over there and buy some falafels," I say, excited.

Baker shakes his head no, pats his canvas sack. "I'm Scottish. Brought snacks."

Darn it. I want to buy special food. It's a festival.

"What would you like?" He brings out trail mix, tangerines, an apple, ginger candies.

"Actually, I'm okay, for now. I just wanted to impulsively buy some food."

"I won't stand in your way."

"I'm okay. I don't want a falafel if you're not having one."

"That philosophy won't get you very far," he says with a twinkle in his eye.

He's right. Someday I'll be able to stand on my own beside a man.

Baker moves aside to let me be in front to watch a guy playing guitar. Baker's very polite. But he doesn't take my hand, or brush his arm against mine. Is he only a friend? Am I reading it all wrong? I need to find out.

We move to the edge of the crowd to watch a guy who's on his own juggling lemons. He's pretty good. Baker stands behind me. Close, but not touching.

He's not going to make a move. I have to do it, or I'll never know. I've got nothing to lose.

I slowly back into him.

He stands his ground.

The heat of his chest against my back feels better than it should. His warm breath on my neck makes me look up at him. I could kiss him. His rugged face creases in a smile, clear blue eyes look down from the shade of his O.D. green bill cap. God, this feels good.

The juggler takes a bow.

We clap.

"Come on," Baker says to me, and takes my hand, pulls me along as he takes off bounding through tall yellow grass.

I have my answer. We're more than friends.

Now I'm not sure I'm ready for whatever might be coming.

He helps me over a wooden fence.

"Where are we going?"

"There." He points to an old, elegant two-story house with posts on a rounded veranda. "Stow House. Historical site. It's part of the Lemon Festival tour."

We move through the crowded house, holding hands. Being with someone shouldn't feel this good. I hope we'll be okay.

We will. We're both sober. We know each other a little.

We walk room to room. I'm too distracted by the feeling of his hand to notice whatever might be interesting in this historic place. I think back to my horrible breakups. Adrenaline starts to flow. This connection feels too sudden, too real. My stomach's getting upset. What if we get hurt?

Then you should have said no to the Lemon Festival.

He said, "Our first bus ride." I love that.

And what if we don't get hurt? What if things work out?

He leads me room to room. He's been here before. I watch his shoulders. He's very strong.

He could have other girlfriends. A different ex, one he wants back. This whole thing's risky.

Yeah. It was easier to get hooked on guys and hop in the sack with a magical idea that there was some deep bond. Now I have to decide what my feelings mean. I don't even know what I'm feeling. A nervous stomach, now. Shoot. This is a real relationship. I don't know if I can do this.

CHAPTER 10
NO SHARP EDGES

October, 1993. A month later.

Baker and I are definitely an item, though I go back and forth asking myself am I sure he's the one. Going back and forth about Baker is exhausting, like shopping. Anything that costs more than thirty dollars I check out in the mirror for over an hour before I can decide.

I just need to decide.

I like him and that's that. He's fun and likes to talk about life. I can't wait to tell Jean about him.

On second thought, I'd better wait to tell her. It wasn't that long ago I was obsessed with Arnold. Better see if Baker and I stick.

At the survivors' meetings, Baker and I don't sit together, but people have figured out we're an item, probably from the way he walks me to my car. They smile, raise their eyebrows.

After a meeting, Scott says, "Hey, so how serious is it?" He laughs. "Have you guys done the deed?"

Embarrassed, I look to Baker to handle Scott.

Baker doesn't smile. "Come on, man."

"You can trust us!" Scott squeals. "Hell, we know every goddam other intimate detail about each other." He laughs.

He's got a point. But I'm not going to be the one who says we haven't done it. Scott's too loud and nosy to tell our personal business. Baker can tell him if he wants, later.

I'm glad we haven't done it. I think Baker's old-fashioned. We've taken a few walks on West Beach, below his house. We hold hands. I told him all about twelve years Catholic schools with nuns. He told me about almost drowning five times. He's interested in me. That's enough for me, for now.

"I'll take you to the *other* beach," Baker says with a meaningful tone at my car after the meeting.

It sounds too serious. "All right, thanks."

"Better wear a jacket. It is October."

He picks me up on Saturday. We drive to *East* Beach this time, get out of the car, bundled up. He suddenly appears behind me. I startle.

He laughs. "It's only me, the man you're going to the beach with."

I laugh. How did he get behind me so quickly and silently? "I startle easily."

"I've noticed."

"You sneak up on me!"

We walk.

He takes my hand. "I think someone pecked you out of your egg too early, and that's why you have that crazy startle reflex," he says.

I laugh. "Not far from the truth, I think. Dad raged at two-year-olds, I'm pretty sure. That's like getting pecked out of an egg too early."

He squeezes my hand, puts me at ease. Pulls his thick long hair out from under his jacket.

"Your hair sparkles in the sun," I say.

He grins, pulls his hair back, lets it slowly fall. "Just washed it."

I'd prefer him with short hair. Short hair's such a turn on. "You like your hair."

"Yes, Ma'am. And no, I won't be cutting it any time soon!" He flashes me a grin.

"Others have tried?"

"None has prevailed."

"I like short hair."

"Mine's not going anywhere. Get used to it."

Damn it.

We walk to the far end of East beach to the cliffs, where few people go. As usual, we keep an eye out for sea glass, pick it up, see if it's ready.

"It has to be ground completely smooth before it can be taken home," he says, like he's the boss. He has been a beachcomber his whole life. He has his ways.

"I used to come to this spot," Baker says, "when I was in the shit." He nods toward a little sort of miniature pier in the sea, a thick plank jutting into the water. "I call it the Wall of Rage. I went out onto that little jetty every time I came here. Waves lapped around me. I raged out to sea, till I was hoarse from screaming at God, humanity, and anything else that entered my mind. I'd rage and curse and spit, until I had no voice. Then I left, spent."

"You have a lot to rage about."

"Nightly whoopin's bare-ass with a belt in front of my brothers. Yeah. That neighbor perpetrator-fuck sucking me. Yeah."

"It's good you got it all out!" Really good.

"Maybe not all."

Shoot. Do I want him if he still has rage inside? Can he help it? Is it right to set him aside for something not his fault?

I reach down, pick up a nice smooth piece of green glass. "Here's a good one." But I feel a shiny edge.

Our hands glide together as he takes it, inspects it. His touch soothes me. I don't care if he has rage. I like him.

"See here? Feel that." He touches the shiny spot on the glass. "Be careful."

I touch the piece of glass, run my finger carefully over the edge he says is sharp. I can barely feel it, but it's there. "It's sharp."

He nods.

"It's not ready," I say.

"No." He looks at the glass. "It needs more time. Has to be pounded by the surf, smoothed by boulders, polished by sand and time." He looks me in the eye. "No sharp edges."

He's talking about us. "No sharp edges."

"You agree, needs more work?" he asks.

"I do. You want to toss it back?"

"No. You found it, you do it."

I toss the little piece of glass, but it lands in the backwash. "Damn." I'm embarrassed. "Can't even toss a piece of glass into a wave."

"You really have a headful of critics, don't you?"

"I do."

He's got rage. I've got fear. He's secure, I'm kind. We're uniquely suited to help heal each other's childhood wounds. A guy named Hendrix wrote that about couples.

We walk on, quietly tossed in the waves of our inner worlds—my fear, his rage. Are we ready to be partners? Can we *will* away our sharp edges?

He drops me off at home. "I wonder if you'd like it if I made us dinner tomorrow," he says.

This is new. "Sure. That'd be nice," I say, though getting closer makes me nervous. I'm not used to this queasy feeling of liking someone who's going slow.

When I arrive the next night for dinner, Baker says, "Good evening," in the formal tone of a butler.

He's full of fun tonight.

He leads me through the house to a long, enclosed back porch room. "This is the sunroom," he announces.

He's a very good actor. "It's beautiful," I say, impressed with the peaceful space where one wall is all windows looking to the ocean. The room is refreshingly sparsely furnished—he's tidy! This is great.

A couch faces the ocean. A little round table and two chairs sit next to a window. A candle burns on the table next to a small bottle of soy sauce.

"It's nice in here," I say.

"Please be seated, madam," he says. "Your dinner will be served shortly."

"Thank you, sir." I take my seat.

Strange. I'm really not obsessed with him. I'm calm with him, calm when we're apart. He's not dashing—he's too lean. He hides under that army field jacket, his armor. His hair's too long, too much like a girl's. But he's rugged, honest, fun.

He comes back and sets two large steaming bowls of stir-fried vegetables and rice on the table. "Are you vegetarian?" he asks.

"No. Are you?"

"Yes, ma'am."

Shoot. "I don't know how to cook like this. And broccoli doesn't agree with me."

He bursts out laughing. "I think maybe you don't agree with broccoli."

"You know, you're not right about everything."

"I'm not?" He gives me a clever smile.

How's this going to work out if he's so opinionated?

Suddenly it's nine o'clock and I can hardly keep my eyes open. "I'm sleepy. I'd better get home to bed. This was really nice. And the broccoli was no problem. I'll make us dinner at my place next week."

He smiles at the candle. "Sounds good."

I think he's happy.

The next week in my kitchen, I'm nervous as I wait for him. I review my simple menu: buttered mashed potatoes, broccoli and carrots. I hope that's enough. I'll mash the potatoes when he gets here.

I look around my studio. It looks drab. Make it cozy. I get up, find the holiday lights in one of the boxes, drape them on the pole lamp, which is missing a shade ever since I stepped on the striped one. I plug them in, turn off the overhead light, sit back down. The holiday lights give the little room a warm glow that soothes my ragged soul. Why didn't I think of hanging these lights sooner?

I hear his knock, take a deep breath, let him in. "Hi. Have a seat. I have to get back to the stove and make the food hot."

From the stove, it's not hard to see Baker. My place is so small, the kitchen and the other little room look into each other. "I have no table. I hope that's all right."

"No problem, ma'am." Baker takes a seat in my little gold stuffed swivel chair in the next room with a clear line of sight to me at the stove. "Your place is nice. Cozy. I like your holiday lights hanging from a pole lamp. You look nervous," he says.

"I get nervous when someone's talking while I'm cooking."

"I notice certain things calm me down," he says reflectively.

"Like what?"

"Walks on the beach. Candlelight. Sex."

I laugh. "Surprise."

"Sex is such a personal experience. No one else knows what you're feeling, but yourself. Isn't that strange? We're the only ones inside ourselves," he says.

"True, we're the only ones inside ourselves. But, how does that seem strange?"

"Well, I mean, unless someone tells you what they're thinking, how they're feeling, or shows you some other way, you'll never know what's inside them."

"That's so true." He looks deeply at things. I pour the hot water off the potatoes. "I'm listening. It's hard for me to talk while I'm cooking. It's almost ready." I mash the potatoes in a saucepan on a low flame. There's no point in mashed potatoes that aren't scalding hot.

"I'll be quiet, then. I'll move back. Far away." He pushes his chair two feet back to the wall. "There. I won't be so noisy and distracting here. Take your time. I'm fine here by myself."

I burst out laughing, seeing him right there. "You're still talking."

"Am I? I guess I am. At least Great Spirit gave us great ways to communicate, even if so much of life is a fucking shitshow. I mean, there's talking, of course. Art."

"I paint."

"No way. Show me."

"Later."

"Okay. There's, literature. Again, conversation, like we're having. Then there's eye contact, without words."

I look at him. We hold each other's gaze a moment.

I smell the potatoes brown, look away from him, turn off the heat. Scoop the mashed potatoes onto the plates.

"So, eye contact. That was good by the way. You're not afraid of eye contact," he says.

He's getting closer without leaving his chair. My body warms up, not from the stove. I glance at him, look back at the food. I make wells in the piles of hot potatoes, fill them with butter. "No. I'm not afraid of eye contact."

"Good. Then there's communicating by doing kind things for another. You're making me dinner."

"Yes. You made me dinner."

"Yes, ma'am. Other ways of communicating—well, sex of course, the most intimate communication possible, because you're giving your whole being over to another's care, trusting them with your body. That's huge."

"It's powerful." Interesting, he keeps talking about sex, without hitting on me. I love it. I don't feel pressured. I butter the carrots. Put mayonnaise on the broccoli. "It's ready."

I carry his plate to him. I sit on the bed with my plate, a few feet away from him. "I have to tell you something. We've been hanging out for over a month, now. I can't tell you how good it feels to be seeing someone without being hustled into bed."

He nods, looks at his food. "This is beautiful, by the way. But, do you have something other than mayonnaise for the broccoli?" He makes a face.

"You don't like mayonnaise? I love it."

"Only on sandwiches. Do you have salad dressing?"

"I do. Thousand Island."

"That'll do. You know," he says as I leave for the kitchen, "I'm glad …"

He waits till I come back. "I'm glad you're comfortable. Some people never are. They don't know what makes them comfortable."

"I'm just beginning to learn what does make me comfortable," I say, drizzling dressing onto his broccoli.

He motions for more. He likes a lot.

"I haven't been very connected with myself most of my life," I continue, "I've been in one relationship after another all based on my magical thinking, neurotic attachments. I mean, they weren't all bad, there was some good in them. But hopefully I've learned from them."

"I'm comfortable with you," he says with a smile, surveying his plate for his next bite.

His smile's so sweet. "I'm glad."

He happily eats.

It doesn't seem possible someone so tender could have rage inside. Maybe he just needs love as a cool salve on his wounds and the rage will leave like a fever. And I only need his confident reassurances and my anxiety and fear will wash away on the tides.

Chapter 11
If You Leave

October, 1993. A few weeks later.

After the next survivor's meeting, Baker and I stand close at my car. It's been six weeks since the Lemon Festival. We hold hands facing each other. He's solid. Not in a physical way, but emotionally, or spiritually, or something. The way he holds my gaze, I want to fall into him, but he doesn't make any move to hug. He stands there. Wind picks up his hair. A wave of heat radiates off his chest. A nice cold wind gusts through my hair, cools my neck.

"I'll make dinner for us Saturday night," I say.

"Saturday." He seems to think about it. Keeps eye contact. "Can't get there until eight."

What is he doing? "Why?"

"I'm going to a meeting. It doesn't get out until seven-thirty."

"Oh." Suddenly I'm nervous.

Damn it. I can hardly bear the wave of anxiety that fills me. It's as though I'm a child who's been left behind. It doesn't make sense. I'm not a child. He's not my parent.

He's going to a different meeting without me, that's all. Why am I a wreck?

I don't think I can do a real relationship. I shake my head at the pavement. It feels like the end of the world, the world I know. He has a life of his own which doesn't include me. That's what scares me. Why?

I *have* to relax. "Okay. Eight will work." Act normal, Marie. "See you then." I get in the car. "I'll make fried onions, potatoes and eggs," I say through the window.

"That'll be great. Thanks!"

See? Everything's fine. As I drive away, I shiver in the cold car. I'll be home before the heater warms up. At the stop sign, I pull my jacket close around my neck. He's going to some meeting, that's all. Maybe he'll tell me later what kind of meeting.

Saturday night, glistening fried onions and potatoes sit hot and ready in the skillet at eight o'clock. I'll cook the eggs when he gets here. I climb on the bed and open the window next to my pillow to enjoy a breeze while I sit and wait for Baker. I look around the small room. I need to cover the stack of boxes with something pretty. I could hang the holiday lights on the boxes. No. How come he's not here yet? I reach my foot way out, kick the gold stuffed chair, spin it. Baker likes his chair. He'll be here.

I need to do something. I watch the door.

Eight-ten, no Baker.

He's always on time.

He's not coming, I can tell, the way I could tell when Dad always said he was coming home and didn't show up.

Hey, it was just a dinner. It's not like it's my life. Why do I care so much if he shows up?

I've done recovery work, I understand my dad travelled months at a time, but it never bothered me. The house was more peaceful with Dad gone. Still, I can't bear being left. It feels safer to end things with Baker than to risk him ending it. I'll just say I'm too busy writing to hang out with him anymore.

How do I know Baker's not coming? He could still come.

Eight-fifteen. The room's getting cold. I close the window. He's not coming. I can tell.

Who else was at that meeting he went to?

I'm not being reasonable. People would say fifteen minutes late is okay. Something came up.

Eight-twenty. Fuck this real relationship thing. Fuck it.

Calm down. He always shows up. Don't worry about it.

I *know* we said eight. We didn't say eight-thirty.

Now I have to deal with him being late. Or not showing up. Damn it! Why do I feel as though electricity from a low voltage taser is running through me? Other people would be fine. I can't handle it. I'm the problem. Forget the whole thing with Baker. He's a nice man. I'm too fucked up. There. We're done. That's a relief. I take a deep breath and sigh.

But I wanted him.

Then fight for him. If he shows up, tell him dinner's cold, and it's unacceptable for him to be so late. Everyone says in a relationship you tell someone how you feel. That way, he won't do it again.

I guess I could wonder if he's all right. He could have gotten in a wreck. Arnold got in a wreck on the way to my swearing-in. It happens. I have no way to find out. I can't call Baker. It's not like he has one of those mobile phones. We both agree those are stupid. I'll wait.

He's fine. He's just getting used to me and thinks it's okay to be late, that's all, I'm sure. He's not some special man, after all. Already taking me for granted. Well, I won't put up with it. He's tired of being on time, being responsible. That won't work for me. He's definitely his own person. That's been plain from the start. But I do matter.

I don't even know him. I've been so stupid thinking I'm the only one he sees. I only see him two or three times a week.

I'm screwed. I need to let go, cut ties. Yeah. This not showing up doesn't work for me. Easy come, easy go. I need to be able to count on whoever I'm seeing. Oh well.

Eight-thirty. He's not coming. Shit. Fine. It's over. And I'm good. It wasn't anything anyway. Good thing we didn't have sex. I'd be all screwed up. He's just an irresponsible friend. We don't have to keep having dinners. I sure don't need him to hold my hand.

Footsteps come upstairs. A knock. He's here. I don't want to lose him but I can't bear him being so late.

Be reasonable. Tell him don't do this again, I'm not okay with him being so late.

I open the door.

He smiles.

I don't move. I'm suddenly angry.

"Can I come in?" He sounds confused.

"I guess."

"What's up?"

"What's up?" As if he doesn't know. Tell him. Be your real self. "You said you'd be here at eight o'clock. You're half an hour late. What happened?"

"I told you. I had a meeting."

I shake my head. I don't know how to do this. He's here. Do I let it go, the way Mom always has done with dad? No. I'm angry. "It's fine. Dinner's cold." I turn toward the kitchen.

He can tell by my tone I'm angry. Good.

"You're angry?"

"No," I say, looking back. He doesn't have a right to know.

He takes off his field jacket, sits in the gold chair. "I don't mind cold food."

I fry the eggs in silence. I'm so angry and hurt and scared I can't ask him how he likes his eggs.

It's not fine. Tell him.

I return, hand him his dinner, sit on the bed opposite him, our knees a few feet apart. "It's not fine. I don't get it. The meeting got out at seven-thirty. You said you'd be here at eight. Why didn't you come over?"

"I was talking with some people."

Girls. Damn it. How long did they talk? Don't let him know you're jealous. "Where's the meeting?"

"A few blocks away."

He spent an hour with someone else? I can't bear this. I've got nothing to lose. "So, you visited for almost an hour? With whom?"

"Some friends." He takes a bite of potatoes and shrugs. "Someone needed to talk."

He's kind to people. "Fine," I say with a softer tone, to sound mature. I don't feel mature. "But you're talking to someone else, when you have a date with me. It doesn't work for me," I say calmly. Now he knows.

He looks down. Why isn't he saying something?

I'm angry again. "You don't see a problem with saying you'll be here at eight and showing up at eight-thirty? Meanwhile talking to someone else a few blocks away for a whole hour? It doesn't work for me." He needs to understand "I can't live like this, not knowing when or if you're showing up." That's the real problem. And talking to other people, probably girls, when he said he'll be with me.

Say you're sorry, Baker.

We're both quiet a long time.

He puts his fork down, looks at me, shrugs. "Maybe I should just leave."

An adrenaline spike makes my arms tingle and my neck hot. He's going to leave. He'll let the little lady cool off. That'll fix everything. No, it won't.

Tell him. "*If you leave, …*" I raise my voice and stop.

How do I finish? I can't say don't come back. I know him. He won't ever come back.

He looks at me, waiting.

I can't believe I said that. I'm so fucked. I *want* him, because I'm myself with him, but now I'm driving him away. How do I get out of this? My mind's blank. I can't finish the sentence. What do I say?

My sober friends say they ask God for help, and help arrives. I've never tried it in a pinch like this. I need a fucking miracle.

I look away, as if the answer is over my right shoulder. God, please help, I say in my thoughts with a deep sigh.

I look back at Baker, his head now bent, take a deep breath. I hear myself say, "…that would not be good." The words come out without going through my mind.

He slowly looks up, smiles, amused.

I smile, relieved.

He nods. "All right."

A ton of fear lifts. Thanks God. I don't want to fight him. I want to get along. No sharp edges. Of course, I mean a lot to him. We've been an item since the lemon festival. "Were they girls?"

"Some were. I'm not interested in them. They're just people. Just friends."

I can hear that. It's not hurting me. He's here with me. He's interested in me, not them. See? I have to grow up.

"I'll try not to be late again."

Good enough. "Thanks. Let's eat."

"Let's eat."

"I'll heat up our food. It's cold."

"That'd be nice."

I go into the kitchen, put the fire under the skillet. Put a good bit of butter in the pan, slide the food into it, breathe, relieved. I don't know if I can do this, have a real relationship. It's all but unbearable.

If it works, it may be worth it. But it feels like it's going to kill me.

Chapter 12
Rocket-Powered Roller Skates

November, 1993. A few weeks after Baker arrived late for our dinner.

After a survivors' meeting, our little group drives to Hot Spots and braves the cold November wind from the parking lot to the café. It feels good to feel extra alive in the cold air.

I've been getting those spells again, feeling as though I don't exist. I don't know what to make of it when one comes. It floats in silently, like a large bird, hovers inside me, quietly pulls all the wires that connect me to normal life until it seems only everything but myself exists. Thankfully it doesn't last too long. Yesterday at work it lasted twenty minutes. I wonder if one of this group can help me.

Inside Hot Spots, we take a large table. I order hot chocolate—I recently realized I don't like coffee at night. Coffee makes me anxious. I'm glad I don't need to be right next to Baker. What a great feeling. He's across from me talking to Scott who's telling him about the high surf today. Ella and Mark talk quietly.

Be sociable. I smile at Dinah beside me. "How was your day?"

"Not bad at all. I've been filling out job applications."

"For chef work."

"Yes," she says, smiling as she turns her napkin around on the table.

"That's so great. Somebody will be lucky to have you."

"Thanks. I'm ready."

She sounds calm and confident. I want that.

I'm relaxed, which is good. From the time Dad started touching me when I was a teenager, I've felt nervous and ashamed to be seen in public. Now, I'm less self-conscious, feel more like a normal person. I love the feeling. And I'm seeing someone who pays attention to me as though I matter, without requiring sex, which is so strange. I think it's having a good effect. Now, if only the spells where I don't exist would end.

Dinah's not as pale and thin as when I met her a couple months ago. Her wispy hair sparkles now. She's doing something right. Maybe she can help me. I'm usually the listener with others, it feels safer. Let her in, a little.

"Can I ask you something, Dinah?"

"Sure." Dinah smiles.

"I've learned a lot about how to recover from incest, you know, good ideas like prizing myself, speaking up for myself, accepting my erratic emotions. But I still get anxious with fear of abandonment that I can't shake. And sometimes I feel I don't exist. I know you relate. I don't get the connection with incest. Any ideas?" I can't believe I told her all that. I sip my hot chocolate and want to retract into a shell, but why not say what I think?

"Big connection," she says. "We were abandoned each time we were used by our perpetrators. You don't exist for that person."

Her words sink in. "When my dad gets me, I disappear into my own Crater Lake for a while—if I don't exist, I can't be hurt. But if I don't exist, I can't have a real relationship. Maybe I slip away afraid of a relationship."

"I think that's exactly what's happening. You and Baker have something, which is scary, risky, right? Until your real self actually trusts you, she's going to take off."

"You're brilliant, Dinah."

"Thanks. Lot of therapy."

"I've never had a real relationship. They've all been neurotic attachments. Did you have fear of abandonment?"

She laughs. "Probably always will, my therapist says, but I'm getting better, slowly but surely."

"That's good. I'm not good at therapy. I always think I know more than the therapist."

"A lot of people don't have a therapist. There's a great workbook. It really helped me. Maybe even more than therapy. It's for incest survivors." She writes the title on a scrap of paper. "Get it."

"Thanks, Dinah." She's so smart and easy to talk to.

A few days later in the evening after work, I pick up the workbook at the Earthling Bookstore. It's thick and heavy. On the drive home, I reflect on how I wanted to start the workbook tonight, but now I feel too lost, the rug's been pulled out from under me somehow, again. I float from one thing to another, barely here. I was excited. What happened?

I watch the tall trees sway in the wind as I drive past.

I know what happened. Part of me vanished, ran away, because she's afraid of the workbook.

I look in my mind toward a shadow hiding among some beige curtains with a large floral pattern. My childhood living room curtains. The shadow's myself.

The other survivor group members say we walk through the weirdness and do the work, regardless of who inside of us is pitching a fit.

It's okay, I tell the girl hiding in the curtains, we'll do it together.

At home, to feel cozy, I turn on the holiday lights still strung on my pole lamp. I curl up in the gold stuffed chair, open the workbook. I need more light. I get up, turn on the overhead light, sit back down. I need a cup of tea. I get it and sit down. I need my pajamas, to really focus. I change and sit back down. I need some crackers and a pen and a box for a footstool. And my big sweatshirt.

I get all that. At last, I sit, thumb through the workbook. It's way too thick. A lot of fill-in-the-blank questions. I'm suddenly exhausted. I can't do all this work. Forget it. I close it.

I take a deep breath. Shoot. Nothing's going to change if I don't study the problem and address it. Try. Start wherever you want.

I open to the middle.

"When I think about hope, I feel:" the text reads.

Hope. Hm. I hate that word. What does it even mean? Several blank lines follow the prompt.

When I think about hope, I feel.

I write:

Anxious and nauseous. Yesterday I was a new person I'd never been before. Come to think of it, I felt hopeful and glad. The person I am tonight is old, familiar, has no hope.

"If I had hope, what could go right?" the workbook asks.

That's easy. I write:

I'd live and die with love in my heart and in others' hearts for me.

That'd be good.

Well. I feel better. I'm doing a workbook.

I skip around the book. A section on remembering reads, "An effective coping tool of children is blocking out memories of abuse."

Exactly. So why remember?

I read on.

Oh.

It says children might forget in order to get through the next day. As adults, we might remember to understand feelings that come as phantom pains. Fine.

I remember everything. I feel everything. I'm having trouble staying connected with my real self, is all.

Maybe it'd be better to start the workbook at the beginning.

The next few days I move as fast as I can through the workbook so I can get better quickly. I told Baker what I'm doing. He said slow down. I said, why?

It feels good to be doing something useful for myself. I need to get better fast. I've made life so hard in the past, getting neurotically attached to one guy after another. I don't want to screw things up with Baker.

One Saturday morning, I quickly answer several workbook questions about sensory memories and memories of abandoning myself. I can't stand the sound of twigs snapping, fire crackling, can't stand being touched the way friendly women at work reach out and touch my arm or put a hand on my back. It makes me want to jump out of my skin. I swear, the kaleidoscope of feelings the workbook brings up makes me dizzy. I set the workbook aside to think about times I abandoned myself. I abandoned myself when I *had* to get each guy I was obsessed with in the past. Baker's different. I feel calmer with him. With the others, I obsessed on every single one of them, with no thought for whether it made sense to be with them, no effort to see whether they were partner material or not.

I needed gorgeous Adam with his low-slung pants, long stride, steely eyes. As long as he wanted me, I felt safe. Though it was only sex and long gazing into each other's eyes.

I needed to have Joe, with his satin skin, white teeth, kind heart. We both got addicted to drugs we couldn't kick together. I had to go.

And I had to have Randy, who needed me with that steady gaze, long arms, irreverent child-like laugh. He cracked my head on the ground once, beat me up once. It didn't change how I needed him.

I had to have sweet, distant Isaac. I got hooked one day by his smile. Stayed fourteen years. That was abandonment.

And Arnold. Over and over, I went back. I was hooked by his deep, warm voice.

I shake my head. So much pain being with them. Pain losing them in the end.

Why did they have to be gorgeous? I think about that. Remember the jolt of adrenaline and the feeling of being hooked onto them whenever I saw them. Their looks were the knock-out punch that let me dissociate from anything that actually mattered.

Well, I had awoken to my Dad's hands on me when I was twelve, and the next day gorgeous Horst Buchholz saved the young girl in the film Tiger Bay. Seeing him save her killed my pain. That's whom I've needed ever since.

A sad hopeless feeling comes now. It feels as though I'll never change, not really, I'll always be anxious, feel panic, stop existing out of the blue, because I've always been this way. It's not enough to not be neurotically attached to Baker, because there's still an empty place within where connection with Dad should be. What can I do?

Nothing.

A familiar sound from down the hall shatters the edge of my melancholy. It's the music of Saturday cartoons and the funny cunning voice of the cartoon character Wile E. Coyote. He's plotting, as always, to get the roadrunner. I picture Wile. E. Coyote hurriedly slapping on rocket-powered roller skates the way he does, because it seems like such a great idea. The same way I do. But he always flattens himself against a granite mountain. He has to peel himself off. Same as me. While the roadrunner beeps and runs away unscathed.

I'm Wile E. Coyote! That's how I abandon myself. *I* slap on rocket-powered roller skates because of my need to get what's missing within. I recall Arnold, Adam, Randy and the rest. I burst out laughing. I'm Wile E. Coyote. I keep laughing. Tears stream first from my laughing and then from my sadness. It's who I've always been, chasing one guy after another, slamming into the granite mountain, hurting myself.

I look across the little oval rug to the darkness under the bed. I don't want to accept I don't have something I need, but I have to, to get better. I don't have a safe connection with Dad, and I don't have a solid connection with myself.

Calmer, more solid now, I set my workbook aside and stand up as I accept the truth. I need a Wile E. Coyote coffee mug to help me remember I can never safely slap on rocket-powered roller skates again. I feel better. I may not need the workbook anymore. I need a real connection with myself.

I stretch, glance around the room for something it seems I'm supposed to remember.

CHAPTER 13
SO SAYS THE GREAT ARCHITECT

November, 1993. The same moment.

Thanksgiving! That's what I'm supposed to remember. How could I forget Thanksgiving's next week?

I want Mom and Dad to meet Baker, to know I'm seeing someone good.

First, I need to invite Baker. Damn. He won't like this. Call him now.

I call him up. "I'm Wile E. Coyote. But I'm not crashing into granite mountains anymore."

Baker chuckles. "Good for you."

And lucky for you, Baker. "So, I was wondering," say it like it's a casual thing, "if you'd like to come with me for Thanksgiving. There'll be a lot of other food besides turkey." Please say yes.

"It's at your parents', right?"

"Right."

"Thank you, but no."

Ow. That was abrupt. "Why?"

"Because I don't like being around perps."

Perpetrators. Dad. Damn. "You don't want to be around my dad."

"No, ma'am, I do not."

Does that mean, he's never going to see my parents?

"Your Mom, I could hang with. Not your dad."

Damn it. "Okay." Why can't he just be kind for one day? I can. "What are you going to do for Thanksgiving?"

"I believe I'll take a long beach walk, think about the Native Americans we slaughtered. It's a fictional holiday for me. Sorry. I know you're probably invested in the linens, candles and turkey."

He knows I am. I've told him about Mom's linens, which were Grandma's linens, with big holes now. Mom regrets not darning the holes when they were small, but she had ten kids, other priorities. She starches and irons the linens. Gets emotional arranging them so the holes are covered. She misses her mother, wishes they could have had a relationship. Which makes me long to help my mother.

"In our house," he continues bitterly, "the Thanksgiving table was over-turned by my drunken father, so, Thanksgiving means nothing to me."

That's so sad. "I'm so sorry."

"You didn't over-turn the table," he says with a softer tone.

This is sad—Baker and I won't share my favorite holiday. I love it because it has such an ancient, moody feeling. It makes me feel tethered, imagining Seattle wind and rain outside the windows, having bread rolls, butter, pies, starched linens shining in candlelight. He'll never love Thanksgiving the way I do, but I need to help him soften up, somehow.

"But you have a nice time," he says.

"All right." I have to accept he won't come. I wanted us to be like a normal couple.

"What are you doing tonight?" he asks.

Not doing my workbook. I think I'm cured. "Nothing."

"Let's go to the Earthling. Look at books."

He sounds happy. Good. I'll be with him, and I'll be tender and wear off on him. "Okay."

"I'll be over at six," he says.

He's complicated. I like him a lot. It hurts to think that he won't meet my parents.

But the truth is, he's not dating my parents.

At six, I hear Baker's steps on the stairs and open the door.

"Come on," he says, "Let's walk."

I get my jacket.

He stops at the top of the stairs, turns with his back towards me. "Hop on."

"You're crazy."

"I'm not. Hop on."

"You'll drop me."

"I won't. Hop on."

I hop on his back. Down the stairs we go. Doesn't feel too steady. He lets me down at the bottom.

"How did you *do* that?" I ask.

"Was nothin'," he says, and laughs.

We hold hands, walk in the brisk night under the street lights. I love the warmth of his big hand. "It's a dark night," I say and squeeze his hand.

"Yes, it is. New moon. We might even see some stars, if we get away from the street lights."

"I wonder if the sun's going to burn out."

He looks at me. Squeezes my hand. "I wouldn't worry about it. Probably won't happen tonight."

He's joking of course, but his tone's reassuring. He's obviously trying to impress me, carrying me downstairs, and it's not for sex.

Baker turns down the dark street I don't like. I stop, pull back.

"What?" he says.

"It's too dark."

He laughs. "And?"

"Let's take the other street with lights. I can't go down a dark street."

"Why not?"

"I was stalked on this street one night, walking to work at a rest home. I was terrified."

"Did he get you?"

"No, I ran."

"It's not even seven o'clock. Come on. I like the dark. We might see stars."

"I can't go. Someone could get us."

He laughs. "No one's going to get us. Come on. You'll see."

He gently tugs my hand.

He's right. It's not likely someone will attack us early in the evening. He likes the dark. Walk with him. I hold tight and go with him down the dark street.

"See?" he says. "No one's getting us." He sounds so sweet, as though we're children.

"They could."

"They won't."

"You don't know for sure," I say.

He squeezes my hand, looks over to me. "Don't worry, ma'am. You're with a trained killer," he says with an official tone.

A trained killer. "The military?"

"Yes, ma'am," he says proudly. "MOS02J20, ma'am. Military bandsman, specialist fifth class, First Army, Twenty-fifth Infantry Division."

I pull his hand to me. He means to protect me. Tears warm my eyes as I scan the shadows. We walk. I'm still nervous. I'm not used to feeling protected.

A strange calm comes with that truth.

Dad couldn't protect me. He was often gone. And when he was home, he couldn't protect me from himself.

Sweet sadness and relief come together. I never understood this. Dad couldn't protect me.

I take a deep breath, release a great sigh. Suddenly, Baker's and my body are moving in tandem as one person, rocking left and right with easy steps, connected, safe. I feel strong. Never mind he won't be at Thanksgiving. My fear's gone.

At the Earthling bookstore, we have fun looking at books on astronomy. I get sad reading the sun *will* burn out in seven billion years. The sun. I can't believe how sad it makes me feel. "Isn't that sad? The sun is going to burn out."

"I guess nothing lasts forever," Baker says.

"Love does."

He gives me a skeptical smile.

"I mean, love's eternal, because it's God. Love's the only thing I believe in," I say.

"Hm," he says.

Back at home, Baker wants to carry me *up* the stairs.

I laugh. I need to protect *him*. "No. You don't need to do that," I say.

"I do." He stands ready for me to hop on.

"You'll hurt yourself."

"No, I won't."

I give up. "Okay." I hop on his back. He carries me upstairs.

I'm in awe of the strength in his slight build. "You're strong!"

"Thank you, ma'am," he says and sets me down.

Maybe he'll want to come in and snuggle. Maybe more. I'd be fine if we did it. "Would you like some tea?" It'd be nice to cuddle, at least. We've never done that. Thankfully I'm not wearing rocket powered roller skates, and there's no granite mountain.

"No, thanks, I'd better get back. Have a good Thanksgiving at your folks."

"Thank you. You have a nice beach walk."

"Will do. Good night."

"Night."

I close the door. Why didn't he stay? I don't understand. Are we only friends who hold hands?

Wait and see.

No. I can't wait. I need to know.

I ruminate about Baker for the next few days. How come he doesn't make a move?

I'm going to have to ask him. That's a real relationship, when you ask someone what they're thinking. Call him up and ask if he has any intentions.

One night, I get a nice cup of tea ready, light a candle, get comfortable sideways in the gold chair, my feet dangling over the arm. I'm nervous. So what? I'm always nervous. I call him up. "Hi, Baker."

"Hello, Marie."

"You sound so formal."

"So do you."

Damn it. He sees right through me.

"What's up?" he says.

"Well, I wanted to ask you something, I'm not sure how to say it, so I guess I just will."

"That's usually best."

"Um, well, actually, I was wondering. Well. Do you have any intentions?"

Silence.

"Are you there?" I ask.

"Yes, very much so. I was reflecting on your question. Could you illuminate for me your meaning? Intentions is a broad category."

"Sure. Well," say it, "I mean, do you see us going anywhere?"

"Do I see us going anywhere," he repeats as a statement. "You know, life's a great journey that goes many places. It meanders this way, sometimes, and then hurries off that way, other times, but the paths we actually travel within ourselves are never ..."

He talks on for half an hour. Beautiful philosophical thoughts about paths and unfolding.

"I hope I've answered your question satisfactorily," he finally says.

I smile. I know nothing more than when he began. He's saying he doesn't know. We haven't unfolded yet. Let him know you're open to him and his answer was good enough. "Yes. It was a fine answer. Thank you."

Strange. Not knowing, doesn't matter now. I like who he is.

After the next survivor group meeting, Dinah calls Baker over to her. "We're on for tomorrow?" she happily asks him.

Shoot.

"Yes. Same time," Baker says.

"Great," she says.

At my car I ask him, "What are you doing with Dinah tomorrow?"

"Oh, beach walk."

"What?"

"Dinah and I walk on the beach," he says.

"I don't want you to walk with her."

He laughs. "Why not?"

"You walk with me. We hold hands. Do you hold hands with her?"

"No."

"Don't you see how it's a problem?"

"No. She and I are friends."

"But it's a beach walk. It's what *we* do together."

"And we still will."

Damn it. I don't want this. I stare at the ground between us in wounded silence.

"She and I have been friends since before I met you," he says.

Crap. I have to accept this. He's saying he wants me to trust him. They're just friends. "Okay." I climb in my car. "Good night."

"Night."

It doesn't feel good to feel at odds with him. I'll see him for dinner at his place tomorrow night. Damn it. I don't think I can do this. Maybe we don't belong together.

The next night, he serves our hot plates of stir-fried vegetables and tofu in the beautiful empty sunroom. I watch the candle flicker, watch his eyes. Someone at the sobriety meeting said think of the positives. I put myself in a good mood thinking of how Baker and I like each other. How I feel grateful I'm the one he's interested in. I put Dinah and the beach walk out of my mind. It works. Baker seems relaxed too. We're getting through these little hurdles. Fucking painful ones, but in the big scheme of things, little, I think. This is good.

After dinner, we take a walk through the neighborhood, holding hands. We're like a married couple. We comment on trees, yards, cars. Baker's a horti-culturist. He points out a small tree. "See that? There's no excuse. It's still tied to its nursery stake." He shows me the damage the stake has caused where it digs into the tree's bark. "Leaves it wide open for disease. As soon as the tree can stand in the wind, the stakes should be removed. The wind will help it grow stronger."

The wind of our turmoil will help me grow stronger if my nursery stake of old rules and beliefs gets ripped out. I picture myself ripping it out—the rule that he shouldn't walk with a woman friend, the belief that I need him to befriend my dad. Suddenly, I feel my strength against the wind. I'm going to grow.

He knows a lot. I love how he cares about trees. And he's confident. I want to be someone who knows something too. I stop at one house, wondering how the cut away curb of a driveway came to be right in front of the house, not the garage. "How do you think that happened?" I ask. "The driveway's in front of the house." I point.

"Don't know," he says, and keeps walking.

"Don't you think it's interesting?"

"Not really."

Darn him. "It's fun to speculate."

"I don't speculate." He looks at me, seems to see my disappointment, comes back. "All right," he says, takes a look at the property. "The driveway used to be over there," he points to a landscaped area.

"No," I say, suddenly realizing how the odd juxtaposition happened. "The house used to be the garage! They've remodeled the garage into a living space, with a porch, so now it looks just like a house!"

He turns and walks away. "So says the great architect," he says with a sarcastic scoff.

I stand still, dumbfounded.

He walks on up the hill toward his place without me.

I feel my face flush as the heat of rage rises. Dad's sarcasm ripped into Mom my whole life. Still does. I won't have it. I follow him. "Why did you say that?"

No answer.

"So says the great architect?" I say. "That's sarcasm."

No response.

"That's not okay," I say, struggling to catch up to his long stride. "You're not some god."

"Are you sure?" He walks on in silence a few paces in front of me.

Is he saying I'm making him out to be a god?

No. He can't talk to me this way and walk off like that.

Forget him.

I'm done with him.

It was nice while it lasted. It's over.

It was nice. Except for walks with Dinah. Showing up half an hour late for dinner.

Shit. I'm over-reacting. This is how relationships go. You have a fight, apologize, make up. Except, he's not apologizing. But do I end it for one remark?

No. Love and tolerance is what matters, my sobriety meetings say. Though he needs to know how wrong it was to say that. I told him. He didn't seem to get it. All right. I won't speak to him. That'll send the message. Hello and good-bye is all I'm going to say, until he apologizes. Mom never stood up to Dad. I won't make that mistake.

We get back to his place, I collect my things. "Bye."

"Bye."

I walk to my car. Don't look back, Marie. He needs to know how you feel.

The next night at the meeting, Scott seems to notice the frost between Baker and me.

"Hi, Scott!" I say happily. "How are you?"

Scott laughs. "I don't know, Marie. You're trying to drag me into a mess I'm not sure I want any part of. Trouble in River City, Baker?"

Baker smiles. "Looks like I'm in the doghouse."

Scott laughs. "What'd he do, Marie?"

I'm not telling Scott. I shake my head.

"What'd you do, Baker? Kick over the flowerpot of her dreams?" Scott laughs.

"Something like that." Baker glances at me with a brief warm look of knowing, the smallest hint of acknowledgment that what he said hurt me.

I can't stay mad at him, now. Maybe he was beaten so badly as a child he can't apologize. It would bring up too much shame or rage. Maybe he'd rather die than say he's sorry. Maybe he only needs to feel the heat, the distance I put between us when I get mad in order for him to recognize he can't be sarcastic with me anymore. I don't know how long you're supposed to stay mad at someone.

A few weeks ago, I read a good section in my workbook on anger. I haven't been angry for a long time until right now. I'll look at the book again tonight. At least I no longer feel I don't exist. I have an angry inner child who won't be talked down to with sarcasm. And if he wants to be with me, he has to be with her.

CHAPTER 14
THE STARDUST MOTEL

December, 1993. A few weeks later.

It's surprising how fast anger can disappear. A few days after I got so angry with him, Baker and I had the best time at the Museum of Natural History and at the Botanical Gardens. He made me howl as he pantomimed ants having a cigarette while they plotted their next move on a little bit of trash—hamburger paper—on the ground. We see each other more than ever since he made the great architect remark. I did the right thing, letting him know I wouldn't allow sarcasm.

He calls me one evening, as usual. "What are you doing?" he asks.

"Adjusting my Holiday lights on my pole lamp. They're Christmas lights now that Christmas is coming."

"It needs a shade, not Christmas lights."

I laugh. "It needs Christmas lights!" I plug the strand in. The magical colorful lights touch my soul. "They make the place so cozy," I say from a dreamy place far in the past, in Seattle, when I was small. "What are you doing?"

"I need to buy some shoes."

"Okay," I say. Why's he telling me? "So, what else is new?"

"Well, I need to get some shoes, probably this weekend."

"Okay." What does he want? "Did you want me to go with you?"

"Yeah. That'd be good."

Seems odd, he wants me to go with him to buy shoes. We must really be a couple. "Where do you want to go?"

"I thought we could go to Two Guys in Goleta. Maybe have a picnic lunch on the beach out there."

"That sounds fun. I'll make us some sandwiches."

"Thanks. I'll bring some trail mix."

"Good. Don't forget it." He needs that trail mix. His blood sugar plummets and he gets anxious and irritated, as if it's my fault. He calls it red-lining.

Saturday morning comes. I haven't talked to Mom in weeks. I ought to call her, say hi. I never tell her what's going on in my life. I'll tell her I'm going shopping with Baker today.

I dial the phone. "Hi Mom. How are you?"

"Hi, darlin.' Doing well. Yourself?"

"Doing well. Baker and I are going shopping for some shoes he needs in a little while."

"Oh?"

"Yeah."

"Well, that sounds nice."

It's so hard to talk to her. I just want a normal conversation. "What are you doing today, Mom?"

"Oh, the usual. Cleaning the kitchen. I've got a few letters I want to get out before the meeting this week at the Area Agency on Aging."

I'm so happy to finally have a real boyfriend, but she doesn't seem to care or notice. Tell her. "Sounds good. I'm really glad Baker and I are getting along well. He's really kind and makes me laugh every day."

"That helps!" She laughs. Well, honey …"

"Right, I don't want to keep you from your letters." I need to push her away first. It's unbearable when she pushes me away.

"Yah, I'd better get at them. They won't write themselves."

"Okay. Nice to talk to you."

"You too, honey. Give Baker our love."

Can't do that, Mom. Baker won't hear of Dad sending his love. "All right, Mom. Love you too." I hang up.

I stomp my foot, angry. She was fine. She was kind. She was busy.

I don't need her! I fucking hate these feelings!

I'm pissed at Mom again for no reason. I've anxiously needed her and been mad at her since I can remember. I take a deep breath, wash my dishes. We're all doing our best, I reflect. That's one of Mom's favorite sayings. I calm down.

By the time Baker arrives, I'm in a better mood. My kitchen's clean and we're going shopping. I'm glad it's easy to put Mom out of my mind.

We drive to Goleta. Walk down the long aisles of Two Guys. This is very personal, helping him buy shoes. Couples do this. We do seem to be a couple. Though still no sex, which is weird. It's been three months since we started seeing each other.

He selects a pair of white athletic shoes, heads for the checkout counter.

"Aren't you going to try them on?"

"I will at home. These should work. They're my size."

I forgot. He hates being around people in public. It makes sense he doesn't want to try them on. We walk up to the counter.

I feel anxious for no particular reason. A big cholate candy bar with lots of nuts will fix that. I pick up a candy bar and take out a dollar.

"Candy?" he says.

"We're going on a picnic. You want one?"

"No thank you, ma'am. Not good to fix feelings with food."

"What feelings?"

"Any feelings."

"Right." Right now, I just want a candy bar. "I'm always anxious, anyway."

"My point."

I don't want to think about it.

At the beach, we sit on the cold sand, turn our jacket collars up, huddle against the wind, try to keep the blowing sand out of our sandwiches.

He looks out to sea, his face beams in the sun. "You can't beat this!" he says. With an expansive look, he takes a big bite of his sandwich. I made it the way he likes it—cheese, a pile of pickles, lots of tomatoes, lettuce, and gobs of mayo. Juice runs down his hands.

I think I love him. His constant passion for simple things lifts me out of my constant petty concerns, like why I get mad at Mom now at forty-three years old. Grow up, Marie. I eat half my sandwich and all my candy bar. I can't imagine going without candy.

We finish eating. "Let's lay back, feel the sun," he says.

He rolls up small towels for pillows. We lay, bundled up against the brisk air, the sun on our faces. He smiles over at me, takes my hand, squeezes it. "Isn't this something!" he says with a tone of awe. We could be standing on the rim of the Grand Canyon.

"Yes!" I say. With him, everything feels so real.

After a few minutes, the candy bar sugar's kicked in. I'm ready to go. He won't want to. I wait a respectable eight more minutes or so. "Ready?"

"For what?"

"I want to go."

"Where?"

"I don't know. I'm just ready to do something."

"We are doing something. We're lying here."

"I know. I'm just antsy."

"Relax."

He always wants me to relax. I like relaxing, but only for a few minutes. He could relax all day.

That must be what they mean about give and take in a relationship.

Ten minutes later, I say, "Okay. Now I'm really ready to go."

"Yes, ma'am." He's not pleased.

I can't help it.

He pops up.

I can't make everything right for him.

We pack up, get to the car.

"Where to?" he says, irritated.

"Sorry, you're not happy, Baker."

"I'm happy. Where to?"

He can't always have his way. "Home, please."

He drives us to my place and parks. "Should I come up?" he says.

"Sure, if you like."

"I mean, I don't want to infringe on your doing something or whatever."

"Don't worry, you won't. I'm sure you can busy yourself."

"Oh, I can busy myself, all right." His eyes twinkle.

I laugh. I'm glad he's letting go of being upset.

"I'll try on my new shoes," he says amiably.

"Good idea."

He's a handful. I'm suddenly tired. It was a long work week. And the sugar's worn off.

Upstairs in my room, he tries on his new shoes. "What do you think?" he asks.

"Nice." They're so bright and white they don't look like his shoes.

He sits in the gold chair admiring them.

I wish I had his energy right now. I'm nine years older than he is. "Are you turning thirty-five tomorrow?"

"Yes, I am. If I live until then."

"Darn it. I forgot it's your birthday. We'll do something tomorrow."

I'm feeling irritated, over-whelmed, sleepy. I put away the sandwich fixings from the morning. More than anything, I want a nap. I can't bear to kick him out.

"You know," I call from the kitchen, "you can stay, or you can go, but I need a nap. I'm sorry, I'm getting cranky."

I finish in the kitchen, turn to go in the other room. He's not in the gold chair. I look around the corner. He's lying on my bed, smiling, arms wide open for me to fall into.

At last. What I've been waiting for. Only, not right now. I'm too tired.

So? I'm tired. This is a relationship. Things aren't always going to be perfect. I curl up in his warm arms.

It feels strange when we start taking off each other's clothes. We've spent so much time together, and now, finally getting naked, I'm shy.

"I have a condom in the drawer," I say.

"Good. Gotta have a raincoat."

He's not shy as he kneels above me, stretches his lean body. He smiles into my eyes, slowly lowers himself to me. He's not afraid of sex, thank God. Not at all.

He makes love with his eyes open, gazing into mine.

We're a real couple now. He's mine. I'm not crazy in love the way I was with the others. I've been calmly wanting Baker in my life. Now, here he is. I'm wide awake with him, but separate from him in a good way, not hopelessly lost, hooked into "us" by some romantic dream-state. I'm not sure what to think.

Later, wrapped up in his warm arms, dusk falling, I wonder if we'll be okay. It's a big step, sex.

Don't hurt him, comes a cautionary voice from one deep inside who's seen me drop men I'm not neurotically attached to.

The warm dark quiet of sleep comes on, my nap, at last.

I wake. It feels late. I switch on the strand of Christmas lights and watch him stir awake. We've never talked about children. It didn't seem right before. Now, it seems too late.

"Your mind is working over-time," he says, sitting up.

We put pillows against the windowsill, sit against them, his arm around me.

"Yeah. I was just thinking, I never told you I want to have children. Not give birth, but raise them. Foster kids, or adopt some kids. It's kind of late to mention it."

"No, we don't need to subject small beings to our care."

"But I want to."

He squeezes my shoulder. "We'll be our own children. You'll see."

He doesn't think we'd be good at it. He may be right. Our hands may be full learning to get along. I'll let it go, for now. It was a big dream before, raising kids, but now it doesn't feel so urgent.

"Your colorful lights are really nice," he says.

"Do you celebrate Christmas?" I ask.

"Not so much Christmas. I celebrate my being a child of God, and all children of God. And if Christ did exist, he was surely a child of God. One of many. I'm not a Christian, in the classical sense."

"No," I say, squeezing his hand. "I don't think you're anything in the classical sense."

"Probably not."

"You definitely march to your own drum."

"As do you. Is there any other way?"

For three hours we gaze into the Christmas lights, swapping stories. This is the connection I've craved all my life. The sex was nice, but this is the thing I need.

"When did you move here from Seattle?" he asks.

"1961. I was eleven. I was devastated leaving our home, the only home I'd known. A part of me never left Seattle. She hangs on Mom in the kitchen, plays in the rain, walks home from school as it gets dark proud of her brown leather shoes. The summer after we moved to California, I had made a friend, Karen. That helped. She was crazy about surfers. We stuffed tissue into our bathing suit tops and walked down to the beach looking for a boy she had a crush on. We were twelve. She lived in a motel her parents owned. The Stardust Motel. It was an interesting place. There was an older couple who belly-laughed wanting us to listen with them to the 'Baby Elephant Walk.' And a strange family with three little boys and too many adults lived in another unit. We only had to clean the rooms of the overnight guests."

"The Stardust Motel."

"Yeah."

"On Mason," he says.

"Yeah."

"Get out."

"You know it?" I ask.

"We crash-landed in Santa Barbara in '62. After staying with Granny, we lived in a few different places. We ended up at the Stardust Motel."

I look at him. "In sixty-two?"

"Yeah."

"How old were you?"

"Born in '58. Probably three, turning four in December. Colin would have been five. Gordon two, still in diapers."

"Three of you."

"Yep. The other three were born later, in Hawaii."

"I was there. I saw you there at the Stardust in 1962. There were three little boys, one in diapers, who played on the walk along the grassy mound in front of the units. They lived in a unit with too many adults."

"That was us. My mom had joined the cult." He laughs. "And you remember the Simples. The roly-poly couple."

"Yes! I was trying to remember their name."

"They played 'The Baby Elephant Walk.'" Baker laughs. "God. I can't believe this. We were both there at the same time. They'd call over anyone who'd listen and play their record and laugh and laugh."

"Oh my gosh! With their mixed drinks in the morning!"

"Exactly! We were really there together. That's crazy," he says.

We shake our heads, squeeze each other tight.

"I feel like it's a sign," I say.

"That we should get out while we can?"

"No! Why would you say that?"

"I don't know. It's a pretty big step. You know, now that we've done *it*."

He's as scared as I am. "Too late." I snuggle up even closer. "Not letting you go."

He sinks his head down on mine.

Nothing can go wrong now.

CHAPTER 15
THE BONDO JOB

March, 1994. Three months later.

I lie beside Baker in the sunlight on his bed in the late afternoon, restless. Our life is fairly self-centered. I want more purpose in my life. Baker said we're our own children, but that's selfish. We have a lot to offer. We could devote energy to fostering children who really need a stable home. I'll bring it up again. Maybe next week. Today, I want to patch the holes in the back of my car to stop the fumes from coming in.

I roll onto my back, spread my arms on the great big king-size bed that came with his ocean view and feel grateful we're together. Though I'm restless. Usually, when I need to do things, he wants to help. Which is good, except now the Bondo kit's been sitting in his garage for three days because whenever I'm ready to do the job, he's not. I can patch the rusted holes myself. He won't like being left out, but I need to get it done.

"Baker," I say, full of resolve. I sit up. I'll be my own person. I can patch the holes if he's not ready to.

"Yes, Marie." He says over his shoulder. He sounds wary.

"I need to do the Bondo job today. I mean, I'm going to do it today."

"I don't know what you're worried about."

"Fumes!"

"And have you been driving?"

"No, because you have."

"Exactly. It'll get done."

"I need to do it today."

"What's wrong with tomorrow. Tomorrow's Sunday."

"I wanted to do it Thursday!"

"Fine! Have it your way. You always do."

"What's that supposed to mean?"

"It means you'll never rest or let anyone else rest until you get what you want. Let's do it. Let's do it now."

"You don't need to do it. I don't want you to do it if you're angry."

"I'm not angry."

"Yes, you are. I can tell."

"You haven't seen me angry."

He gets up.

"I don't like when we're like this," I say.

"Like what? A couple of nimrods in the shit because one of us can't sit still?"

"No, upset with each other."

"Get used to it, baby."

"What's that supposed to mean?" He's angry. Only three months since we started sleeping together and it's all falling apart.

He dresses, goes out to the garage.

Well, at least it's going to get done.

He starts pushing big boxes around.

"What are you doing?" I ask.

"Making space."

"For what?"

"You said you wanted to do the Bondo job!"

"I do! The car's out there on the drive! Let's go do it!"

"Well, it needs to be in here where the dew won't get on it! Or did you read the instructions?"

He read the instructions. That's sweet. "I just don't want us to fight anymore. We fought last week too. Let's just get along, have some fun with the Bondo job."

"Not gonna happen," he says sourly.

"Why not? We get to decide our attitudes. We're both sober. Let's have fun."

No answer. Fine. Be miserable, Baker. I refuse to be miserable. I get the package of Bondo.

"What are you doing?" he says.

"Reading the box."

"I already read it," he snaps.

"So?" Now I'm angry. "I want to read it."

"Well, if you want my help, pull the car in here."

"Don't tell me what to do."

"Fine. Do it yourself." He puts his hands up, walks away.

"I don't want to do it myself! I want to have fun doing it together! My sisters and I would have fun with this!"

"I'm not your sisters!"

"No, you're my partner but you're not acting like it!" Forget you, Baker.

"Like I said, do it yourself."

I can do it myself. I should have. But now, I can't bear it if he walks away. I'm in a freefall seeing him go. "Get back here!" We've never fought like this. Damn it. Miserable, I get the keys and pull the car into the garage.

He comes back with a putty knife. "Thought you might need this." He drops it on the garage floor.

"Please help me do it."

"I don't know if I can."

"Why?"

"You want to do it yourself."

"I don't."

"You're sure?"

"Yes."

"All right. We need to prep the area. Here's some wet dry." He hands me a few sheets of black sandpaper.

Relief floods in. I may not be neurotically attached, but I sure hate abandonment. "We can't just slurry the Bondo on?"

"Sure, you can. It'll fall off within a week. But go ahead."

His tone has no humor. "You're so cold."

"Just stating the facts."

"It's your tone."

"Better get started."

I knew he could get cranky, but I didn't know how hardened he is. I don't want this kind of relationship. "What do we do?"

"Take all that rust off."

"You're joking."

"You wanted the job done, let's do it."

"I thought you just mix some paste and glue a patch on."

"Not in Baker's platoon."

"This isn't the military," I mutter and follow his lead, kneel on the garage floor.

He sands a patch of rust on one side of the back of the car. I sand on the other side. We work in silence. He's maddening. I need to lighten him up. "What do you want do tomorrow?" I ask pleasantly.

Silence.

"You're not speaking to me?" I ask as fear rises.

Silence.

"It's not right to treat someone like they don't exist," I say calmly, feeling dread mount within.

Silence.

The problem is, I can't bear the agony that him not speaking creates in me. I reach around in the soup of my childhood for the reason it's so painful. It seems obvious. Dad used to stop speaking if I disagreed with him. He'd go to his library. I couldn't make him come back. Then he went on the road. There was no repair. I need to get over this dread I feel, somehow.

For the next half hour, the feeling claws at my stomach, a steady painful reproach for making him angry enough to act like I don't exist. Except, that doesn't make sense, because I didn't make him cruel enough to treat someone this way. The back of the car's still a rusty mess. I didn't realize the holes would be a problem when I bought it. I glance at his fixed scowl. I didn't cause this. He's wrong to not speak to me. Dad was wrong too. No, this definitely isn't the kind of relationship I want, or can stomach.

These days everyone says you have to ask for what you want, tell your partner how you feel, don't settle for less than what you want. I've done all that. It doesn't frigging work.

Another fifteen minutes pass. I say, "I think it's good enough."

No answer.

"How long are you going to stay angry?"

"I told you. I'm not angry."

He spoke. The claw let's go of my stomach. I exist.

I need a better reference point than him and my dad to know I exist.

We work on it another half an hour. The sun's gone down. Baker turns the garage lights on.

"I'm hungry," I say.

He must be starving. Food will settle him down.

"Let's eat," I say.

"You wanted to do this. We're doing it."

I look out to the last evening light, lonely to my bones. I don't care about the car anymore. Don't care about Baker. I picture the rest of my life in one long fight with him. I should never have slept with him. He wasn't like this before we started having sex. What changed? I remember Joe, my first husband, changed when we got married. Suddenly he thought I should dust.

Baker opens the Bondo package. Takes out strips of patch material. I get some scissors, find some gloves. He mixes a portion of the Bondo paste with the hardener. Puts some around a hole in the car, presses a patch onto the hole, and spreads more paste. The patch curls up.

"Godammit!" he yells.

Now he's angry.

"Hold that!" he yells.

He can't yell at me. I won't allow that. "Don't yell at me!" I yell back and hold the patch.

He slathers more paste on. The patch sticks to my gloves. It begins to harden. I press it on and peal the patch off my glove as I pull my glove away. The patch is crooked, wrinkled.

"Get another patch!" he barks.

"Why are you barking at me?!"

"Because it's hardening and it'll be wasted! Just do it!"

"Don't order me to do things!" I get another patch. Hold the corners so it can't curl. "Put more here," I say.

He ignores me.

"More here!" I yell.

"Can't you see I'm putting it here!" he yells.

"You're impossible to work with!"

"Well so are you!"

He mixes more paste and hardener. Slurries it on my new patch.

I slap the patch onto the old one, to plug the holes in the wrinkled patch.

"What are you doing?!"

"I'm patching my car!"

"It had a patch! You fill in with the paste! Put the next one over here!"

Why does he have to be so mean about it? *"Fine!"* I'm angry.

Poor Mr. B. has to listen to all this.

After half an hour of yelling, all the patches and paste are used. The car looks like it has a cast on its butt. We clean up in silence. He goes in the house.

I walk away from the garage, all nerves and pain. I sit on a boulder near garden steps. There's nothing left of us. I look out to the blackness of the sea.

It's over.

I look up at the stars. Yep. Better to be alone. I set my jaw and nod. We tried to have a relationship. It didn't work. I don't know how my parents did it. Yes, I do. Mom didn't yell back. I'm not going down that road—sixty years of being barked at and belittled. It's too bad we couldn't pull it off. Baker's a really great guy. I'll be sad to say good-bye.

CHAPTER 16
BLACKSMITHING

March, 1994. Fifteen minutes later.

I sit in silence a long time on the boulder thinking of ending things with Baker. Waves of sadness cascade within. I feel crazy. I tap the boulder I sit on and pull on my hair to ground myself.

Baker comes back outside, walks over. "Pulling your hair out?"

How can he sound so relaxed? "Yes."

"Come here."

"No."

"Come here."

I look up at him. Be honest. "I don't want to. I don't want to be with you anymore. It's not working. I want to be alone." I look away toward the ocean. That was easy. I'm surprised I just said it, and it came out so easily. It's true.

"I need you to come with me."

He knows I can't resist when he says *I need you.*

"What do you want?" I stand up. "You won't cajole me into acting like things are fine."

He reaches out his hand.

"I don't want to hold your hand."

"Come on," he says tenderly. "Give me your hand."

Damn him. I shake my head no.

He reaches closer.

Shoot. I'm caving. I hold my hand a few inches away from myself. A big fat sorry would help, Baker. But he doesn't say sorry.

He takes my hand, swaddles it in his big warm hand, leads me over to the garage.

"What are we doing?" I ask.

"Admiring our work."

He's so romantic. Still, I'm angry and laugh a mean scoffing laugh. "It looks like shit."

"It heard you say that," he says with a small twinkle in his eye.

Things have feelings in Baker's world. "The truth will set it free," I mumble.

"You're right. It does look like what you said. But I think we learned a lesson."

"No, we didn't. We didn't learn a gosh darn thing. What lesson?"

"Not sure yet." He smiles at me.

I frown, squint my eyes at him. I'm still sore.

He puts his arms around me.

"How can you act like things are fine?" I ask.

"Things are fine."

"No. They're not. I decided to leave you, sitting there on that boulder."

"I hope you don't."

"That was *awful* fighting like that! I *never* want to fight like that again. It was horrible!"

"It wasn't so bad."

"It was bad, Baker! I hated it!"

"You hate a lot of things."

"Hush. I don't."

His body's hot like a toaster.

He's trying. He's messed up from what happened to him as a child. I'm messed up too. Can it hurt to try again? The worst will be another shouting match. I hated that.

I would hate to lose him.

I put my arms around him. We hold each other a long time, look out to the sea of our crappy Bondo job, children on the shipwrecks of our pasts. A breeze rustles the old dead garden behind us, lifts my hair, cool's my scalp.

"Baker."

"Yes."

"Do you think we're going to make it?"

He looks me in the eye with a fun smile. "Sure."

"Why? That fight was *horrible.*"

"That was nothing."

"Nothing? It was three hours of horrific hating each other. We won't make it if we have another fight like that." I use a note of warning. I have a limit.

"Don't worry, dear."

He called me dear. I love it. He's attached. "Why not worry? We'll never make it if we can't get along."

"We'll make it. Don't worry. We're just blacksmithing."

"What do you mean?"

He pulls back to look me in the eye. "Blacksmithing. That's when you stoke the fire with bellows, get the iron red hot, and then pound the fuck out of it. Shape it into the relationship you want. Not the relationship someone else has, but the one we want."

He's serious. That sounds brilliant. Is it? I don't care. "We're that messed up? We can't just get long?"

"You saw what happened. We both wanted to be in charge. Blacksmithing, dear."

He said it again. Dear. "I don't want to fight anymore."

"Good luck with that." He smiles into my eyes and holds me close.

I need to tell him I want to raise children. "You know, we talked about children. You said we're our own children, or each other's child. But I think it's selfish not to devote our energy to fostering children."

He looks me in the eye. "I don't want to make the mistakes my dad made."

"You're not your dad."

"Don't be so sure."

"But I really want to raise kids," I say, looking down.

My mind feels a nudge that I'm missing some important point in my own argument. Yes. Answer this: is feeling a lack of purpose in my life enough of a reason to foster kids?

"You really want to raise kids, but have you thought it through?" he asks. "What it takes to help foster kids who've already been traumatized? It's one thing to work on ourselves at survivors' meetings once a week and totally another to help young children day in and day out. I'm not equipped for that."

Listen to him. He's got anger inside. And I've got a lot of anxiety. We could screw up. I hadn't thought about that. What was I thinking? Of the sweet times. The fun nurturing times. What about the conflicts? Are Baker and I equipped to be adults in the face of the inevitable anger of traumatized foster children? We can't handle a Bondo job. I'm impulsive. Don't be impulsive about this.

It hurts to let go of this dream, because I'd love to nurture young beings, but I think he's right. We could do more harm than good.

Whatever I need from raising children, I'll find somewhere else, with less risk of screwing up. "Okay," I say.

"We're the children we need to raise," he says.

"It sounds so selfish."

"Who else is going to do it?"

CHAPTER 17
No Ex's

June, 1994. Three months later.

I'm tired of shlepping my things to Baker's all the time. Me going to his place makes sense, his place is bigger. My bed is small. Mine may even be a child's bed. We've been together six months. Nine months, counting walks on the beach. Why don't we live together? It'll make things easier.

I give that some thought for five minutes, to be responsible.

Call him. "So, I was thinking," I say, when he picks up the phone.

"Don't think so much," he says.

"Don't tell me that. Don't ever tell me don't think so much."

"Excuse me, Your Highness."

I want to strangle him.

His poor mom, raising six boys after she kicked his dad out. "Never mind. I wanted to talk about something."

"Now?"

"Why not now? You don't even know what it is."

"I know it can wait."

"How do you know that?"

"Because when you want to talk, I've done something wrong."

"What? That's not true."

"Yes, it is."

I laugh. "No, no, no. I'm not upset at you."

"But you're upset."

How can he tell? "I'll just say it.

"Please do."

"I think we should live together."

Silence.

"What do you think?"

Silence.

"Okay. Here's the thing," I say. "Three times a week I shlep my stuff up to your place. It's a pain in the butt. We're together, we could save money if I didn't pay rent. You have space. Plenty of space. Mr. B. probably thinks I live there already."

"He probably does."

"So why not try it? If it doesn't work, I'll move. Rooms are easy to find." I won't have to move. We're getting along great ever since the Bondo job.

Silence.

"Baker. Why aren't you talking about this with me?"

"I don't know."

"Is it your privacy?"

"No. Like you say, you're here a lot, which is good. It's working."

"It seems to."

"Yeah. No, it works, the way things are. Why change things?"

"Because it's really inconvenient for me. You get to stay where you are. I, on the other hand, get home from work, pack a bag, go to your place. See?"

Silence.

"What is it, Baker? What do you see as the problem?"

Silence.

"If we can't talk about it, how can we go forward?" This is a real relationship. We have to talk.

"I suppose you're right. I just don't know."

"Don't know what?"

Silence.

"Baker, what don't you know?"

"Don't know how we'd handle the money."

"The money."

"Yeah. I grew up on assistance. Food stamps. How would we handle the money?"

What a relief. "We can handle our money any way we want. We can have separate accounts. Joint accounts. Split the bills. Pay them together. I don't care how we handle the money."

"Oh." He sounds relieved. "All right. Sure. Let's do it."

Amazing. We talked. It was so easy.

A week later, Scott piles all my belongings into his big purple station wagon, ties the big things on top of it, moves me up to Baker's place.

"Hi, Mr. B.," I say, as usual, except this time I carry boxes past him.

He doesn't seem to mind.

"Did you tell Mr. B.?" I ask Baker when I'm all moved in.

"No. Did you?"

"No."

"He probably thinks you live here already."

Now, it feels strange to leave work and no longer drive home to my place. I drive home to Mr. B's house, always relieved to see Baker's car. For some reason, I expect him to stop coming home. In the mornings, I drink Baker's special coffee he makes in an espresso maker, instead of mine brewed in a small pot. It's different. I'll get used to it.

"What did you do with those carrot ends?" Baker asks one night in a panic as I make a salad.

"Threw them away. Why?"

"They don't go in the garbage!" His stern voice cuts me.

Is he crazy? I didn't see this coming. "Where else would they go?" I ask

"Compost."

"Oh." He's very particular. "Sorry. I'll fish them out."

"It's all right. You don't need to do that."

His tone tells me he's relaxed now, thank goodness.

A few weeks later, I confirm by observation what I've been suspecting. When he makes our coffee in the espresso maker, and adds water, his cup of coffee's stronger than mine. He's watering my coffee down, so he gets more actual coffee, the rascal. "I'll make the coffee tomorrow," I say.

"Go for it."

"Because you make yours stronger!" I say.

He grins.

One night watching Jeremy Brett in Sherlock Holmes, I reflect how we get along pretty well, and love each other a lot, but I miss writing in the mornings. He likes us to visit over coffee before work every morning, and at night after work I'm too tired to write. It's a relationship. I have to accept I'm not single anymore. Not being able to write is a noisy machine of frustration which always runs in the background. I need to figure it out.

I walk into the bedroom one night. He relaxes on the bed on an extra-long phone call. I can tell by his soft tone it's a girl. I don't like that. Like me, he's in a relationship. I give him a look.

He gives me a look.

I go back out to the sunroom, guts astir. Damn it. He has friends who are girls. I knew that. Can I live with it?

No. No, I can't. I hate it.

I try to write in my workbook, but I can't focus. I need another session with that therapist, Michael Andersen. Get my bearings.

After a while, Baker joins me in the sunroom.

"You were talking to a girl."

"I was."

"Who?"

"Does it matter?"

"You're with me now. It matters."

"It was my ex, Barbara. She called me. I don't call her. She calls me once in a while."

I shake my head no. "No ex's."

He nods. "All right. I'll let her know."

That was easy. "Thanks." This is great. He's reasonable. This is a real relationship.

CHAPTER 18
HEALED BY A T-SHIRT

June, 1994. A week later.

I drive home from work and feel sad that Dad's not invited to the party coming up for the June birthdays in my family. It's good he's not invited. But it makes me so sad I wish I could help him see what he does, somehow. But I'm still not on solid ground myself with my own recovery from trauma. I can't focus on Dad.

I begin climbing the Mesa hills toward home at Mr. B,'s house. As usual, panic rises from thinking Baker won't be home. I always spend the last three blocks in panic. I'm so used to panic and anxiety, I don't let it bother me, especially because when I turn down the drive, I always see Baker's blue VW fastback, his Granny's car, and feel relieved he's there, as he always is.

But this evening, suddenly things become slow motion as I glide down the drive. I see the familiar panic dissolve as effervescent crystals in my nervous system. I feel the warmth of calm flow in when I see his car. I feel good. But is it normal to panic every day when I come home? No. It felt normal, but it's not.

Once inside, I greet Baker with a kiss. "Hi. How was your day?"

"All right, I suppose, if fixing little old ladies' bathroom faucets can be considered an all-right day. At least I get a lot of variety. Always something at a senior housing complex."

He said he got this full-time job because he's in a relationship now. He's so sweet. I'm not telling him about the panic and relief that come every night on my way home. It's too weird. I'm done getting neurotic attachments, but I may not be as well as I thought. A sad overwhelmed feeling comes. I'll never be able to work with Dad, help him sort himself out if I can't sort myself out.

"What do you think about dinner?" Baker asks.

"Grilled cheese sandwiches. I need something soothing."

"Yes! And coleslaw. I'm on the slaw."

"I'll make the sandwiches."

A deep missing-Mom sadness suddenly flows into me, for no reason. My eyes well up. It's been a long time since I've had this happen. It always feels like

I'm losing my mind. "Excuse me. I need to cry for a minute." In the bedroom, I curl up in a ball on the bed with the familiar anguish.

He follows me in. "Everything all right?" he asks.

I shake my head no, unable to catch my breath. Tears flow.

He climbs on the bed, rests his hand on my back.

After a few minutes I can talk. "It feels as though my mom's looking for me a block away, at night. I'm calling for her. She can't hear me. That's insane, huh?"

My tears pour out, soak the pillow under my cheek. I let myself sob. "All I can see is Mom looking for me. That's so weird. Mom knows where I am. I'm here with you."

Baker sits quietly.

After ten minutes, I take a deep breath and sigh. The sorrow flows away like a tide. "Sometimes it feels I've been grieving Mom my whole life. I don't know what I'll do when she dies. How can grief happen so fluidly? I take it for granted, same as breathing, always missing my mom. Not this bad. It's been a while since I've had a bad spell like this one. They started when I was a teenager. It's been a few years since one's come on. The feeling of her looking for me on a street at night. I'm kind of a mess."

"You're not a mess. You're Marie, a recovering child of God."

I squeeze his hand. "Thanks. I might as well tell you. I get anxious three blocks from home."

"Really?"

"Every night, I panic three blocks from home. Then, as soon as I see your car, I'm calm. That isn't normal, is it?"

"I don't think so."

"Especially since you're a homebody. You don't vanish."

"I am a homebody. That you can count on. No, I don't vanish."

"Do you miss your mom?" I ask.

"Not the way you miss yours. Like I've said, she was always around."

"So was mine."

At work the next day, I sit in my converted closet, the file clerk/librarian's office, pause in opening invoices to reflect on the panic I felt in the driveway the night before. What if I think more about Baker, focus on how he's a good guy and is in my life? That might take away the panic. I'll do that.

Except, I can hardly bring him to mind.

Try again.

Nothing. No image of him comes up. That's strange.

Come to think of it, I don't think about him at work.

Never.

I don't know if that's normal. I don't call him, or think about him at all. I'm at my job, he's at his.

I picture my old boyfriend, Randy. There he is, I can see him plain as day. Tan face, long curls, wide grin. I think about Baker. No image at all. He's an invisible spirit person. I feel crazy.

Try again. I know he has long chestnut hair.

Nope. Can't see his face. Or *his* hair. Only hair. This is crazy.

I think I'll try the therapist again. Maybe he can explain what's going on.

A week later, the sun feels good on my face as I walk from my car to Michael Andersen's office. I remember the first time I came here to see him for therapy. It was sunny and I hated it. I'm making progress. Inside, I smile at the giant pink and turquoise prints. They have no charge. Yep, progress.

"You said on the phone you're having a problem with jealousy, insecurity," Michael says, as we take our seats.

"Yes. I'm jealous of other girls, women, but Baker's really loyal. It's just that he has friends who are women, who he sometimes talks with on the phone, maybe walks with, I'm not even sure he does that anymore. I'm on edge whenever he's on the phone with another woman."

"How so? Describe the feeling of being on edge."

"It feels I'm literally on an edge, ready to fall."

"Fall where?"

I picture it. "I'm going to fall into nothingness. It's terrifying. I want to die."

"Those are strong feelings."

"They are."

He looks at the floor. He doesn't know what to make of my feelings.

"What should I do?"

"Jealousy can stem from a lot of things. Low self-esteem. Lack of one's own interests."

"My self-esteem is pretty good, and I definitely have my own interests."

"Attachment issues can make a person insecure," he says.

"I'm insecure."

"How's your relationship with your mom?"

"Normal. Very attached. I feel needy. Then I get mad at her for being busy."

"Sounds like anxious-avoidant attachment."

It has a name. That's a start. Should I tell him about the sadness? I don't want him to think I'm weird. But he might help me figure it out. "Sometimes,

I sense my mom's looking for me, down a street at night. I panic, trying to tell her where I am, but she doesn't hear me calling for her. I usually have a good cry, and then I'm fine." Don't tell him anymore weird things. He'll think I'm making them up to get attention. I really just need to get squared away enough not to blow it with Baker. And to be able to help my dad if I can, because as long as Dad doesn't apologize or change, he can't see the grandkids, there's no peace in the family and Mom's stressed out.

"Hm. How often does it happen?"

"It'd been a few years, then a spell came on last week."

"Yeah, could be attachment trauma."

"Except, my mom was always home. I was always with her."

He shrugs. "We'd have to talk more about it."

What else is there to say?

"Why don't you write about those fearful feelings?" he asks.

"I've written so much about them. Nothing works."

He's at a loss.

I almost forgot. My coming-home-from-work panic. "While I'm here, I wanted to run something else by you. It's probably nothing. It doesn't really bother me, except for three blocks."

I tell him how I panic the last three blocks before home, then I'm fine when I see Baker's car.

Darn it. I've told him too much. He'll think I'm inventing problems, needy for attention. Oh well. "And I was thinking about this at work, and realized I couldn't picture Baker's face. Then I realized, I'm never anxious at work, because I never think about him. Never call him. It's like he doesn't exist. What do you think?"

"I don't know. I've never heard of anything like this. But it sounds like it could be an object constancy issue."

"What's object constancy?"

"It's a developmental stage in infancy. The ability to know people or things still exist, even if you can't see or hear them. You know, a very young infant doesn't miss a parent who's left the room, or a toy that's hidden. She hasn't developed the ability to know the thing still exists when out of view—object constancy. But at around eight months, infants' minds become able to grasp that when Mom leaves the room, she's missing, so they become distressed.

"If you can't picture your boyfriend when you're apart, it's as if he doesn't exist. Yet you're very connected when you're together. It could be an object constancy problem. Did anything traumatic happen when you were an infant?"

"Not that I know of. I'll ask my mom. How do I fix an object constancy problem?"

The therapist raises his eye-brows. "Not sure. Talk to your mom. See what she says."

The following morning, while dressing for work, I think about how infants carry blankets around as a representative of their parent. "Baker, can I take one of your T-shirts to work?"

"Why?"

"I need to see if it helps me with my object constancy."

"I don't know. I'm partial to my shirts."

"An old one. Pick one you don't care about."

"I care about all of them. If you take one, it'll miss me."

Oh dear. "Please? It's important. It's my baby blanket."

"Well, since you put it that way. It's for your inner baby. But don't lose it, all right?" He plies through his T-shirts, chooses a plain tan one. "Don't lose it."

At work, I leave his tan T-shirt folded on my desk. I look at it. Picture Baker giving it to me. I can see him! It's working!

Throughout the day, I look at the T-shirt and picture Baker. It works! I'll leave his shirt here for thirty days. That should fix one part of me.

Now, I just need to call Mom to find out if any trauma happened when I was a baby that would explain why I'm insecure. She's usually too busy to talk. It's excruciating when she is. But I don't need to talk to her on the phone. Only make a date to come up there and visit her.

I'm going to get well, whatever it takes. And when I do, I can help my dad. It breaks my heart to see him excluded from gatherings, because I'm sure he doesn't mean what he does, and could change, if he had help. But he doesn't trust anyone. I know he'll trust me, because I'm honest and not afraid—well, except to stand up to him, because he'll roar. But I'll get over that, someday, and he'll know the truth when we talk. I have to be patient.

CHAPTER 19
LITTLE RUBBER LEGS

June, 1994. The same week.

In a few days I get up my nerve and call Mom. She picks up the phone.

"Hi, Mom. Sorry to bother you, but I was wondering if I could come up there to talk with you sometime."

"All right." She sounds nervous.

"It's nothing bad."

"Oh good." She brightens. "How about we meet at Pea Soup Andersen's. That way we'll meet halfway."

She probably wants to spare me having to interact with Dad. Or she might want to spare me the drive. I'll just be glad to see Mom. And since we'll have a truly private conversation, I can ask her if she knows anything about Dad's childhood that may have affected him and the way he acts out.

A few days later, I watch her cross the Pea Soup Andersen's parking lot, her wisps of short white hair flying in the wind. She's so small, shrinking. She's eighty. It hurts to see her go through all the mess with Dad at her age. Though she had her part in keeping everyone quiet for years, not wanting anyone to rock the boat, until we did. We'll have a nice visit.

We settle in a large green booth. I'm going to ask her first if she knows anything about Dad that would help explain him.

"So, how are you?" I say, after we order our bowls of soup.

"Oh, I'm all right. Your father's been a *wonderful* help around the house lately. I've been under the weather."

She wants me to like him. "I'm really glad he's a big help, Mom." He never was when you were raising ten kids and he sat relaxing with his paper. Though he did have migraines. Okay.

"So, what was it you wanted to discuss?" she says.

She still sounds nervous, though I told her it's nothing bad. She's not sure it's not another boundary, like, I'm not going to see her or Dad anymore. I'm done setting those boundaries. I cut him off for a while. I cut her off too, for four months. It was horrible telling Mom I couldn't handle her glowing tales of Dad, and I needed to not see her. And I was more miserable not seeing her, than I was relieved to not hear about how wonderful Dad was.

"Well, two things. Neither one is bad. I was wondering if you can think of anything about Dad's childhood that could have made him …boundaryless, the way he can be."

"I see." She gives her head a little shake, probably to compose herself. "Well, let's see. His mother wore the trousers, as they say." Mom nods. "But no … nothing that I know of. I mean, he started working as a young child. A lot of children did in those days. I suppose something could have happened then, nothing he's ever talked about, but young children on the street are always vulnerable. You know, he had his own newspaper corner when he was five."

"Yeah. But nothing at home?" I recall the bad feeling I used to get as a child at nap-time at his parents' house, Grandma and Grampa Wells.' Grandma never let us wear our undies to bed. That was weird. And once, when Patricia and Marietta came home from a stay at Grandma and Grampa's, Patricia was unable to speak for three weeks. No one paid much attention. We thought she was choosing not to speak. Something bad could have happened to her. Probably did.

"At home? Well," Mom's voice grows quietly strong, "now, I don't know if he wants this to be public knowledge, but his mother did bathe him until he was twelve."

What? Wow. Everything just changed. Dad's an incest survivor. All these years, Mom and Dad have known that. "Twelve?" Poor Dad.

"That's right. He told me that."

Try not to look stunned. "Twelve is old to be bathed by your mom."

Mom nods in agreement.

"Wow. That'll affect a person. What made her stop?" I ask.

"He finally put his foot down," she all but growls with a note of pride. "As I say, his mother wore the pants in the family. It couldn't have been easy for him."

That's an understatement. I think of the comparable experience if Dad had bathed me until I was twelve. The thought's unbearable.

Dad was traumatized. I knew it.

"Now," she looks up at the approaching server, "I don't know if that has anything to do with things, you know, with the way he is. But I imagine it could."

"Yeah." I'm sure it could. Suddenly I don't have much appetite. I tell the server who sets our soup down, "Thank you."

"Shall I say grace?" Mom says.

"That'd be nice."

"Bless us, oh Lord …"

I picture it happening in a small bathroom in the 1920's.

"… gifts which we are about to receive, from thy bounty, through Christ our Lord, amen. Let's eat!" she says with the same gusto she always had when I was young, before she happily calculated, some nights, the cost of each plate of food. Eighteen cents! Or, twenty-two cents! She felt proud to stretch the money to feed ten kids.

"Now, what was it we were talking about?" she says.

"Dad. Grandma bathing him. That was huge." I feel like a burglar, having broken into his private story. "Was there anything else he told you?"

Mom blows on a spoonful of soup, shakes her head. "No, nothing else that I can think of."

Maybe Grampa molested him too. Grampa didn't have good boundaries. He hit on me, ran his hand up my thigh when I was twenty-five and asked for sex. He wanted to pay me; said he had lots of money. He kept saying I reminded him of Grandma whom he loved so much. He told me about Grandma's Lysol birth control douches every Wednesday and Saturday. I didn't mind learning about that, but is it really what you tell your granddaughter?

Lysol. Could that have affected Dad as an embryo?

"That's okay. That was a lot. Granma bathing him till he was twelve."

Mom nods. "Yah."

There's nothing more to say about it with Mom. "The other thing I wanted to ask about is nothing bad either. I saw a therapist, because I get jealous, because Baker makes other women laugh, has women friends. And I also noticed I can't picture Baker when I'm at work."

I tell her the whole story about object constancy and attachment. "So, the therapist said jealousy can be related to attachment problems. I told him I'm attached to you, but he said to ask you if there was any trauma during my infancy." I hope she remembers something.

"Gosh. Not that I recall."

Darn it. "Oh. Okay."

We eat our soup. I wanted something wrong with me I could fix.

"No," she says. "I'm thinking, trying to remember those years, nineteen-fifty, fifty-one, two, but not coming up with anything. Now, your brother Christopher fell from the buffet, as an infant. You would have been seven then. But as far as when you were an infant, nothing remarkable comes to mind."

"Well, that's probably good. Just thought I'd ask." I won't tell her how I get crying spells, terrified she can't find me. She'll feel sad and helpless.

"Now, a little later, you weren't really an infant, you were, let's see, fourteen months, or so. That might have been something." She takes a sip of soup, a bite of bread.

She doesn't realize she has a cryptic way of saying things. "What might have been something, Mom?"

"Well, that's when I gave birth to your sister Jean. You certainly wouldn't have known what was going on, but I was very sick. Almost died. I was in the hospital two times. So, I was gone for a total of six weeks. Jean was born premature, Cesarean section, you know. I was bleeding. I had taken so many pills," she laughs, "the nurses didn't appreciate me laughing when the blood from the transfusion poured out all down my arm because the blood wouldn't go in. I thought it was funny. They finally had to use my foot."

"Wow. I knew you had a C-section with her. I didn't realize you almost died."

"Yah. And when I came home, they told me you had refused to eat while I was away. Said you had sat outside on the curb waiting for me." Her white hair bobs as she nods. "I'll never forget when I saw you. You had little rubber legs from not eating." She shakes her head with sad, teary eyes.

I wouldn't eat. "Really?"

"Yah."

I missed her. Of course. "Thanks, Mom. I never knew that."

"It never came up."

"So, I missed you."

"You did indeed."

She was gone six weeks. I try to imagine a one-year-old missing her mom for a day, two days, a week, two weeks. This is why I sometimes feel so mad at Mom for no reason—she was gone too long.

"And I'm quite sure you were farmed out to relatives for part of that time. Your father couldn't look after everyone."

I was sent away to stay with people I didn't know. My eyes well up. The dream. Dad hugs me, lifts me away from him, hands me off to a strange man with a woman, at night under wet maple leaves across from our house. In the dream, I scream and scream for Mom. The people were probably an uncle and aunt I never saw before.

I can't make Mom feel worse by telling her about my dream and my crying spells, but they all make sense now. I blink back tears, relieved. It all makes sense.

I'm so glad I asked her. Little rubber legs. Wild. I feel so relieved. I'm not crazy. She was gone and I longed for her. I was handed off to a stranger. That's why I cry when it seems she can't find me. I screamed for her in my dream. She must have been looking for me. And I probably *was* wearing baby shoes the last time I felt safe in my life. That's why I need white high tops now.

There's a reason why I've always been insecure. What a relief. Now that I understand, I don't need to be jealous anymore.

And Dad was bathed by his mom. God only knows how that affected him. I need to tell Cecilia.

CHAPTER 20
IT'S NOT HURTING YOU

July, 1994. A few weeks later.

Baker and I relax on the couch after dinner in the spacious sunroom. I love how empty this room is. There's only the couch, our little dinner table and chairs, and now a couple of boxes of my things in the corner, which I was sad to put in here. They look messy. But there's no room in the garage.

"I'm thinking of taking a trip," Baker says.

"Really? For both of us? I can take time off."

"No." He looks at me. "It's more of a solo venture."

"Oh. Is Dinah going?" That popped out. I smile to make it a joke.

He sighs, impatient. "No, Dinah's not going. How many times do I need to tell you?"

"Sorry. Sorry. I shouldn't have said that."

"No, you shouldn't have."

Fuck. I'm still insecure. "Where are you going?"

"Sacto."

"Why?" That's where his ex lives, and his ex before that one.

"I've got a truck up there. Somewhere. Not even sure where it is now. It's been five years since I've seen it. And a storage unit."

"Oh. So, you're going for a weekend?" Not for weeks.

"No, I thought I'd take my time. Take two weeks. Stop in the Bay Area, see my brother. See some old friends in Sacto. Thinking about taking a Greyhound up, renting a small moving van to come back."

I'm so scared I can barely breathe. Don't pick a fight. "But why can't I go?"

"Because I don't want you to. That's final."

"What kind of partnership is this, then?"

"The kind we say it is. There's no need for you to come. I have a lot of things to do up there."

"Are you coming back?" My fingers dig into the couch.

"I'm coming back."

"All right. You can go."

"I wasn't asking your permission."

"I mean I won't be mad at you."

"I don't care if you get mad at me."

"Don't you care if it hurts me if you go?"

"It's not hurting you. You think it's hurting you. It's not. It's just a trip to get some stuff, see some friends, see about my truck."

My terror of being left makes me remember shy Marsha who dreamed of having a yellow convertible and who wished her husband would get hit by a bus. For an instant, I want the relief I would feel if Baker suddenly didn't exist.

Something about what he's saying makes sense, yet it's so painful it leaves me breathless. The part that makes sense is barely coming through the nervous static in my mind. There's nothing wrong with this trip. I'll have all the time I want to write. Now's the perfect chance.

A week and several tiffs later, at the bus station, I bravely wave good-bye to Baker.

The next morning, I'm sure he's not coming back—it makes sense, he's going back to his ex and didn't want to tell me, that's all. Otherwise, he would have taken me along. I'll be brave about it. All good things come to an end. Nothing lasts forever.

At one o'clock in the afternoon, it's obvious, I'm delusional thinking he's gone for good. Of course, he's coming home. I can picture him smiling at me. We're a good couple. Why would I torture myself thinking he's not coming back?

When night falls, I know it's over because I can feel it. He's gone. Bleak, I get in bed, awash in agony of knowing he's left me. I leave the bedside light on, stare at the ceiling, finally fall asleep.

By the end of the next day, I'm exhausted by the same rollercoaster I rode the first day. I'm too tired to be in agony and I fall asleep quickly.

By the end of the third day, I can't take it anymore. Sure, relationships are hard. But I can't do this level of anxiety again tomorrow. Luckily, I toss and turn in mortal dread for only an hour.

Day four. I'm in neutral. Wow. This is great. Hardly thinking about Baker. Going to work, shopping for Mr. B., going to lots of sobriety meetings. It's as though Baker barely exists, which is good. It was too stressful going up and down worrying.

The next day is hot. I'm grateful for the garden shade when I have lunch with Cecilia. I can't wait to tell her about Dad and his mom bathing him until he was twelve. Mom didn't say don't tell anyone. She said he wouldn't want everyone to know. I suppose that's the whole world. I have to tell Cecilia. She goes to therapy and might know what it means.

"I had lunch with Mom. I wanted to find out if I had any trauma as an infant, because my therapist said that could be why I'm so jealous."

"And?"

"Mom said no, not as an infant, but when I was fourteen months …"

We crack up because one-year-olds aren't infants to mom.

I finish telling her about how I got handed off to strangers and got little rubber legs missing Mom so bad I wouldn't eat, and that's how I became insecure.

"Wow. Good thing you asked her."

"Isn't it? I asked her something else. About whether Dad had ever mentioned anything about his childhood that could have led to his lack of boundaries."

She smiles. "Yes?"

"Mom said Dad told her that his mom bathed him until he was twelve."

"His mom *what*? Bathed him until he was *twelve?* You've got to be joking."

"No. Talk about no boundaries. Grandma only stopped because Dad put his foot down."

"Well, that could sure explain a lot."

"Yes. I'm sad for him, and for Grandma. What was Grandma thinking? Who was boundaryless with *her?* I'm glad to hear a plausible explanation for Dad's behavior. I think something glitched out in him when Grandma did that, for *years.*"

"It sure seems likely it's where he lost his way. Wow." She nods a few times. "Wow. It all makes a lot more sense."

"Doesn't it? There's nothing we can do, knowing about Grandma, but it helps just knowing it. Dad needs real help."

"Good luck with that," she says.

"I could help him, someday, when I'm not so screwed up myself."

"You mean you could be his counselor?" Cecilia laughs a sweet, gentle, compassionate laugh. "No, sweetie. I don't think so. It would take a veteran therapist to pry open Dad's floorboards so Dad can see what's in there."

She doesn't understand. Dad'll never trust a therapist. But he'll trust me, one day, somehow. I can feel it.

It's been two weeks since Baker left, and I'm calm. Life is good, though I haven't been able to focus enough to sit down and write even once. I sit up in bed with my sketchbook and sketch my toes. It puts me in a trance.

The phone rings.

"I'm near Salinas," Baker says. "Should be there by four this afternoon.

"Wow. Great." I feel nothing. I'd better focus and get my feelings back. Say something nice. "It'll be good to see you."

"You sure? You don't sound convinced."

"No, it'll be good." I can hardly remember him. "You know me, I'm weird."

He laughs.

His laugh makes me feel him. What a relief. "I made you laugh," I say.

"You did. Not many people can."

"I noticed. Well, hurry home. But drive safe."

"Yes ma'am."

Suddenly tears come up and I tremble with relief. Weird. Was I scared this past week and didn't know it because it was suppressed?

A few hours later, a medium-size moving truck comes lumbering down the drive.

Oh dear.

Baker turns the truck around, backs up to the outside door to the sunroom, hops out. He comes over with a big smile, gives me a kiss and a hug.

He came back. "Let's see your stuff."

"Later. Need to eat something."

We eat fried egg sandwiches and salads.

"That truck's not *full*, is it?" I say warily.

"Pretty much."

"I thought you'd have a few boxes like mine."

"Well …"

At ten o'clock that night, our footsteps echo in the dark cavern of the truck as we carry the last item out, the wooden frame of a futon bed.

"Let's set it in the garage, for now," he says.

"Yeah. The sunroom's full."

I brush my teeth to get ready for bed, mourning the loss of the spaciousness of the sunroom. No wonder his place has been so tidy. None of his stuff's been here. Everything feels different now.

But nothing's changed. And he did what he said he would. Got his stuff and came back.

Chapter 21
By Going to Sleep

March, 1995. Nine months later.

This afternoon we're drinking sodas at Baker's brother's place in Hawai'i, near where Baker grew up on the windward side of O'ahu. The trees outside the door of the upstairs apartment stir in a light wind. When his mom left the cult, and his dad joined them, they lived in a group of old houses built literally on the beach not far from where we are now. Those old houses are torn down now. They made a beach park where they stood. It's so peaceful here.

Yesterday, we swam in the warm, shallow, placid, crystal clear, blue waters of his childhood. And this morning, we all floated at a different beach in big waves that lifted us until our toes couldn't touch the bottom and then lowered us. It was exhilarating.

The other brother who's still in Hawai'i lives on Kaua'i. So we've had places to stay on two islands. It's been great being here, but I'm glad we're going home soon. I miss crisp cool air.

The phone rings.

"It's for you, Baker. Guy says he's your boss," his brother says.

Baker and I look at each other.

Why would Baker's boss call him here? Probably can't find something. They perform building maintenance together at a government sponsored senior housing complex.

I'm glad we're leaving in two days. I like Baker's brothers and their families, but besides it being too hot and humid for me, I'm too needy a person to get along with Baker here. He's always helping his brothers' wives, whom I love, but who're younger than I am, and more beautiful with dark satin skin and long black hair. Baker makes them laugh. I get jealous, even though I know why I'm insecure. If he's not making them laugh, he's going somewhere with a brother. I can't relax. I'm okay when I have him all to myself, but I don't, here. Last night I complained. I said you don't talk to me. He glared at me and walked away. I just want to go home.

We left my co-worker Danny in charge of looking after Mr. B. I hope things are going okay.

Baker finally hangs up, looks at me. "Mr. B. is dead."

"What?" He was old, but he wasn't sick. "What happened?"

"Neighbor found him on the floor beside his bed. His stepson had been unable to reach Mr. B., so the stepson called the neighbor to check on him."

"Where was Danny?"

"Wasn't around."

"Shit. Poor Mr. B. They'll think we left him all alone," I say.

Baker shrugs. "They think he fell. May have died first, then fell. Can't do anything now."

"How did your boss find out?"

"Police found my work number next to Mr. B's phone."

"Do the police want to see us?"

"Nope. Natural causes. No robbery. Good thing we're leaving for home soon."

"Yeah. We're going to have to move," I say.

"We'll see about that."

"What do you mean?"

"I mean we'll see."

His tone and scowl tell me he's done talking about us moving. He's dreaming if he thinks we don't have to move.

Back on the continent, Scott picks us up from the airport, drops us off at the bottom of Mr. B.'s driveway. "Got to go, working over-time," Scott says, after he and Baker unload our luggage.

I have a sinking feeling as I watch Scott drive away up the hill.

The sun's gone down, the air's got a chill, the ocean looks cold. I hope the house isn't locked. Something's different. The garage is shut. That's what's different.

Baker tries opening the garage door. "Locked." He tries the other doors. "Place is locked up tighter than a drum."

"You don't have a key?" I say, impatient.

"Never needed one," he snaps.

Shit. I would have had a key. It's getting dark. I'm tired and hungry.

He goes around the house again, comes back grinning. "Found a window."

"Great."

"Come and give me a hand."

I follow him to a small high window. "It's too high. Too small," I say.

"It goes to Mr. B.'s office. I can make it. I just need a boost. Put your hands like this." He locks his fingers to make a step.

He's crazy. "I can't hold you."

"Yes, you can."

I bend forward, clasp my hands.

He kicks off his slippers, quickly steps a foot on my hands, which surprisingly hold, and hops up to the window's ledge, pulls himself up, wedges a shoulder under the open window, pushes the window open more, slowly disappears into Mr. B.'s office. He's in. Thank goodness he's lean. A quiet crashing sound comes from inside.

Soon, he opens front door. Baker beams, puts out his arms and gives me a great long squeeze. It's all I need to relax, to feel connected.

We walk around the house, look in Mr. B's bedroom. A small spot of blood on the carpet by the bed doesn't tell us much.

"Can you believe it?" Baker says. "He's gone. Outta here. See you later, suckas, he's probably saying." Baker sounds envious.

"You're not sad for him?"

"Are you kidding? Poor fuck stuck in that wheelchair, missing half a leg, having outlived two wives and his bat-shit crazy sister, on so much Baclofen he was unable to differentiate between his television remote and his telephone? Nah. I envy him."

"You want to die?"

"Well, not just yet. But there's got to be a better place than this to hang out. Hopefully Mr. B. found it. Let's find some grub."

We rustle through the cupboards and fridge. "What's wrong with life on earth?" I ask, looking in the fridge. "Found some potatoes."

"Great. Here's an onion. That'll get us through the night."

"You're easy to please," I say.

"Yes ma'am." He beams at me.

God, I love him. He's so alive. And fun. He's mine again, doesn't belong to those women in Hawaii. He peels the onion, pours a lot of oil in a skillet, turns the burner on.

"You didn't say what's wrong with life on earth," I say.

"Oh, don't get me started. What's wrong is a bunch of greedy fucks thinking they've got the world by the short hairs kickin' dirt in everybody's face because they can."

"True. But our life's pretty good."

"Yes, it is, little Miss."

I don't like being called little miss. Tell him. Better now than five years from now. "I don't like to be called little miss."

"Why not?"

"It's patronizing."

"Don't give me that crap."

He's a Neanderthal, I swear. "It's not crap. I don't like it!"

"Good," he says, suddenly ice. "That's settled." He turns off the stove, walks away.

"Baker, come back."

The bedroom door opens and closes.

Such a baby. I follow, stop at the closed door. "That's no way to leave a conversation," I say. "Baker."

Silence.

Why's he so temperamental? I try the door. It won't open. He's holding the door knob. I smile. "Open up!"

Silence.

I laugh. "Open up right now, mister, or you'll be …" I shake the handle.

He opens the door, bursts out laughing, takes me in his arms. "Or I'll be what?"

"You rascal," I say.

"No, you're the rascal."

"Did having five brothers make you argumentative?"

"Did having seven sisters, two brothers and a perp for a dad make you argumentative?"

Why did he have to mention my dad? "Don't talk about my dad."

"Why not? He's a perp."

"I said, *don't talk about him!*"

"Why not?"

"He's my dad!

"Just telling the truth."

"*Don't talk about him!*"

"I don't see what the big deal is."

"Fine. I'll talk about *your* Dad."

"Go ahead. Talk about him all you want. He's a dick."

We silently go back to the kitchen.

I'm tired of fighting. We need to eat, plan our move.

We finally sit down to glistening golden piles of hot fried onion and potatoes.

"You can't buy this," he says, shaking his head in awe of our dinner. "How great is this? We were able to get into the house, find some grub, the utilities are on. We can take a hot bath. All our needs are met. It pays to be simple, dear."

"It does. But I was wondering, why do you think we might not have to move?"

"The stepson could want us to be caretakers till the place sells. Could be months. A year. And maybe Mr. B. put us in the will."

We howl laughing. Our standing dream, someone might will us a house. We could never buy a house. We have no savings. And we don't make much money.

"Well," I say, "if we do have to move," which we will, because Baker's dreaming, "let's splurge and rent a nice apartment for a year."

Because in a large nice place, maybe we can relax and learn to get along better. "We deserve it. Then, after a year," when we know how to get along, "we can get a small place, save our money."

"We'll discuss it when the time comes."

He's so bossy. "Don't you like to plan?"

"I like to be present."

"I need to have a plan."

"You need to relax. Hot bath?"

He's so cute with his sweet smile, sly eyes. I can't stay mad at him.

A week later, Baker's angry because the stepson let us know we have one month to move out.

For days, Baker's so angry at the stepson, he won't talk about renting a place.

He is being uprooted from a beautiful place high above the ocean. Still, life goes on and Baker's stuck. So be it. He's good at being lively and making me laugh. I'm good at planning. I'll make the calls.

I find a large storage unit, and scour the Want Ads for an apartment. We probably should be frugal, but then I keep getting a feeling it would be good to splurge for a year, rent a nice two-bedroom apartment and a small storage. Then, later, after we weather the storm of this new relationship, we can downsize.

A few weeks later, we follow a landlord up outdoor concrete stairs that have a gravel finish. Depressing. We'll put plants on the steps to dress them up. The landlord beams as he ushers us into a spotless spacious living room painted white, with a light beige carpet, a large window looking out to tall eucalyptus trees and a creek below.

"A creek," I say, feeling hopeful. Surely a creek right outside will calm us down, help us get along.

"Water runs in it until summer," the landlord says proudly.

We wander through two bedrooms, a bath, a small kitchen.

"What do you think?" I ask Baker.

"Can we afford it?"

"Just," I say quietly. "I added it all up. Nine hundred fifty dollars plus utilities for this place, plus my debt repayment of five hundred a month, storage one-fifty, and miscellaneous. We can do it."

"I don't know," he says.

"What's wrong?"

"It's a lot of money."

"Well, I did the math. We can afford it." He never looks at the bank statement. "My checks are pretty big." He makes ten dollars an hour, more than twice the minimum wage. I make sixteen.

"All right. Let's do it."

"You like it?" I say, to be sure.

"Of course, I like it. Let's put our bed out here in the living room. It's got the best view of the creek."

"Great idea. Fall asleep to the sound of the water. Tell him we'll take it."

"You tell him," Baker says.

"No, you." Baker needs to do it to get more confidence.

Baker takes a deep breath. "Yeah, so, it's pretty nice. Nine hundred-fifty dollars?"

"That's right. First month and five-hundred-dollar cleaning deposit. A hundred fifty of it is for carpet cleaning, so that part's not refundable."

"Okay. Sounds good. We'll take it, if that's all right."

"Your references checked out. You can give me a cashier's check, or cash."

"Marie, we brought cash, right?"

"Right."

We sign a one-year lease and give the landlord the cash. He gives us keys and leaves.

"Nice chap," Baker says.

"He's really nice."

I walk around some more, plan where to put things. "How about your Granny's sewing machine in here?" I say from the second bedroom.

"We'll see."

Mom always said, "We'll see." Baker won't plan with me. I don't feel connected when he won't plan. But things could be worse. This is part of being in a relationship, having differences and not needing to fight about it at every turn.

"Okay."

We move in. Someone said to butter our cats' paws so they'll lick off the scent of the old place and won't try to go back. We do that. It's sweet watching them lick butter off their paws in our new digs.

A few months later we invite friends over to see our new place. Before they arrive, Baker and I scrap over Baker's dismissive tone. I won't accept him talking down to me. So, when our friends arrive, I cool off from the fight by busying myself in the kitchen for a bit while Baker regales them with antics and stories about Mr. B.'s passing, Baker climbing through the window, dealing with the jerk stepson, as he calls him.

Now I'm done being angry. It feels so good not to stay mad. I'll remind him to tell the story of how we buttered our cats' paws. "Baker," I say lightly.

"*Yes, mother*," he says with impatient irritation.

It cuts deep. He sounds like my dad ridiculing my mom at a party.

A few people laugh.

My face flushes hot with embarrassment. There's nowhere to hide.

Ella says, "Whoa, Baker, out of bounds."

"It takes two," Baker says, with a hostile glance in my direction.

He's still mad at me? Too bad. He can't put me down in front of our friends. When everyone's gone, I'll tell him he can't do that to me.

Ella hangs on Baker's neck when she says good-bye. She's just a friend, I keep telling myself, as I panic, seeing the truth of why he puts me down—he doesn't want to be with me anymore. Of course.

When they're all gone, I have no fight left. I go to bed without a word. Stare out the window into the dark canopy of tall trees. No moonlit clouds or stars to comfort me. Only darkness. I have no heart to say my prayer. All I come up with is, God, please help.

Baker cuddles up to my back, wraps his arms around me. I don't know him anymore.

I lie still, wonder how we can stay together.

I panic when I envision being apart.

He's so tender, loving and kind, and vulnerable. And he's cruel. No doubt because of having been so badly abused. But him having been traumatized doesn't mean I can live with his cruelty.

Humans have always confronted the unbearable and found a way to get by, somehow. By leaving, by staying. By going to sleep.

Sleep finally drifts in, warm as Hawaiian waves.

Chapter 22
You Were Little

November 1995. Eight months later.

I sit back on the futon bed in the living room and shake my head. Baker and I get along so well, then every few days out of the blue comes trouble. Dinner's cold in the kitchen. Baker's still not home from work. He said he was meeting up with Dinah, but he'd be home by seven. It's seven-thirty.

Cold and dismal, I put on a jacket to lower the gas bill. I feel like painting a grim self-portrait of me in my jacket with stark shadows in the background. I had thought this big beautiful apartment would help us settle down with each other, so we wouldn't have such hair-trigger reactions. If anything, we're getting worse. I've been going to a child abuse group run by a counselor, learning more about abandonment. Of *course,* that's where my insecurity comes from. I've known that a long time. Which is why I'm jealous. Surprise. Neck-up knowing all this doesn't change how I feel. I watch the front door, as if that will make him walk in.

Now, at my sobriety meetings, one of the steps we work is supposed to get rid of character defects by asking God to remove them. I've begged God to take away my jealousy. Nothing's happened. The previous step says be entirely ready to have God remove it. How could I be more ready? I want to scream, I'm so ready.

Entirely ready? How do I know I'm entirely ready for my jealousy to be taken? How does anyone know when they're entirely ready for something?

A scene of a baby nursery comes to mind. The crib, diapers, little clothes. They're ready for a baby. Someone looks over the room, as if the baby's already there, to see if they're entirely ready for a baby. They act as if the baby's there to find out if they're entirely ready for the baby to come. So, to be entirely ready to have my jealousy removed, I need to act as if it's already gone. That feels true. I take a big quivering breath and try on the idea, the feeling, that my jealousy is already gone. Instantly, I feel better.

Of course, I also just heard Baker's boots on the steps.

I smile when he walks through the door.

He grins back at me.

It works. Act as if my jealousy's gone. What a frigging relief.

A few weeks later, he comes home at nine-thirty. I come unglued. I can't bear him being unpredictable. "No," I say.

"No, what?"

"No, this doesn't work for me."

He shrugs off his coat.

"Well?" I say, terrified he's seeing someone else.

"Well, what!?" he snaps.

"Don't you even care?"

"Care about what?"

"Me! I'm your partner. You didn't come home."

"Well, last I looked, I was standing right here!"

Nothing I say goes in. "Where were you?"

"I was with Scott."

"Fine. You didn't tell me."

"I didn't know you were my nursemaid."

"No, I'm your partner. Partners tell each other their plans."

"Partners don't freak out when something unplanned comes up."

Fuck. "I can't live like this."

"Like *what!?*"

"Not knowing when you're coming home."

"I'm *always* home!"

Am I asking too much? Am I the problem? "You could have called me."

"From the beach?"

"You were at the beach for three hours?"

"We had dinner first! I didn't know we were going to walk on the beach!"

He's right. But I can't bear not knowing. He doesn't understand that about me.

We argue until eleven o'clock. We're no closer to making up than when we started. I need him to say he won't do that anymore.

"I'm going to the harbor," he says, picking up his field jacket.

A jolt of panic scrambles my thoughts. He could meet someone. At eleven p.m.? Sure.

I can't bear the anxiety in my body, but somehow, I know he's not the cause of it.

Suddenly my mind is quiet, clear. I feel it—I'm killing the relationship. I need to get a handle on my jealousy, or I'm going to lose him.

The nursery comes to mind, with the crib and all the little clothes and things. Act as if my jealousy has been removed. I picture it. What would I say if I weren't jealous? I take a deep breath. "Okay. See you when you get back."

Baker nods, opens the door, closes it behind him.

I've done my part. I didn't scream, don't go, and threaten to break up. God, if you're listening, I'm entirely ready to have jealousy removed. Please remove it.

I float into the kitchen. It worked. The jealousy's gone. My anxiety's gone. But sadness so powerful my sides ache wells up. Tears pulse from my eyes. I don't know why. I sob so hard from some painful sorrow I can hardly catch my breath. I lose strength, let myself collapse to the kitchen floor and weep. It's not Baker I see in my mind's eye. It's Dad, leaving when I was six, going on the road for business. He was gone for three months. I missed him. I wail, missing Dad as if I were six and he'd just left. I never thought it bothered me when he left on those long trips. But of course, it did. I was six. My protector, who made everyone laugh was suddenly gone for three months. Then he was back for a few weeks. Then he was gone for a few months.

I sit up, wipe my face, catch my breath, sob a little more. I had no idea this pain was inside me.

After a while I get up off the floor, drink some water, put myself into pajamas, and into bed. I leave the lights on for Baker. I'm truly calm.

An hour later, I hear him come up the steps.

Well. Acting as if I'm not jealous is definitely the thing to do.

Baker gets into his PJ's, crawls into bed.

We wrap our arms around each other.

"I'm sorry for not trusting you," I say.

"And I could have checked in."

"That would be good."

"Your hair's wet."

"I was crying." A sob comes involuntarily. "Not about you. When you left, I saw my dad leaving on his long trips when I was six. I collapsed in tears. I never even knew I missed him." Tears come up again. "Of course, I did." I need to go see my dad.

Baker holds my head close to his chest. "Of course, you did. You were little. You needed your dad."

He acknowledged I need my dad. Baker's more bluster than bite.

"And I'll try not to call him a perp," he adds.

He gets it. I love my dad. "Thanks."

Baker tenderly strokes my head with his thumb. Sometimes he's too aloof. Sometimes I'm too clingy. But we're going to be all right.

"The neighborhood's quiet," I say.

"Yeah, but you can still hear the traffic on De la Vina Street."

"Yeah. I hear it. You know what I miss living here? Grass," I say.

"You're clean and sober."

"Not that kind of grass. Grass you put your feet on. Someday, I want to live in a place where I can step out the door and step on grass."

"That'd be nice."

"Wouldn't it? In the country. Not too far out in the country, but where you see horses now and then."

"You'd like that."

"Yep. Someday. They say if you don't think about what you want, you can never have it." My eyes are so heavy, I close them.

"Makes sense."

"I'm going to envision the country!" I say, so sleepy I'm in two worlds.

"You do that."

"You don't believe envisioning it'll work."

"Not really."

"Me neither."

"Can't hurt," he says.

"No. Can't hurt. Grass under my toes." I'm so sleepy, I'm starting to slur.

" 'night," he says.

" 'night."

CHAPTER 23
MY TOES IN THE COLD GRASS

February, 1996. Three months later.

I can tell by her footsteps my co-worker Betty, the always smartly dressed paralegal, is coming my way. The chance for a fun chat with her breaks my focus on how to train Baker to not make fun of me when I'm being serious. Like this morning, when I said I can't take seeing the mess anymore, and he said, admit it dear, you can't take seeing I have more stuff than you. Three weeks ago, he was going to clean it up—stuff strewn on the living room floor that he'd brought home from work, discards from residents. Three weeks. I wonder what Betty wants.

Working here at the law firm in my little closet office with no door, I've learned the footsteps of every single partner, associate, paralegal, and secretary who works on this floor. About thirty people. They step lightly, heavily, quickly, slowly, meandering, hurried. Each one has a rhythm in their heel-toe movement. I've been here almost eight years. It makes sense I know peoples' steps.

"And what can I do for you, Betty?" I say just before she arrives.

She appears in my door, her sparkling blonde hair pulled back tight, her glossy lipstick smooth across her wide smile. "You knew I was coming."

"I'm very smart."

"You are!"

"I know your footsteps."

"And you're smart. What are you doing working as a file clerk slash law librarian when you're an attorney?"

"I like peace in my life."

"God, so do I. I spent the most heavenly weekend reading on my back porch."

"Sounds grand. I wish I had a back porch. I wish I could enjoy reading. I have to start every paragraph over and over."

"How did you get through law school?"

"Stubbornness. It took me nine hours to do assignments the others did in three hours."

"You probably just never became a fluent reader."

"Really?"

"Seriously. Keep reading. It's fun when you're fluent."

"Thanks."

"How are you and Baker doing?"

I grin. "I want to strangle him. I want a tidy house. He brings home boxes and bags of things people have thrown away. Some of it good, but it has to be gone through, sorted, dealt with. We're both wound too tight. We scrap. He says being in the army mellowed him out." I laugh. "If this is mellow, I'd hate to see what he was like before."

She laughs. "You obviously love each other."

"We do. He toughens me up, in a good way."

"Hm," she says, and seems to ponder. "He was in the army."

"He was. Army band."

"Where do you live?"

"On De la Vina."

"An apartment?"

"Yes."

"How much is your rent?"

"Nine-fifty. Why?"

"You guys should buy a house."

I laugh. "We could never do that."

"Yes, you could."

"How? We don't have savings, and we don't make a lot of money."

"I've been looking myself. The prices are at an all-time low. You're paying high rent, almost a house payment."

"But we have no down payment."

"You don't need one. Baker's a veteran. Honorably discharged?"

"Yes. He even got a commendation for his sense of humor."

"You're kidding."

"No. He showed it to me. It's official."

"Well, as a veteran, he qualifies for a VA loan, which will cover the down payment."

"Are you serious?"

"I am. Talk to your bank. They'll tell you how big a loan you qualify for. Then look for a house in that price range. You're going to do it?"

"Yes. I'll look into it. Thanks. It sounds way too good to be true. But what do we have to lose? What did you need from me?"

"Oh. This." She hands me a note with a file number. "Thanks. No rush."

"Okay. Thanks, Betty."

"Any time." She waves, sashay's away in her little black heels.

Baker doesn't like change. I doubt he'll want to buy a house.

I call him at work.

"Hey, I wanted to ask you something," I say.

Silence.

Damn, he's hard to talk to sometimes. "Why are you silent?"

"Because I know it's not going to be good."

"Why?"

"You know me, dear. Being asked a question is like being bludgeoned and left for dead. Nah. Go ahead. What's your question?"

Say it all fast. "Betty my co-worker says we can use your VA benefits to buy a house with no down payment."

"We don't need to buy no house. What's wrong with where we live? We just got there and you want to move."

"With a house there's no landlord to raise the rent or kick you out to move his family in."

"We're fine where we are. You always project the worst."

God, he frustrates me. I need another approach. "Okay. Was just a thought."

"Good. Got to get back to work. Addy's disposer is clogged."

"Okay."

"It's always eggshells. Out of eighty-four elders, you'd think a few would remember."

"Right."

"Sorry dear," he says. "I know you want to buy a house. We don't need one."

I won't argue. I'll ask Jean how she talked her husband Ron into getting a house. "Okay. See you tonight," I say.

Baker adds, "Let's stay home and watch a movie on Saturday. You're always running errands."

"Okay," I say. He's so sweet. "That'll be fun."

"See you tonight. Love you million jillion," he says.

"Love you million jillion."

I call Jean.

"Jean, how did you get Ron to agree to buy a house?"

"Why? Are you and Baker going to buy one?"

"My co-worker says because Baker's a veteran and prices are low, we could get one without a down payment."

"That's right. Ron's a veteran."

"But Baker's not interested. Did Ron want to buy a house?"

"Not really."

"How did you get him to?"

"Well, I went house hunting, came home and said, 'Honey, I found the cutest little house.' Marie, want to go house hunting?"

"Yes! I'll talk to the bank and find out our price range this week."

"Let's go Saturday."

"You'll need to be married to use his VA benefit," the loan officer says.

Shoot. Well, first things first. Find a house. "Okay."

"According to your records, you would qualify for a loan," she goes on.

"Really?"

"Yes. Because you've been making high monthly payments for a year. Your rent, your debt consolidation payment. It's very impressive. You'll qualify for a hundred-and-forty-thousand-dollar loan."

Is she kidding? Because we didn't save money by renting an *in*expensive place, but paid out a lot each month, we qualify? "Is that enough for a house?"

"You'll probably find something in that price range. Not in Santa Barbara. Unless it's a condo in Goleta. Look around. Check the Multiple Listings."

At home, I mention matter-of-factly, "We qualify for a home loan." Don't say the amount. It'll scare him. "Because you're a veteran and we've paid high rent and high bills for a year."

No reply.

That's okay. Let the idea percolate. Leave it alone.

On Saturday, I say, "I'm going to visit Jean today."

"You promised we'd watch a movie together in our pajamas today."

Shoot! "I know. I'm sorry. When I get home, I'll watch a movie. Okay?"

"All right. You owe me. So, what are you and Jean going to do today? Swap horror stories about Ron and I?"

I laugh. "No, dear, we're just going to visit. Maybe shop." For a house.

We kiss.

"Okay. Don't break the bank."

"I won't. See you. Love you."

He gives me a suspicious smile. "Have fun."

He knows I have a secret. I don't know how he knows.

At a real estate office in Oak View where Jean lives, a little town forty miles from Santa Barbara, Jean and I pick up a list of properties in our price range. I don't want a condo in Goleta.

"I love looking at houses!" she says. As she drives us to the first address, we pass horses in a pasture. I remember my dreamy wish to live in the country someday.

The first place on the list is a tiny one-bedroom house with no garage, sits on the main drag, offered for ninety-thousand dollars.

"It's darling."

"Too small," she says.

"I love it. But you're right."

We climb a hill to a beautiful ranch style home with an incredible view. The sign has a red *Sold* label on it. Darn it!

We descend to the main road, then climb a smaller hill, turn down a one block street with nice houses on the high side. The address we want is on the low side, down a long flight of stairs. Still, the vista from the street is a mesmerizing expanse of sky and mountains surrounding the little valley of neighborhood homes. We're in the country!

"We're not supposed to bother the residents without the realtor," I say, taking a brochure out of the plastic case on the For Sale sign.

"Let's ask them if we could peak inside," Jean says.

"The brochure says $155,000."

"Yes, but the print-out is from today. They dropped the price to $139,000!"

A woman our age lets us take a quick look at the living room. "It's three bedrooms, one bath, two car garage." she says.

It has grass outside the front door and grass outside the back door! I don't care what the bedrooms look like. I can't wait to get home and tell Baker.

Jean and I go back to the real estate office.

"Any luck?" a stout, friendly black-haired woman asks. "Sorry I was unavailable earlier."

"This one," I say, pointing to the listing.

"Okay. You'll want to move quickly. There's another couple circling that property. And the seller just dropped the price on it. He's overseas, in the service. Wants a quick sale."

"What do we do next?"

"You and your husband make an offer. I'll take it from there."

"All right."

Back at home, I walk in the door, and say, "Honey, I found the cutest little house!"

"Pajamas. Now."

"Okay." I can't stop grinning. Do as you promised, then tell him.

Even though it's a great movie, watching is torture.

When the movie's over, I turn to Baker.

"What's this about a house?" he says.

"Well, Jean and I happened to be looking."

"You just happened to be looking."

"Right. So that you wouldn't have to be bored by driving around."

"And?"

"We found a house in our price range. But we have to get married to make an offer. You and I can go see it tomorrow, Sunday. Then, get married Monday. Then go back to Oak View and make the offer."

"You think we should do this."

"Yes. It won't cost us much more than we're paying now. And our money will be going into something that's *ours*, not someone else's." He'll like that.

"And you want to get married."

"Well, I wouldn't mind. It's like we're married already. We have to use your VA benefit, and to use it, we have to be married. Would you mind getting married?"

"No. Shoot, I'd rather pay ourselves each month than some landlord."

"Me too."

"So, you like the house?" he asks.

"I love it. It's in the country. Grass outside both doors."

"Crazy. All right."

All I can think about is stepping outside at night, looking up at the stars, my toes in the cold grass. Everything's going to be all right.

CHAPTER 24
SOMETIMES, THE WATERS ARE CHOPPY

November, 1996. Eight months later.

Alone in the dark car, I sit parked outside Mom and Dad's house in Santa Maria for Thanksgiving dinner. I'm feeling weird about myself and I think I know what the problem is. I haven't written in a long time. I don't understand why that would matter. Most people I talk to don't feel some need to write. I sure do. But it takes a lot of time and focus, which I had when I lived alone. Well, soon I'll write, and I'll feel better.

I'm glad Baker stayed home watching our cats in our new house in Oak View, which it's still hard to believe we bought six months ago. He'd have been cold to Dad if he'd come with me to Thanksgiving dinner, even though Mom and Dad drove all the way to Oak View last week to deliver a tiny dwarf lemon tree to us as a wedding gift. I knew they were coming, but I was still shocked when they pulled up with the tree tied in their trunk. They seem too old to be driving, let alone delivering a tree. And why all these months later? We got married in March. I didn't ask, but when Dad explained it's best to plant a new tree just before winter, I had my answer. It was so thoughtful. And tonight, everything's so sad because of Dad. He won't admit what he does.

I should go in the house, but I'll sit here in the car a minute more. I want to forget painful things. Let it be Thanksgiving.

Melancholy comes. I recall how we kids helped Mom starch and iron linens that came out dazzling and beautiful despite giant holes in them from years of her having no time to mend them. We polished silver, rolled pie dough, scraped our little hands breaking into little pieces a pile of hard stale bread crusts which Mom had saved all year long for dressing. Best of all were the dinner rolls with real butter.

Thanksgiving's hard now. It's been eleven years since we confronted Dad for touching us girls. Still, the air's heavy with hurt and a lot of people don't come to Mom and Dad's house. I came because I can't bear to let Mom down. Not showing up wouldn't have any effect on Dad's behavior. Nothing has. I want to see the stars.

I get out of the car. I wish I could fix things, get Dad to apologize. He's stubborn. Or blind, more like it. His trauma being bathed by his mom until he was twelve must have altered his mind to make him adamant that he's done nothing wrong. He's not normal, I'm sure of it. If only I could help him see that.

I look up at a long faint cloud high in the sky—the Milky Way galaxy. My mind tugs at it for something to get me through the night. As a teenager, I couldn't bear to see Dad alone, watering the lawn at night, after being alone on long business trips. He wasn't safe to get close to, still, I sometimes nervously went outside, kept him company. He taught me about stars. "And yet we doubt there's God!" he'd say, surprised by the vastness of the universe, the smallness of human awareness. I'd be cynically thinking what good is God when bad things happen? Still, Dad made me think more deeply.

I march up the walk carrying a grocery bag with dinner rolls and real butter, recalling how I had the stars to turn to in my dark times in my life: at Twin Palms Apartments, in Contra Costa County, on Bear Creek Road, in the studio on Garden. I made it through all those times looking to the stars. Thanks Dad. I smile. I'll make it through tonight.

I'm going to thank Dad tonight for helping me think more deeply. I don't care that I had to be light-footed on the lawn when he got too close. At the time, I thought my kindness could help him lower his guard and someday admit he was wrong. I still think so.

Something gently brushes the nerves of my scalp. God. Or an angel. Why not? Time to go inside.

In the kitchen, the smells of turkey and pumpkin pie pull me out of my little melancholy. "Hi, Mom." I set the bag down.

"There you are!" she says, tufts of white hair sparkling above her sad smile and moist eyes.

She appears smaller than ever. She's eighty-two. She won't live forever. I can't bear that thought. "How are you?" I ask.

We kiss and hug.

"Oh, about as good as can be expected. You know, we'll be a small group again this year," she says.

"Yeah. Well, we'll still have fun, Mom." I look through to the living room. About ten adults, and since some have relented, a few children. There used to be forty people. People stay away because of Dad.

Mom sadly looks around, nods, smiles. "The show must go on!"

"That's right."

She wishes we could all just get along. We can't just get along, Mom. Can't act like it doesn't matter how hurt and betrayed people feel. "I'll get the rolls in the oven."

"Would you? It's just about time," she says.

The smell of the fresh rolls sends me back in time as they fall from their packages onto cookie sheets.

I don't feel as hurt and betrayed as some of my brothers and sisters do. Not even angry. There could be something wrong with me I don't know about.

I join the others in the living room.

There's Sarah. So beautiful with her Liz Taylor smile. No one's ever seen Sarah without makeup. Her second daughter's been battling cancer for three years. It's unthinkable, the pain Sarah hides under her beauty. Her boyfriend, Sal, a shy willowy man, sits with a few small children—my great nieces and nephews. Sarah says something that makes Andrew, her thirty-year-old, six-foot-four son laugh. Cheerful Bridgette in a bright-white blouse and burgundy slacks sets a dish of candied yams on the buffet, moves other dishes around to make more room. Jean's wearing eyeliner tonight. She looks good in a denim jacket and jeans, waves hello. My brother Martin, in a plaid dress shirt comes and gives me a hug. I'm glad I made an effort with a nice pullover white blouse with good drape, jeans and cute boots.

The outlaw sips a drink in his chair. "Marie!" Dad calls out in a warm welcome. Smiling, he slowly stands on spindly legs, hobbles forward.

How I want to give him a hug. "Hey, Dad!" I extend my hand to shake. He won't like not hugging. "Your knee's bothering you," I say to deflect my pain.

He sees my hand, loses his smile. We shake.

"My knee's not too bad. Where's Baker?" he asks, turning to sit back down.

"He couldn't come."

"Well, tell him he missed out on a feast! Or, wait, he's vegetarian. Well, I hope he doesn't waste away!"

I don't like Dad's caustic tone. Why is Dad suspicious of people who don't eat what he eats, who don't drink what he drinks? What a sad way to live. "No, he won't waste away. He eats twice as much as I do!"

Dad can be paranoid. Be kind. It'll calm him down. "By the way, thanks again for our wedding present. The lemon tree. It seems to be doing well. It's so darling. Lemons are expensive and soon I'll have all the lemons I want."

"Well, you're welcome. Have you found a good place for it?" Dad says.

"Yes, Baker planted it near the driveway where it'll get a lot of sun."

"That's the way. He knows a bit about horticulture," he says, his voice softer.

I'm glad he admires Baker's way with plants. "It's his passion," I say.

"It's a dwarf Meyer, so, you don't have to worry about its roots breaking up your concrete foundation the way a standard-size Meyer lemon would do. Those grow to be very large. The tree we gave you will grow to about eight feet, is all."

He already explained this when he and Mom brought the tiny tree to us. He's eighty-one. He can repeat if he likes.

"It'll be perfect for us. I can't wait to get up one day and pick lemons from our own tree." Dad is thoughtful. Always has been.

"Mom said you and Baker bought a house!" Andrew says.

I haven't seen him in over a year. I love the mirthful smile he always has. He makes me feel sane. "Yes. We bought a house back in March. And we got married too, because we had to use Baker's VA benefit to get the down payment financed. We looked at the house on a Sunday, got married Monday, and made an offer that afternoon."

Andrew laughs. "And you weren't planning on getting married before that?"

"Not at all. We've both had a few marriages that didn't work out." Excruciating marriages. "We were getting along fine so, we'd thought we'd skip marriage, until the house idea came along. We said as long as we didn't let being married change us, it'd be okay. The big question was what to wear, of course, with one day to plan. We wore our favorite clothes. My white high-top sneakers, denim skirt, denim jacket. Baker's field jacket, army fatigues, a Hawaiian print shirt."

"Of course," Andrew smiles. "I can see you guys doing that." He gets me.

"You want to hear what happened?" I ask.

"There's more? Yes."

The room grows quiet to hear the story. It's great to have stories to pass the time, relieve the pain of being around Dad.

"So, we found this minister in the Yellow Pages," I go on. "She met us at the Court House. She was a little bit of a thing, about eighty-five years old. She had wiry hair pulled up with bobby pins, black horn-rimmed glasses with little jewels. She wore a purple choir gown with stains on it including egg that ran down the front. I thought, she's casual, like us."

People laugh.

"We didn't know where to stand to get married. She pointed to this little knoll in the sun above the sunken gardens. Baker helped her over the thick grass. I was grateful she could meet us on such short notice.

"We all stood there in the sun on the wide, lawn. While she looked in her folder for something, Baker and I chatted. We were in awe of how fast it had all come about—finding a house, finding the minister, about to be married on a beautiful day. Baker said something like, 'Can you believe it?' and we cracked up with disbelief and happiness, you know. We were planning to make an offer on the house that afternoon. It was all a bit much, we had never thought of ourselves as homeowner types, so we were laughing.

"I was looking forward to hearing some sweet words of encouragement from the minister. Next thing, she says sharply, 'It's time to start.' She launches into a stern scolding about how matrimony is a sacred step not to be taken lightly, and we had better be ready to take it very, very seriously.

"I wanted to bust up laughing so badly. Luckily, I felt Baker's hand grip mine tighter. It felt like we were teenagers she'd caught in the back seat of a car. It was all we could do to keep a straight face."

People laugh at the story.

"She was the boss. It must have been our clothes, and our laughing that set her off. But it was good, what she said. A little crash course on marriage. Then she married us"

We laugh some more.

"Where's Baker?" Andrew asks.

"He couldn't come." I give him a knowing look with my eyebrows.

Andrew nods.

He gets it.

"So, are you and Baker still getting along?" Andrew laughs.

"We are. Most of the time." Except during the forty-minute commute home from work. And Saturdays when we need to do chores.

"No couple gets along all the time," he says.

"That's true," I say.

Though Baker's bitterness almost every night for the whole drive home from work is wearing on me. He won't speak when I get in the car, so I meditate, since I have to close my eyes with his reckless driving in our little three-banger Geo Metro. Then we get home and we're usually okay. "We're determined."

Baker's heaven to be with when he's not in a bad mood. I think his childhood affects him. Good thing he's working on that at inner child meetings. I want to help him too. I've been to some of those meetings. They say I have to work on myself. I wouldn't have a problem if he'd behave.

"Dinner's just about ready, you guys," Mom says in the doorway. She appears more relaxed, maybe from the laughter. "Come and carry the rest of the food. Your rolls are ready, Marie."

In the kitchen, Dad slices the turkey. He looks lonely. We don't crowd around him for bites of turkey the way we used to before we confronted him. He called us sluts and whores for even *thinking* he would touch us inappropriately.

That hurt, coming from Dad, but it's such a childish reaction, on the other hand, it's hard to take it seriously. It's not him. Something about all of this is not him.

He seems to be more than one person. One who thoughtfully drives a hundred miles to deliver a dwarf Meyer lemon to Baker and I, though we didn't marry in the church, something that matters a lot to Dad. Another person who's cranky and disrespectful, putting Mom down with cutting words. Still another who when a shadow crosses his eyes, changes into someone else before he reaches across or around and inappropriately touches us. Some of my brothers and sisters say he knows exactly what he's doing. I don't think he knows what he's doing, nor understands why people are upset with him.

I'll go over and be friendly, at least, take my chances on getting touched, which isn't likely. He's got a knife in one hand, a fork in the other.

I walk over. "Hi, Dad. Need someone to test the turkey?"

"Don't get too close," he snaps, cautioning me as he would a child. "The knife's sharp."

Stung. I turn around. "Okay." He doesn't know the actual sharp knife is him pushing me away.

Mom gives me a sad look. I nod. She lives with his erratic moods. His rebuke smarts. I'm grateful I don't live with him. I pile the hot dinner rolls into Mom's stainless steel cake bowl.

Mom smiles at Dad.

Uh oh.

"Could I get you another platter for the turkey, sir?" she asks playfully.

Wrong move, Mom.

"Yes, Evelyn, you may get another platter!" he says, as if weary of her oppressive helpfulness.

Damn. Dad sounds just like Baker. That's amazing. The same irritated put down. Am I like Mom?

Mom shrugs sadly, puts a platter beside him.

And, if she hadn't asked, Dad would've bitterly asked why wasn't there another platter ready. A lose-lose situation. It's the same at home. In trouble for helping, in trouble for not being helpful.

I can't do anything about it tonight. I dust myself off within, put salt and pepper on the table.

Dad carries the turkey in.

I go back to Mom in the kitchen. "You all right?" I ask.

She gives me her teary-eyed wide-mouthed smile and laughs. "Sometimes the waters are smooth, and sometimes they're choppy. Let's go eat this feast!"

God, she's resilient.

I enjoy my dinner. We eat mashed potatoes and gravy, rolls and real butter, turkey, cranberry sauce, string bean casserole, candied yams, pumpkin pie, mincemeat pie.

"It's a wonderful dinner, Evelyn," Dad says warmly.

The storm has passed.

"Thank you, Edward," Mom says, having dusted herself off. "Would like to try the string bean casserole?"

"No, thank you, Evelyn. Let's save the vegetables for the children."

Everyone laughs at Dad's standard reply to an offer of vegetables.

"Not everyone's here," Dad says, "but I'm glad everyone here could make it."

He seems relaxed now, so I relax. I feel alive in the Milky Way Galaxy here at our little table in a moment of time that somehow stretches billions of years. We all matter to each other. That's all that matters. No one's perfect. Dad laughs as he banters with Sarah about whether the Pope's interest in national freedom is a matter of faith and morals. On one level, Sarah loathes him. On another, she's willing to connect. I sit mesmerized by human depth.

Soon the little ones get down from the table, play a chase game on all fours. Little Martha, who's only two, bursts into a loud, tearful wail. She probably got left out of the game. It's hard to be two years old.

"*Hey! Hey! That's enough!*" Dad's roar, equivalent to an emotional sonic boom, makes me jump.

Martha's shoulders jump as she startles into silence.

The whole room is silent.

A light goes on in me. Dad can't tolerate crying children. He does roar like a lion at two-year-olds. I've always thought so, but I thought my memory might be faulty, because, who would do that to such a tiny being? Now I know for sure where my startle reflex comes from.

I want to tell Dad how wrong it was to rage at Martha.

I can't. I could no sooner speak to Dad about him roaring at little Martha than I could lift this house from its foundation. Why can't I confront him? I need to stand up for her.

I can't. It feels the same as expecting a computer to do a function for which it has no program. Well, that needs to be fixed.

Not tonight.

I'm full from dinner. Still, I want to eat another pile of hot mashed potatoes, gravy and more pie. I go about dishing up food in a trance, hear voices and sounds, but feel far away. I've gone somewhere I'll come back from as soon as

I've eaten so much, I'm unwell.

The house slowly fills with sounds again, this time with more quiet conversation. The food puts me in neutral, calms me down.

The good-byes come. I hug everyone except Dad. We shake hands.

"Don't be a stranger, Marie," he says, his tone kind. "I love you. Always have. Always will." That's his anthem.

I believe him. I don't understand him.

He knows he hurt me. He doesn't know he hurt Martha. I'm too afraid of his roar to tell him. "All right. Thanks, Dad."

Relieved to be driving home, I remember something—I forgot to thank Dad for teaching me to think deeply under the stars. Damn it. Well, he was kind to me, but a jerk roaring at Martha. It's just as well I didn't thank him.

That's not a kind attitude.

No, it's not. It's petty, superficial spite.

True, he shouldn't have roared at Martha. But who am I to judge him? God knows, I've done my share of bad behavior. Leaving my first husband who was in a wheelchair. I can rationalize and say I had to, because he wouldn't try to quit heroin. But did I have to leave him the way I did? Over-night for the tan curly-haired neighbor?

No, I can't judge anyone.

January brings several days of a cold snap. Early one morning in the dark, I go outside to see the frost. It's beautiful, glittering on the roof of the car, mimicking the stars. Or do stars mimic frost? They could. If frost came before stars.

The little lemon tree looks weird—its leaves are all brown. Is it dead? I hurry into the house and bring Baker outside. "Is it dead?"

"I'm afraid so, dear."

"It can't be dead!" Tears fill my eyes.

"I'm sorry. It is. Lemons aren't deciduous. They need their leaves for photosynthesis all year round." He shakes his head. "It couldn't take the frost night after night."

"I can't believe I let it die. I didn't check on it." Frantic, I wiggle a branch of the poor helpless little tree to wake it up.

"Neither of us checked on it."

"Maybe it has a spark of life still! I'm going to put a trash bag on it tonight to protect it."

"It won't help, dear. It's dead. I'm really sorry," Baker says gently.

This pure little being was a tether between me and Mom and Dad. I choke back tears. Tears will make it true. I can't let it be dead.

I don't care what Baker says. When evening comes, as soon as the sun goes down, I put a black trash bag on the lemon tree. "Please don't die. I need you to live. I'm sorry I let the frost get you. Please don't die."

In the morning, when the sun hits it, I let the lemon tree warm up for half an hour under the bag, to get good and warm, then I take the bag off.

Every night, I cover the little tree and every morning I warm it, then let the sun shine on it all day, day after day.

I check for signs of life.

Nothing.

Why did I let this happen?

I go to work with a broken heart. When night comes, I'm not ready to give up. I cover it again, and again.

After a couple of weeks of covering the tiny lemon tree every night, one morning I see tiny bumps here and there on the branches. I show Baker the bumps.

"I'll be damned. New growth, dear. Congratulations. You saved it."

I choke up and cry. "I don't know why this tree means so much to me."

"Well, it's a gift from your dad."

Baker doesn't follow his comment with his usual wisecrack.

He's right. I need the connection with Dad. The life in the little lemon tree gives me hope for me and my dad.

All day at work, my longing for the thing writing gives me breaks over me like that giant wave that drenched me at the breakwater. When I get home, I can't wait to write any longer. I break ranks from our usual routine of watching Sherlock Holmes together and tell Baker, "I'm going to write tonight instead of watch a show. You can watch one of your shows you like."

"Thanks, dear!" he says.

That was easier than I thought it would be.

I sit down at my computer, hungry. For what? For myself. It's been weeks since I've really connected with myself. I don't know why I need to write, but I do. Most other people don't need to at all, it seems. I have to. I want to accept that about myself. Honor it. Writing's not a hobby. I need it to tether myself in a deep place to what's meaningful. Or else I have no anchor.

I write about Thanksgiving, Dad roaring, the Milky Way Galaxy of life, and how the lemon tree survived. At two o'clock in the morning, stiff, my arms a bit blue from cold, I turn off the computer, stand up slowly, drugged with happiness to love life, as painful as it sometimes is, and climb into a warm bed. And I'm going to buy a guitar, so when I don't have time to write, I can play moody chords and feel connected to myself. I close my eyes and see myself playing Etta James' "I'd Rather Go Blind" with closed eyes.

CHAPTER 25
I CAN FIND WHAT I LOVE

August, 1998. Almost two years later.

After work, Baker drives us across town toward the freeway for our forty-minute commute home to our house in Oak View. I glance out the window of our black Geo Metro, a little three-cylinder car that gets fifty miles to the gallon and loves to go eighty. Down the cross-streets I notice scenes that I could paint. I'm dying inside from lack of doing anything creative. There's no time to paint or do anything I really love these days, with the forty-minute commute, and being in a relationship. And my job of eight years as a law librarian and file clerk has become so bone-deep boring, a constant frustration robs me of my inner-life thoughts. I have no energy to think deeply about things, like fixing my relationship with Dad, and working on myself—my insecurity, mainly—or even just being myself. It feels like my job will actually kill me. That's a problem. I need to do things I love, to honor myself, get a better sense of self. That'll help my insecurity, which will help all my relationships, especially with Baker and, of course, Dad. The answers are within you, right? Yep. The boring job at the law firm's got to go. It's killing me. "I need to quit my job."

"Why?"

"I'm bored. I feel suffocated there. I've been reading it's important to do work you *love*. I want that—work I love! A few years ago, I wrote that list Dinah said to write of things I love. Visit is at the top of the list, and I sure do visit at work. People open up to me. I can't help it. But I can't bear to open one more library invoice. For some reason, I keep obsessing on red velvet theatre curtains. I need to make some. It's crazy, because I'm not even connected to a theatre. I want to paint portraits, too, but I can't make a living painting portraits. Maybe I could make puppet theatres, with red velvet curtains that open and close on wires that overlap! I've been figuring it out at my desk how to make the curtains work. That's what I need to do. Make red velvet theatre curtains, for puppet theatres."

He's not interested in what I'm saying. "I could make puppets for a living. And handbags. I saw this beautiful satin fabric in a small wholesale store run by two guys in short-sleeve shirts. One guy said in a deep reverent voice, 'This is *nice* goods.' Meaning the fabric. I knew what he meant. It was the end of a bolt of gorgeous rose-colored satin made of heavy rayon. They're from back east, I think. It would make a beautiful lining for tapestry handbags."

Baker takes the freeway on-ramp. Soon, we'll be home.

"But the red velvet curtains are what I keep obsessing on. I can't get them out of my mind. It feels I'm being called…by something deeper than myself to make them."

A loud truck horn blasts above us.

I look to see a semi-truck bear down on our little Geo Metro. "Baker!!!" I yell over the sound of the horn of the semi-truck which Baker's cutting off as he gets on the freeway. The truck's a giant bird of prey. It blots out the sun. The Geo will go eighty, but it doesn't have pick-up. Angry, I close my eyes, relax back against the seat ready for the crash.

Nothing happens.

I open my eyes.

Baker's smiling. The truck dropped back.

"*That* was *so wrong!!!*" I yell. "How *dare* you? You risked our *lives!* I'm never riding in the car with you again! *Ever!!!*"

I fold my arms, gaze out my window. What am I doing with him?

He doesn't have a clever put-down or even a joke, the way he usually does when I complain about a close call. Good. "I'm buying another car. You can kill yourself, if you want. I'm done riding with you."

It feels good to tell the truth.

As we climb the hill from the coastal plain to the inland valley where we live, he finally turns to me. "Sorry dear. I was out of line."

I've never once heard him admit he was wrong. This is good.

"That was bad. I shouldn't have done it," he says.

"No, you shouldn't have. I'm still never riding with you again. We almost died! You can't just say sorry and everything's fine."

"Then I'm sorry I said sorry!" he snaps, angry now.

Ah, damn. Now we have to have a gloomy night because he's ruffled. Well, he can have a gloomy night. I'm not going to. I'm going to practice chords on my new guitar. It has a beautiful tone. Though I'd rather play lead on an *electric* guitar. How come I only see men playing electric guitars? I want one, and my own amplifier. Hit a few moody minor notes on an electric guitar and I'll be happy.

Baker plays drums and harmonica with some buddies Thursday nights but it does me no good. Baker always says no, I can't come, even though I can sing pretty well, I think.

We're almost home. That was good how I yelled at him so he knew I meant it when he nearly got us killed. I've never done that before.

Yes, I have. I've gotten so angry at him for dismissing me I've screamed at him and slammed the heavy front door. Only created radio silence for three days. He's done the silent thing a few times. I feel like the bug in Kafka's "Metamorphosis" when he does. Before I flunked out of college years ago, I made a good pencil drawing of that bug with the apple stuck in its back. That poor bug. I've been reading up on abuse. It's abusive to not speak to someone. It's called stonewalling. I told him it's abusive not to speak to me and I won't tolerate it. He still does it, but not for three days anymore, which is progress. I don't know why he still does it. I'm reasonable.

I don't like being angry. I sure don't want to live my whole life pissed off. I can be done being mad at him now. There's no rule for how long to stay mad.

I only wish I knew why he dismisses me, puts me down. I get weary fighting about it. Making him a sandwich helps, but doesn't change his behavior. Does he need to do it for attention? He gets plenty of attention. It's probably insecurity from his childhood. Or what he saw his dad do to his mom. He understands all that. He still does it.

"What do you want for dinner?" I ask as we pull into our drive. I'm done fighting for today. "I'm still blown away that we bought this house," I say, looking at our yard.

"It's amazing, dear. Who would've thought a couple of ruffian children, one with little rubber legs and the other with a heart the size of a raisin would get it together to buy a house?"

I laugh. "Your heart's bigger than a raisin."

"It is?" He smiles.

"A walnut," I say, with a sly smile.

"Great. I have a walnut heart. Well at least it's not the only nut I have."

I shake my head.

We get out.

I can't stay mad at him. "Spaghetti!" I say happily.

"Yay! Sketty!" He takes me in his arms. "Should I sleep in the metal box in the yard tonight?"

"We don't have a metal box in the yard."

"We should. I could sleep in it."

"Hush." He makes me tear up when he says things like that. I remember hearing how they held him naked in front of twelve people when he was five years old and poured a five-gallon bucket of ice water on him. No wonder he doesn't think much of himself.

Inside I don't care about the semi anymore. I check the message machine. "Hi, Marie, it's Cecilia. I think we need to talk about Mom driving."

"Baker, can you make the spaghetti? I need to call Cecilia."

"Sure can, babykins."

He knows he's not quite out of hot water for the semi stunt. Good. Though I hate being his mom. I want him to grow up.

I get on the phone. "What happened?" I ask Cecilia.

"Apparently Mom had an accident. Or two, judging from the dents. Dad called, asked me if a couple of us could ask her about them. She didn't mention them to Dad. I'm not sure why he doesn't want to ask her. Maybe he's afraid someone needs to take her keys away and wants support."

"Oh dear. Okay."

It's hard to imagine Mom unable to drive. How will she survive, home with Dad all the time? Cecilia and I make our plan to go up on Saturday and get off the phone.

"I need to go see my parents with Cecilia Saturday. Mom has dents in her car. No one knows where they came from."

Baker laughs. "I'll tell you where they came from. Same place any bumper car gets dents."

"Bumper cars don't get dents."

"Your Mom's does."

"You can't talk about my Mom's driving."

"You talk about my driving."

"Because you almost got us killed today!"

"But I didn't get us killed!"

He doesn't get it.

The next day, more alive than usual after the semi-truck close call, I go to the music store and try a few electric guitars. Why not? I need something in my life that reaches deeper than shelving books and making dinner. I don't need an expensive one.

I drive home with a Fender Squier, a little Traynor amp and a feeling of the greatness that people will sense when I play on stage, not because my playing will be great, but because there's greatness in my soul, in everyone's soul, that needs expression. A few slow notes and they'll feel it. I laugh at my day dream.

I show Baker my new guitar.

"All right, dear!"

He does have good qualities.

On the weekend, Cecilia and I drive up to Santa Maria.

Dad's glad to see us, his posse, and warmly shakes our hands at the door. It feels good to connect with him on a mission to help out.

Mom looks up from her newspaper at the kitchen table. "I can hardly see to read. Can you believe it? I never thought this could happen to me," Mom says.

"What does the eye doctor say, Mom?" I ask, sitting down with her. If her vision's not good enough to drive, her eye doctor would know.

"Macular degeneration. Nothing they can do."

"Damn it. I'm so sorry," I say.

"Well, I'm not blind yet!" she laughs. "How are you two? This is a pleasant surprise, seeing you here."

"We just thought we'd come and visit," Cecilia says. "It's been a while."

"Yes, it has," Mom says. "Let's go into the living room where we can all sit down like civilized people. Would you like some coffee?"

"No, thanks," Cecilia and I both say.

In the living room, Cecilia sits down near Mom. "So, Mom, we were wondering about something."

Mom's face becomes clay.

"Nothing bad," Cecilia says sweetly and laughs.

Mom bursts into laughter. "Thank goodness! We've had enough wonderings about something, haven't we dear," she says to Dad.

"Enough for a life time, Mama," he says.

"No, it's not bad," Cecilia says. "We were just curious about how dents could have gotten in your car."

"Oh, yah, that." She brushes the air with her hand. "Well, you see, I didn't want to alarm anyone." She looks at Dad. "So, I didn't mention it, honey. It was, oh, a week ago, maybe several weeks ago. Right here, I mean down there," she nods at the window, "at the bottom of Meigs, on Cliff Drive."

Oh dear. That's a fast boulevard.

"We *both* were surprised!" Her eyes light up with that dancing mirth that's gotten her through rough patches her whole life. "I mean, we hit each *other*! It wasn't one person hit another person."

"Who was the other person, Mom?" I ask.

"A nice gentleman, my age, eighty-three."

No one wants to lose their license.

"Did you call the police or the insurance company?" Cecilia asks.

"Oh, heavens no. I mean, we *both* agreed," she smiles with the recollection, "it was a *real* accident."

I watch Dad and Cecilia. We're all trying to keep a straight face. "Mom, there was another dent, in the back. That must be from something else," I say.

"Yah. That was the tennis shoes."

"I see," I say.

"They weren't a good fit." She shrugs. "I ought to have known better," she says with remorseful regret.

"I see. Better than what?" I ask.

"Better that to have worn those shoes!" She shakes her head in wonder at her mistake.

"And the shoes made you hit something?"

"Yah. When I meant to hit the brake, the shoe stuck, only a minute, on the accelerator."

Shit. "Darn it. But the dent's in the back. What did you hit?"

"The rubbish can. It was behind me. Like I said, the shoes weren't a good fit for that sort of activity."

Her face is red. Poor thing. She's ashamed.

"I'm sorry, dear," she tells Dad. "I should have told you."

"Well, all's well that ends well," Dad says. "I'm just glad everyone's safe and sound."

He can be so good to her.

"Mom," I say, "Do you think you should still be driving?"

Mom looks at Dad.

"Oh," Dad says, "I don't think there's any question of that. A few fender benders could happen to anyone."

He can't bear to tell her no.

"That's right," Mom says. "And of course, it helps to have the proper footwear. Will you two be staying for dinner?"

"Thanks, Mom, but we can't stay," I say.

Mom and I walk into the kitchen.

Cecilia spends a few minutes with Dad. She's good with him.

"Oh, Marie!" Mom laughs. "My eyes aren't what they used to be. My legs don't have their usual strength. I'm afraid this old lady's losing some ground."

"I'm sorry, Mom." I can't bear to think of her ever dying. "But remember, you're only eighty-three."

"Promise me one thing."

"Sure, Mom."

"Promise you'll never put me in a nursing home."

She and I have seen a lot of nursing homes. She's helped make them a lot better with her years of work on the Ombudsman program, a watch dog organization. I wouldn't mind living in a nursing home when my time comes. But she really doesn't want to. But how can I promise?

How can I not? "I promise, Mom, I'll never put you in a nursing home." If the time comes, we'll find another way, somehow.

Cecilia and Dad come into the kitchen.

I hug Mom good-bye.

"Bye Dad. Love you," I say, shaking his hand at the door.

"Love you too. Always have, always will," he says.

Whenever he says that, I wonder about love. He means it, yet he hurts us when he gets a chance with his hands, so how can he love us? Yet I hurt people I love, so not hurting someone isn't the criterion for love.

Cecilia and I howl laughing most of the way home recalling Mom and the conversation about a real accident and proper footwear. I don't mention my nursing home promise to Cecilia. We finally talk about whether Mom should still be driving.

"Don't look at me," Cecilia says. "I won't be taking her keys away."

"Me neither. Not yet. Having older people drive is one of the risks we accept as Americans. No one wants to turn in their keys."

"Although the time is coming, sooner than later, for Mom," Cecilia says, glancing my way.

"It's true. I talk big. I told Baker earlier this week that I'd never ride in the car with him again. The next day I did."

"Why did you tell him that?"

"He cut off a semi and almost got us killed."

"In your Geo?"

"Yes."

"Oh dear."

"And not to change the subject, but I want to leave my job," I say.

"Oh?"

"I've been there eight years. I'm bored to tears. I want to try craft fairs. Make things, beautiful things, like puppet theatres with real red velvet curtains that open and close. I'm obsessed with red velvet curtains. I don't know why. I can't get them out of my mind. They haunt me. And I bought an electric guitar."

"Congratulations on the guitar." she gives me a funny smile. "You really think you can make a living doing crafts?"

"I need to do something different. I can hardly bear another minute in my job. I have a 401K I could use part of."

"No, sweety, don't use that, unless there's a real emergency."

She doesn't understand how desperate I feel.

"But, seriously, good for you for buying an electric guitar!"

"I love it. I only play a few minor chords. Oh, my God, Cecilia, it resonates in a deep part of me who feels so lost in her little navy-blue uniform on a dark rainy late afternoon. When I play the guitar, yellow lights come on in the houses and I'm almost home. I don't care if I never get there—I'm almost home."

"I see." She gives me a tender smile. She understands me.

"You see, the last two years I've stayed at my job only because it seems I'd be ungrateful to walk away from a job people would kill for," I say. "Benefits, good pay, nice co-workers. But now I know I have to go. I have to do something I love, or I'll lose my mind. I can't make Baker not dismiss me with his jokes, or make him drive better, or make Dad see himself and what he does, but I can find what I love."

She nods.

We ride in silence. She knows my minds made up, which helps me know it too.

CHAPTER 26
THE PARADE OF LIGHTS

December, 1998. Four months later.

It's cold at the harbor at night, wearing only a thin jacket—I didn't think of the cold when I got dressed. I lug two card tables and a large bag stuffed with wares to my space. I'm doing what I love, but somehow it doesn't feel like it. I don't feel myself. I've been wanting to write to settle myself, because writing's my salve. But it's been months since I've written anything, because I've been so obsessed with shopping for hardware and fabrics, making things, researching fairs. I'll be too tired when I'm done here tonight, but tomorrow I'll write.

The local toy store owner suggested I get a space here at the Parade of Lights, a fair with boats lit up like Christmas trees in a parade in the harbor. I'll sell my fabric handbags and felt puppets. I'm so happy he put my puppet theatre in his display window. It's beautiful—a wooden box with all sides cut away by my cabinet-maker friend, bolted to cherry-stained legs, with deep red velvet curtains that slide on a wire covered from view by a red velvet valance. I'm so happy with it. I put a three-hundred-dollar price tag on it. That's what it cost to make. I was in a trance. It took forever. It's not practical.

I feel self-conscious setting things down here at the harbor, people walking by. I want to go back home. But I paid the eighty-dollar space fee so I'd better get over myself and set up my two card tables. I love the rose-colored satin and deep red velvet table covers I made. On the satin one, I set out eight tapestry handbags I sewed, with satin lining and braided straps. They're beautiful. A few are made of upholstery fabric, one a soft woolly snowy white fabric. On the velvet cover, I lay out the puppets. I spent more time playing with them than I did sewing them. They look so alive with their big eyes and wide mouths.

I sweated in my little sewing room for three months figuring out how to sew these things. I *have* to sell them tonight.

Done setting up, I look around. It's nice here. Lots of people. Friendly vendors. A few boats bob on the black water where dazzling darts of light show the small waves.

No one comes near my tables. I'm an odd duck is why. They can see I am.

Who quits their good job to swelter for months in their sewing room then freeze in the ocean air a few nights before Christmas?

I've lost my mind.

An hour later, a good crowd watches the Parade of Lights. Still, no one's shopping at my tables.

What was I thinking? I'll make a living selling tapestry handbags and felt puppets? I am losing my mind. Why *did* I quit my job?

I was strangled by the tedium. I watched my life drift away in wisps every day. It broke my heart to work all day and not get to do things I love. That's why I quit.

You know what? As long as I'm here, I might as well have fun—do what I love, make things come to life, that's what I love to do. I put a small green puppet with a big red mouth and yellow spikes down her back on my hand. She looks all around with her big black eyes which are surrounded by whites, all made of felt.

She catches the interest of a pale, skinny little red-haired boy in only a T-shirt and jeans, about four years old, who shyly comes near. His parents aren't thinking, letting him be out here in the cold with no jacket. Where are his parents?

"Hello," the puppet says. "What's your name?"

The boy's eyes get big as saucers. "Ricky."

"You didn't think I could talk!" she says.

He grins, shakes his head no. "Whath your name?" Ricky asks.

"Uh, I'm Melissa."

His eyes stare into her eyes. "Hi, Melitha."

"Hi Ricky. I'm freezing cold Ricky! Are you cold too?" Melissa asks.

"Yes!" he says. "Don't you have a coat?"

"No," the puppet says, hanging her head. "No one ever made me a coat. Where do you think I could get a coat?"

"At the store!" He beams.

"What a good idea, Ricky." The puppet bounces, excited. She bounces over, close to my face, stares at me. "I need a coat," she says.

Ricky laughs.

"Okay, we'll get you a coat at the store," I say.

Ricky claps his hands. "Don't worry, Melitha, you won't be cold anymore!"

A young woman, in a heavy white sweater and a gorgeous white fur hat, strolls by. She holds the arm of a man in a puffy gray jacket. They smile at me, nod appreciatively. "Come on, Ricky. The others are waiting for us," she says, without stopping.

They don't care that Ricky's entranced with Melitha. They walk on ahead. Don't they know he's cold and too small to be left behind that way? Anyone could snatch him up.

"Don't forget to get a coat," Ricky says, sad now, to Melitha as he turns to go.

"I won't. You get a coat too, Ricky! Bye," Melitha says.

"Bye ..." he says.

"Was nice to meet you, Ricky," the puppet says.

Ricky looks back with a bright smile. "Nithe to meet you, too!" He waves, disappears into the crowd.

My heart longs to look after him, to make him laugh. Help him have a sense of self.

Hey, maybe I'm supposed to do childcare. I'd treat kids like they matter.

A half hour later, a frozen popsicle, I pack up my things. Better to find out sooner than later, I'm not cut out to be a vendor. I sold one handbag, discounted to five dollars because that's all the money they had.

I think about Ricky's wide eyes and big smile, toss the puppets into their sack, look at the puppets sitting in there. They'll sit in this bag for years. I could have given the green one to Ricky. Darn it! Why didn't I think of that?

It's too late. He and his folks are gone. I fold up the table covers, heartbroken that I didn't give Ricky the puppet.

My eyes search the direction he went with his parents. After a few seconds, I make out a white fur hat under a building's security light.

They're here, but they're too far away.

Besides, it's a ridiculous idea. You don't run after some kid to give him a puppet. People will think you're weird.

I blew it not thinking to give him the puppet. I mope, turn a table over, fold its legs.

Grow up.

I try on the feeling of being hardened, so I don't feel my regrets. The hard feeling makes me feel sick. I look back at the tiny white fur hat. It's not too late. What am I afraid of? Looking stupid? Seeming needy? Appearing strange? So what?

I fetch from the bag the green puppet with its big eyes and yellow spikes and run through the crowd.

I'm out of breath when I get to Ricky and his parents. "He really liked this one," I say. "I thought, if it's all right, I could give it to him." I catch my breath.

"Sure," his mom says.

"Here, Ricky," I say, holding out the puppet.

Ricky takes the puppet, stares at it. No smile. No words.

It was a bad idea. He didn't want the puppet. He liked the puppet *talking* to him. Now it's only a big pile of felt in his little hand. Shoot. I've ruined the illusion for him, and I can't get it back. I look strange standing here. Leave.

"Well, bye," I say, embarrassed. "Merry Christmas."

I walk back to my things almost unable to bear my anguish for failing. Why such anguish? What's wrong with me? I don't even know the kid.

What was I thinking? He's four, at most. He doesn't understand puppets. Why was I so invested? I need to get home. Something's wrong with me. Everything means too much to me. Everything's painful. I stand the tables against a lamp post, put the bags next to the tables, out of the way of the foot traffic. Yeah. I need to hurry home. Like every other anguish, this will pass in a few days.

Something soft and warm grabs my leg. I look down. Ricky, holding Melitha, buries his head against my thigh. "Thank you!" he says in his high voice.

"You're welcome!" My fiery ball of pain becomes twinkling stars of joy in my heart. The real parade of lights. "You're so welcome." I pat his head, choke back tears.

He smiles up at me. "Bye!"

"Bye!"

I watch him run until I can see he's safely back with his parents.

Life's not what it seems. His parents may be too trusting of a crowd of strangers, but it doesn't mean they don't love their son. They probably showed him how the puppet works and told him to go thank me.

Back at home, I lie on the bed. Baker lies beside me, propped on an elbow. He brushes my tears that stream back into my hair.

"I don't know why I'm crying," I say, through deep quiet sobs. "I sold one bag for five dollars. I'm crazy thinking I could be a vendor."

"You are crazy, but you tried."

"I did. I worked hard."

"That's an understatement."

"And the sweetest little boy loved my green puppet. I gave it to him."

"Good for you."

"He hugged my leg and said thank you. I don't know why it makes me cry. It's as though I've been frozen, and now I'm thawing. Why does everything mean so much to me?"

"You're awake. You see and feel things. You're not sleepwalking through life the way a lot of folks do."

He may be right. A memory of a sunny street comes, where I'm walking to work, elated, because I just found out I was pregnant. I was with Isaac at the time.

More tears flow.

"I had a miscarriage once, when Randy and I broke up. But later, with Isaac, I was pregnant, and ecstatic about it. When I told Isaac, he said he'd leave me if I had the baby." I pause, choking down tears. "I chose Isaac. I was too scared to be a single mom."

"Sorry, dear."

"I'm finally thawing from the abortion. It was over twenty years ago. I thought I had let it go. Even told Mom." I shake that memory away. She didn't get my grief. Told me wonderful help is available for pregnant girls these days. "I never think about the little being. Her, or him." A flood pours from my eyes.

Baker slowly strokes my forehead with his thumb.

"Our house is big enough," I say. "I could use my 401K to get new carpet, paint, put up a chain link fence. I would *love* doing childcare. That's probably what I'm actually supposed to do. I never saw that before this little boy was so enchanted by my puppet. I want to take the childcare classes and open a place here at our house. I won't make enough money if I work at a day care center or school. We're supposed to do what we love. That's what I love. Children."

"We'll talk about it."

I panic. "I need to do this."

For the next year, while I take early childhood education classes, Baker stonewalls discussion about what it takes to make our place a daycare.

"You won't even be here!" I say, exasperated.

He won't discuss replacing the carpet, putting in a chain link fence, painting the house.

"You'll be gone at work all day. Kids will be gone when you get home! It's my IRA money I want to use! Why won't you discuss it?"

"Your mind's made up," he says.

"It is. But could we talk about it? I feel alone."

"You brought that on yourself."

Why am I with him?

I don't have money coming in. If I don't act, my IRA will soon be gone, using it for bills. If he's not on board, I have to do it on my own.

I choose a deep aqua-teal color for the carpet, order an extra thick pad, hire a chain link company, do the painting myself.

CHAPTER 27
TELL ME MORE

July, 2002. Three and a half years later.

Tonight, I sit in a hard desk in my third week of a college night class, Math for Elementary School Teachers. Life's not turning out how I wanted. I have plenty of time to reflect, because I'm not paying attention. I can't see myself teaching math to children.

Childcare didn't work out—I only got three kids to come to daycare at my house. I loved looking after them, but didn't make a living. Then I got a good gig working for a school, cooking at the school during the day, doing after school childcare in the afternoons. But it doesn't pay in the summer.

The bored math professor drones on about sets while I practice cross-hatching tiny portraits of strangers in my notebook. My nausea isn't from skipping dinner to counteract a few days of eating sweets. It's from the thought of teaching math to children. I need to honor my feelings. And self-help books say I need to do what I love. It won't be this.

I loved being an after school childcare teacher. Watching over the kids playing under oaks on a sprawling playground. Parents were in awe of how much their children loved coming to childcare, in awe of how thirty children from three to six years old played riotously but peacefully under my watch. They said they'd never seen anything like it.

I told the parents, whenever there's a scrap, I call, "Childcare people!" The children all come running. "What are the rules?" I ask. They all say, "No hitting or kicking and be kind." I say, "Good, now go play." The children always figured it out.

Now and then I glance at my professor as a I doodle, to give the impression I'm listening.

The children didn't need to be singled out, shamed, scolded, lectured, though I've seen plenty of teachers do that. No. It makes me sad to think I'm not going back. The kids were smart as whips. They got it. And when a child flew off the handle, I told the child it was okay, they just needed to grow maturity by staying home one day. When they came back after one day off, they beamed, chest out, said, "I grew maturity!" It showed in their play. Too bad the job doesn't pay.

I flipped a coin a month ago: heads, teach elementary school kids; tails, be a counselor. I've tried Math for Elementary School Teachers. Counselor it is. Four years of school. It's going to be a long haul. So what?

I want to close my notebook and walk out now in the middle of math class, but that would be rude. Tough it out, build some character.

I quietly laugh. Build character? Living with Baker I have plenty of character, the way he challenges my patience every day. I don't know what to do. I put off thinking about it, since there seem to be no answers. He's so fun-loving, I'm blissful. And he makes me belly-laugh every morning when we have coffee and write in our journals. But the evening comes, and he's usually aloof, ignores me. On weekends, he just wants to relax. When I want us to get something done, he uses sarcasm to block me, or cold refusal.

He loves the paint job, the chain link fence, new aqua-teal carpet I had put in, though he refused to talk about it. Sometimes I think he's mean on purpose, except he's helpful in all kinds of ways and always makes me laugh. But it's not enough. There's something else going on. We have an odd partnership.

He says he doesn't like change. How's that going to work? We're going to fight every time something changes?

I did finally stop changing the house around every few weeks the way I loved to do, when he finally spoke up and said he can't stand me changing the house around. How could I have known how badly it affected him? He would come home, see the change and wouldn't speak to me. I never knew why.

We're stuck. I don't want to break up, can't change him, can't see my part in our problems.

We don't talk about finances either. We talk about life, the cats, dinner, being in the moment.

That night at home, relieved to be done for good with Math for Elementary School Teachers, I can't wait to tell Baker I'm going to enroll in school to become a counselor. The house is empty, though. I forgot. He's out playing music with his buddies in a friend's garage. I'm tired. I can't think about my next career move tonight. I curl up in Mr. B's old stuffed chair we bought from his nephew for fifty dollars, and open the local alternative newspaper for a fun read. The paper opens to a full-page ad: "Change your career in just four weekends. Become a certified chemical dependency counselor."

I laugh. That's exactly what I want to be. A counselor. In four weekends? Not four years? I love to listen to people, help them understand themselves. I'm an alcoholic, a drug addict, so I'll relate to the clients. I study the fine print. It's taught by Dr. Ruth Matheson who's been offering the course for thirty years. Wow. She sounds legit. It's a miracle. Fifteen hundred dollars. That's a lot. But it's only four weekends. It's worth it. Only an hour's drive. Classes are all three weekend days. Baker could take the course with me. He'd be a great counselor. He talks for hours with people from the inner child groups. He's looking for a new career too. He's been doing massage and grounds maintenance near where we live. The class is a hundred miles south. We'll rent a motel. We have enough of my IRA left. Classes start next week.

After four weekends with eight other students in Dr. Matheson's little upstairs offices, Baker and I are finally at our last session. Dr. Matheson explained to us all how the laws are going to be changing, and in a year or two, a two-year degree from an addictive-disorders college program will be required, but until then, our certificates she'll give us are all we need to be counselors. This is perfect. I'll get to see if I really like it before going back to college.

I still can't get over how Dr. Matheson has all this energy at eighty-six years old. She's small and powerful in her light brown wig, powdery rouge and lipstick. She has to take a nap before the afternoon sessions, but then she's right back at it. Luckily, Baker and I were able to stay Friday and Saturday nights at the home of an aunt of his, not far from the class.

I love Dr. Matheson. She's so kind and smart. She's coming over to coach my partner and me. I've never known such a warm person as Dr. Matheson. She doesn't really teach us how to be counselors, she *moves* us to do it, to have warm personal regard for the clients in the role plays. It's a powerful technique. Today, we're peer counseling, so it's not a role play. It's real.

"Who'll be the client first?" she asks.

My partner, Maggie, a young woman with dark unwashed hair raises her hand. "I will."

Don't judge. She's two years sober, has three children, works, comes here. No wonder she doesn't have time to wash her hair. She wears a nice printed top and black jeans, nicer than my T-shirt and blue jeans. I'm off my rocker trying to judge her.

"All right," Matheson says, "Tell your counselor your problem."

"I can't seem to calm down," Maggie says with a nervous laugh. "I've been sober two years, go to meetings, work the program with a sponsor, but sometimes I get *so* anxious, like a panic, I can't help thinking of drinking."

Two years sober is a long time to still be preoccupied with thoughts of drinking. What do I say? Sometimes, when no words come to mind, none are needed, Matheson always says. Don't always tell the client what you think, have the client tell you what they think. "Tell me more," I say.

Maggie's face flushes. "Okay. It's as though I don't belong anywhere, and I feel as soon as I'm found out—I don't even know what about, but found out—I'll be abandoned."

So, put myself in the client's shoes, that's the point. Not to carry her anxiety, but to help her see her strengths. "You're brave coming here and telling a counselor how you feel."

She tears up. "Thank you. No one's ever told me I'm brave before."

Matheson touches my shoulder. "Good. Now, thank her."

Thank her for.... "Thank you for trusting me," I say.

Matheson nods, and moves on.

The young woman nods. "Of course. You're so kind."

No one's told me I was kind before. I don't know what to say now. Matheson always says don't cut a client away from you by asking clinical questions. Help them see who they are. My client didn't realize she was brave. Her tears welled up. "Tell me about being brave," I say.

Suddenly tears pulse from her eyes. She gets a tissue, dabs around her mascara, takes a minute. "It's funny, I haven't thought of this in years. Your question about being brave made it come to mind. I had to watch my baby brother a lot. One time, when I was four years old, my mom said she'd be right back. She didn't come back for a few days." She furrows her brow in some new understanding, takes a deep breath. Her mouth trembles as new tears come. "I was brave." She laughs through her tears. "I was so scared. I sang to him so I wouldn't be so scared. And so that he wouldn't cry so much." She nods with a look of pride. "But when my mom came home, she saw his dirty diaper had given him a bad rash. She beat me. She wouldn't speak to me for days. I thought it was my fault."

My tears well up. I look her in the eye.

"It wasn't my fault, was it?"

"No. It wasn't your fault. You were abandoned. And when your mom came home, you got in trouble when you were found out, so to speak, because she made you think you had given him a bad rash. You had no idea. And you were punished and then abandoned again."

She nods. "I was, wasn't I? I was found out, when I didn't even do anything wrong. And I was abandoned. Oh my gosh."

I nod.

"I haven't thought of that day for years. And I was brave."

"Yes, you were. You still are."

"Thank you. I feel so relieved. You're good at this," she says.

"Thank you. Do you know where you're going to work?"

"Yes. I'll intern at the Salvation Army."

"Good. You're going to be a great counselor. You always see what people do right. I'm going to intern at an intensive outpatient rehab. It's funny, I go to meetings with addicts and alcoholics, no problem, but to work at a facility makes me nervous, like I'll get mugged by an addict on my way to my car."

We laugh.

"I already met the clients I'll work with," she says. "They're really kind, and helpful. They're grateful someone wants to help."

"Thanks for telling me. I feel better."

"Okay, your turn," she says.

"Okay. I'm always in a double bind, you know, damned if I do, damned if I don't situations. And sometimes, the inner conflict's so overwhelming, I feel disoriented. I don't think of drinking, I think what's the use of anything. I'm damned if I love my dad, damned if I don't. A lot of my siblings are mad at him. He touched our breasts our whole lives. But the very thought of not loving him breaks my heart. I don't think he can do better."

"Okay. Tell me more."

She's good. "I think we all do our best. I *can't* be bitter about him. He's sick. People need to keep their kids away from him. He's never acknowledged that he's hurt us. He's never admitted he's wrong about anything in his life. He raises his voice if people disagree with him. Can't tolerate any perceived challenge. That's sick, isn't it?"

"What do you think?"

She's really good. "I think he has a kind of sickness."

I can't wait to be a counselor.

CHAPTER 28
STAND IN THE WIND

October 2003. A year and three months later.

At two o'clock Saturday afternoon, Baker walks in scowling, takes off his field jacket, sits in his chair, turns on a football game. I know he was hanging out with Carla.

He's been hostile for three days straight this time. I can't take it anymore. I need to talk to him. I've been a counselor for over a year, so you'd think our talks would go pretty well, but they never turn out good.

I have to balance warm personal regard for Baker with nurture for myself, which is speaking up for myself, the way Mom never did with Dad. "You didn't tell me you were staying after yoga for three hours with Carla," I say at last. I know he was with her this afternoon.

"She needed to talk. You should try yoga," Baker says with a smug smile, changes the TV channel to another game.

Remember to pause, the number one rule in conflict resolution. I take a breath. "Don't dismiss me. You know what I'm talking about. You and I were going to walk down to the river lookout today. But you spent the afternoon with her."

"Let's walk now," he says coolly.

He's not willing to admit he's having an emotional affair with her. Or that he's blowing me off. "No, I'm too angry to walk." So far, so good. I'm sharing my feelings, not blowing up.

"If you're angry, sounds like you could use some cookies—isn't that how you deal with anger?"

"Fuck you!" I shout.

So much for warm personal regard and not blowing up. "I need you to be more respectful," I say, calmer.

He gives me a fiery look. *"I need you to get off my case about how I should live!"* he roars.

I hit a nerve. Good. I won't respond.

Yes, I will. "And I *won't* go to yoga because I *hate* yoga with all those women in their skimpy outfits bending over, all around you, falling out of their tops! I hate it!" That felt good.

The few times I went to yoga I had to watch the teachers in their low-cut tight outfits put their hands all over him for God knows what reasons.

He smiles, amused. "Hate's a strong word."

I give up. Eight years of bliss and hell with him. Mostly hell, now.

I challenge him, he disconnects, puts me down. I could say he didn't give the cat enough food, and he'd ridicule me for liking sweets. His hurtful words or lack of words put me on eggshells. I can't speak in my own house without a sarcastic or dismissive retort, unless I'm saying something he wants to hear, like dinner's ready.

Something's got to give. "Why do you have to be this way?" I say calmly. "I can't take it anymore."

"Then you shouldn't've married me," he says in a flat, cold voice.

"I can't believe how cold you are. I married you because I love you!" I yell.

"Yeah, well, how's that working for you?"

God, he's cold. Wake up. Be honest. "It's not working for me. I never signed up for this and you know what I think? I'm just going to forget about ever *trying again* with you, because *you don't care! You don't love me, probably never have!* You say you do but that's a good show because I *believe it, when it's not even true!*"

Did that even make sense? "You can't admit when you've done wrong, Baker!"

Like Dad. Damn. It's true.

Baker gets up, grabs his jacket.

I panic. "*Where are you going?*" I yell and grab my purse.

"Well, clearly my best is not good enough here. Maybe I'll go where I won't be accused of sarcasm and ridicule and that other word you like to use. Being dismissive, yeah, that's it. Good word."

"Oh, no. You're not leaving. *I am!*" No one's ever leaving me again. I grab my journal, get to the door first, slam it as hard as I can on my way out.

No one will ever leave me again.

I start my car, step on the gas, startle myself when I skid in the gravel alley as I back out and speed away. Great skidding sound. He heard it. It shows how hurt I am.

He won't get it. I don't think he can. I thought his kindness meant he can empathize. I shake my head, sad.

No, I won't be left again. Getting dropped by Arnold cured me of that for good.

I'll miss Baker.

I don't care. I'm done with this nervous, walking-on-eggshells feeling which I can never shake anymore. I won't put up with being talked down to and being stood up.

I drive through the cross-streets toward the highway. How do I know Baker and Carla aren't having an affair?

Because he has so many women friends there'd be cat fights over him.

Damn it. Why do I have to love him so much? I'm screwed. I knew he was a handful from the start. But he was fun and darling and warm! He still is! He holds me when I still sometimes cry missing Mom, who's not gone. Holds me a long time after we make love. I knew his childhood made him angry. I thought Baker was a lion whom I was sure I could tame because I can love that much. Like I thought with Randy thirty years ago. I'm insane.

I hit the freeway glad to be free. Baker, you don't love me! Because if you did, you would never be dismissive or sarcastic. You're just like Dad when he talks to Mom!

Except, I think Dad does love Mom. So, Baker might love me. Shoot. It doesn't matter. I won't live like this.

A sudden longing for brown leather shoes points me toward the department stores of Santa Barbara. I need those shoes so bad. I don't care how much they cost.

Thirty miles later I park outside Nordstrom's in a kind of trance. I'm calm on one level. Baker's far away. If I can just find my shoes. They always had them at the department store, Frederick & Nelson, when I was little. I enter Nordstrom's, look around. Over there!

Brown leather lace-up shoes. Darn! They all have pointed toes. No! No! No! They won't work. Round-toe shoes are what I need.

I try the men's shoes. None have round toes.

I leave and sadly drive to the old Blue Onion restaurant. The shoes are only a way to avoid your feelings, avoid facing the problem, I tell the little girl within me.

No, they're what I need, she says.

Don't argue with her, Marie. You won't win.

I pull in at the old Blue Onion on State Street. I'm back to the present.

I said I was leaving. It sounds great to tell Baker I'm leaving. The reality of leaving is actually awkward, having no place to go. Motels are too expensive.

I need to think.

I take a booth, set my journal in front of me, survey the large, peaceful empty restaurant. I used to drink wine here. I've changed a lot since then.

A waitress brings water and a cup of coffee.

When I was nineteen, I had a rented room two blocks away. I sketched at that coffee counter. I thought I was Van Gogh. I met an older guy who came to my room for a portrait. He paid me fifty dollars. I loaned him my Cadillac that Dad had sold me. He didn't bring it back. Police found it unharmed in a field three days later. God, I was stupid.

When I was fifteen, cruising in the back seat of my girlfriend's car, I wished we hadn't passed up this restaurant, I wanted French fries so badly. I couldn't speak up then.

And I can't speak up now. How did that happen?

I rage, complain, lecture saying reasonable things, but I'm missing something. I can't actually speak up. I don't know what that would sound like.

God, please help me. I'm a frigging counselor. I teach communication to couples, clients and groups. Clients try the tools and say they work. You'd think I could communicate with my own husband, but, no. The minute I tell him how hurt I feel, he reacts with a putdown and we disintegrate into a battle.

Why?

Because, telling people how you feel probably only works with people who *care* about how you feel!

That's true, isn't it? Of course, it is. I need to stop telling him how I feel. It just draws more fire. I'll tell my clients too, not to tell their feelings to someone who doesn't care about how they feel.

I think Baker does love me, but he really doesn't care how I feel. My feelings are mine he tells me. Damn it! He's so kind and fun when he's himself. Then he vanishes in plain sight. Where does the real Baker go?

I set my journal aside, too angry to write. How does Baker think it's okay to dismiss me? All I said was, "I need you be more respectful." I said it in a nice tone. Didn't use the inherently shaming why word, why don't you. And yet the way he reacted you'd think I'd set a pet on fire. Thankfully he doesn't *usually* yell, but he did today. I *had* to say something, he's been relentless with sarcasm and that dismissive tone for three days now.

My brain needs a rest. It feels fried. Partly because I'm dehydrated. I down my glass of water, pick up a National Geographic left on the back of the booth. The waitress brings the coffee pot. I smile and cover my cup. Coffee makes me anxious. I have it in a restaurant to give my life an epic feel, is all.

I thumb through the magazine. I don't want to go through another break up. But I don't see how I can stay. I'm kind and reasonable, but it doesn't get through to him, so then I suddenly see white—not red—everything white's out, I'm so angry, and I explode. I usually can't remember what I said.

I turn the magazine pages. Oh my gosh. What a darling baby elephant! It stands by its trainer. I asked my counseling supervisor once, "Why are all babies so cute?" He looked amused and said, "So their parents don't kill them." I howled. He's right. Babies are such a challenge, being cute is nature's protection. Baker's cute.

The article says every time the trainer leads the baby elephant to a big log, he drops the rope past the elephant's eye, then ties the rope to the log. When the baby tries to follow the trainer, the baby can't, it's held by the log. When the baby grows too big for the log, all the trainer has to do is drop the rope past its eye. Full-grown elephants won't even try to walk away.

Oh my gosh. That's who I am. Deep inside, I sway, unable to move. I'm a drop-tied elephant, unable to speak up. A cue I learned as a child made me think I can't move, can't talk, can't calmly be myself. All I can do is react. How was I controlled as a child? When anyone spoke up, Dad got sarcastic, dismissive, or roared, and went away. We all shut down. I'm brainwashed to believe I can't move—can't be myself. I can feel it. That's why I can yell, but I can't speak up. I'm a drop-tied elephant. I'll bet we all are in some ways. I can't wait to tell my clients.

I'm mild, so I won't be left. Then, I finally explode. That's the problem—I don't meaningfully speak up. I want to run home and tell Baker.

Because this isn't who he really is. He's loving and kind, or, he used be, before things got like they are now.

A gnawing inside comes as I recall something—Jean wants me to read this book about men who abuse women. In it, the men tell their own stories. That's not Baker, I told her, he's never hit me. She said it's abusive to dismiss someone.

I sip my coffee, sit back to think about that. I don't want to admit she's right.

I push the coffee away. My stomach's hurting again.

Damn it.

Jean's right.

It doesn't matter if he loves me, if he's abusive.

I know from my counselor training we can act out from our trauma. I had hoped being kind to Baker would help him see what he's doing and stop. But being kind hasn't helped at all.

I can't change his behavior. I need to change mine. I need to find my part in it. I'll take the bull by the horns. Go to the library. Look at books on abuse. See if victims have some part in it. Children don't. But what about adults? Some are real victims, but I can't help feeling sure I have some part in it. My recovery program trains me to look for my part in things. So far, I haven't seen what it could be. Determined to discover my part once and for all, I get up to leave.

I pay my bill, head downtown.

Inside the library, the beautiful tall windows and woodsy smelling stacks make me feel like an outlaw because I'm here to look up abusive behavior, a don't-talk subject for some reason. It's too personal. I feel guilty.

Shame makes my cheeks burn as I peruse the few books on abuse. It's affecting me deeply, living with being dismissed. Each book is about men being abusive. None talk about abusive women. And there's nothing about the other person's part in it. I know I have a part in it. It doesn't make sense I wouldn't. But the books assume the other person's always a victim. I'm not. These books aren't helpful to me at all. I need to know my part in it, since I'm the only one I can control.

Frustrated, I leave. I need to go home to think it through.

Back at our house, Baker's car is gone. Good. I need to focus. I gloomily walk up the drive.

A bright spot of yellow catches my eye. It looks like the heavy jasmine arbor, which is so thick it makes the kitchen dark, has sprouted two yellow roses. I can hardly believe my eyes. It takes a second to understand what happened.

For ten years, I've pruned and watered two rose plants, one white and one yellow, that grow under the jasmine arbor. Baker assigned them to me. Each year, while Baker's crimson, red and coral roses flourish in full sun around the yard, mine, in the dark, put on only two roses each, and grow no taller than the kitchen window. Every year, it breaks my heart to see them not grow. I love them with all my heart and tell them so.

I walk over to see with my own eyes now, how the yellow rose plunged into three feet of darkness of the arbor's old growth. It was determined. It grew through darkness toward the light, until it popped out into the sunshine. I laugh with delight.

No matter what, aim for the light.

Inside, I get a straight-back chair so I can focus better, move it into the middle of our living room, get a nice cup of hot water, and sit down to think. What's my part in our abusive relationship? I've got to find out.

I reflect how I've often appeased him by making him a sandwich, since he may have gotten too hungry, or I imagine he needs love more than I do, his childhood was so violent, so I do extra things for him to be kind. I think if I show how I love him, he'll begin to see he doesn't really want to hurt me. But no matter how kind and helpful I am, over the years, we've gotten worse and worse.

Screaming at him when I explode stops the current fight, but another one starts within a day or two, with his needling criticisms. So, screaming doesn't actually help. And slamming doors doesn't convey how much pain I'm in. Neither do tears, which I usually shed in private, as I ask God for help. The answer I always sense is love. Love not only Baker. Love myself as well.

So.

The sun's gone down. The house grows darker with that late in the day bleakness. The bleak feeling gives way to a sweet comfort of knowing I'm present, completely with myself, completely connected to myself. My mind travels into the dusk outside the French door. I know I have a part in our problems. What is it? I sip my hot water. Plunge into the dark.

Forget the fights. What does any partner want and need?

A partner.

What's a partner?

Someone who loves and respects you and stands beside you.

Stands.

Oh.

Little lights flicker within, form a pattern of love more than sweet, more than kind. Honest love which is able to stand in the wind and require respect, because that's the truth—love requires respect. I've been kind, warm, tender. But I haven't stood in the wind to tell the truth—I require respect. I've told him he's a dick, which is only name calling. I've said stop talking to me that way, which is only telling someone else what to do, never works. No. I've never stood in the wind of his attacks and said I require respect. Not with a threat added on. It's not needed. It's embedded in the honesty of the word require.

I picture living the rest of my life the way it's been, the way I've been.

I won't do it.

The way Baker is, works for Baker. It doesn't work for me. I can't change him or anyone else. I've been telling Baker what to do, when I don't *know* what Baker needs to do. For all I know, he needs to act out the rest of his life. It's none of my business if he does.

My business is what I do. I'm on eggshells, constantly nervous, my stomach hurting. I have to leave if he can't be respectful. Simple. Painful, but simple.

I don't have to leave yet. But if I have to, I will. That's the truth. I sigh, relieved at last.

I've never told him I need respect. Never said I don't accept hurtful words. I need to tell him what *I* need and require, not what *he* needs to do.

I've been a doormat, been nice, pleaded, yelled. But I haven't been truthful.

I haven't had a spine.

That's it, isn't it? I've been spineless. That's my part in it. He deserves a partner with a spine. Oh my gosh. I owe him an amends for having been spineless all these years. Fighting with him doesn't mean I have a spine. Standing in the wind does. I can't wait till he gets home.

I'm happy, hopeful at last. A yellow rose sprouting above the jasmine. Either he'll change, because he won't want to lose me, or he won't, and I'll go. Either way, I'll get well. No more walking on eggshells. Time will tell. Ocean liners don't turn around in five minutes. He'll need some time to change. Couple of weeks probably. I get up, turn on the kitchen light, make another cup of hot water. I recall persuading Baker to try hot water as a beverage. It took months, but he finally tried it. One day he brought me a cup of hot water. "P.D.T.," he said.

"What's P.D.T.?" I asked.

"Perfect drinking temperature."

Since then, he loves hot water and always says, "P.D.T.," or "P.F.H.," pretty fucking hot, when he brings me a cup of hot water. He can change.

I love him so much. But something mean inside has got a hold of him. He's the only one who can sort that out.

I signed up for a partner. So did Baker.

I hear tires on the gravel. His car door opens and shuts. It's dark outside.

"Hi, dear," I say, when he comes in.

"Hello," he says, formally.

"The waters hot, if you want a cup."

"Thank you."

He's not going to like this. But it's going to be better, being a real partner. Here goes. "I owe you an amends."

"Oh?"

"Yes. You deserve a partner with a spine. I've been a doormat. I'm sorry. From now on, I'll have a spine."

He pours his hot water, frowns at me, shakes his head. "Whatever you say."

The next morning, it's his turn to make coffee. He gets it started. At the foot of the bed, he turns on the holiday lights we always use for a cozy feeling. He goes out, comes back with the coffee chatting a monologue with God. "What's that God? Sunshine, then storms and death. You got it." He looks away. "Guys! The Big Guy wants us to deal with that Petrie dish experiment He accidentally spilled. Yeah, working title Humankind. That's the one. It's gotten out of hand over there in Sector G. He needs a clean-up crew stat. Yeah. Sooner the better.

They're about to nuke themselves." Baker climbs in bed, turns to me. "Morning, dear," he says sweetly. "Let's walk to the river lookout after we journal."

I'm glad I've found a way to stay with him, because I love him no end.

We enjoy our walk to the bluff where we gaze across the dry river bed to the yellow hills beyond, comment on how despite the drought, we're fortunate to have ended up where we are.

He takes it all in, shakes his head. "Right. There's no God."

We laugh. He can make fun saying God wants to do us all in, but Baker taught me a principle he learned somewhere—divine love always has met and always will meet every human need. I believe it. No matter how painful life becomes, divine love flows if I don't become bitter.

Hopefully it'll rain this year.

In the evening we have fun making soup, garlic bread and cookies, for Sunday dinner with Sherlock Holmes on TV. I'm happy. I will have to stand in the wind. Probably not tonight.

A few days later, I work an early shift, get home at six. Baker comes home with a stormy look. I get nervous.

Act normal. "Any thoughts on dinner?" I ask.

No reply.

Being dismissed by his not replying doesn't hurt in the usual way. I'm a click removed. I'm not helpless. I know I can't stay if he can't be respectful. I can speak up. I don't have an impossible task, anymore.

He sits in his chair, turns on a football game.

"I require respect," I say.

"I require respect," he mimics with a scrunched-up face and squeaky voice.

"And I don't accept that either."

"You don't accept what?" he challenges.

He knows what. He's baiting me.

Sparkling lights glitter around in my brain. I understand. This is exactly where I would fight. Whatever you do, Marie, don't take the bait. Right. Don't ever take the bait.

I've said my piece. I'm not trying to change him. I'm only telling him what I require. Whether he changes, is out of my hands. There's nothing more I need to say. Good.

I go in the other room and get comfortable with a book I can hardly focus on, I'm so happy I told him I require respect, and so upset with him for being so mean. The bad thing is I can't focus to write. My life is going by and I haven't written about it in weeks. I won't fight anymore, though. I won't take the bait. I'll keep saying my piece, and let him figure out what he wants to do. If he doesn't change, I'll leave, because I need to get my life back.

He won't want me to leave. He'll change, I'm pretty sure.

CHAPTER 29
THE NEW NEST-BED

October, 2004. One year (a lifetime) later

I get home from work at ten thirty at night, as usual when I work nights, and sit in my car on the street above our house. The street light's too bright to see stars, but the waxing moon's a bright fat crescent in the western sky. I watch it a while. Get oriented to the optical illusion that the moon appears to be setting. We're hurtling east at twenty-four thousand miles an hour. I used to be thrilled by these thoughts. Now, I'm beginning to feel cynical, to feel nothing really matters. That's a problem.

It's been a whole year of my having a spine, but there's been no real change in our relationship. Sometimes we get along and have fun, but more often we have splintery exchanges. We haven't fought a lot, because I'm usually able to walk away after telling him I don't accept being talked down to or whatever. So, the problem's not the heat of fighting, but a slow grinding away at what matters in life. I'm very tough, and that's a problem.

I watch the moon, think about the future. Do I want to live the rest of my life like this? That's the only question I need to answer. Because this is how it's going to be.

Nope. I don't.

Good. It's done.

I always thought I'd be so sad to leave, that there'd be no way I could go. Now, I'm like, I want to survive and have a good life. I'm not sad at all. What a relief.

The next day, I look on Craigslist and start with the least expensive lead.

Three miles away from our place, I knock on a door of a pretty white house with beautiful landscaping. All I really need is a nice room, hot plate, little fridge, my own bath.

An unshaved man opens the door. "Yes?"

Don't judge. "You have a room for rent?"

He puts his cigarette in an ash tray, motions me to follow him around the outside of the house to a small cottage.

This looks nice, more than a room. Lots of windows. I could definitely start my new life here. I didn't think I'd feel so calm leaving Baker. I know the reality will hit later. But I can shed my tears in a pretty cottage which is only four-hundred dollars. It's sad Baker's not going to change and it's time for me to go, but I've given it my all.

The landlord goes to the back of the cottage, unlocks a door to an added-on room, judging from the painted plywood. "This is it."

Oh. The eight by ten room has water damage coming down from the ceiling into swollen drywall, and mold growing up the walls from a dirty brown carpet.

"Got your own bathroom. Hot plate," he says. "Four hundred dollars."

"I see. Uh, thanks, but it's too small for me. You rent the cottage?"

"Eleven hundred. Occupied."

"You got this area." He pulls a dirty tan curtain aside to reveal a curtain rod.

"Yeah, still, I don't think it'll work for me. Thanks so much."

I walk to my car, feel sad for people who have no choice but to live in rooms like his. I'm glad I have two more places to try. I head out to the big old gray farmhouse Tim, who's teaching me guitar, suggested I try. He's the only person I've told I'm leaving. He won't tell anyone. His hands are full with his own boy-friend.

The farmhouse, out a few miles, isn't far from the freeway. I met a few of the people who live there one time when I attended a music gathering. It felt like a time warp back to the sixties. They all had long hair, wore flowy hippy clothes and smoked a lot of pot, but maybe that was because it was a party.

I knock on the kitchen screen door.

"Yeah, come on in!" a man yells from upstairs.

The kitchen appears chaotic with wooden boxes stacked around, old pots and utensils hanging all over the walls, baskets hanging with old dried produce. Counters covered with dirty dishes, takeout containers spilling from the garbage, the smell of marijuana thick.

I don't want to live here.

A man with long ash blond hair comes partway down the stairs, buttoning a shirt in a hurry. "Oh. I thought you were someone else."

"Tim said you might need a roommate."

"Yeah, guess so."

He doesn't seem interested in showing me around. It occurs to me now, I'm older than these people by fifteen years. Still, I should at least look. "Could I see it?"

"Sure. I'm just trippin.' Thought you were someone else."

He's high. He turns back up the stairs. Leads me to a small bedroom, no closet. It's big enough for a bed and a dresser. "I think it's six hundred dollars," he says.

I stuff my hands in my pockets. "Okay. Thanks. I need a little bigger place."

He shrugs, goes off down the hall. I see myself out.

I don't need a room. I need an apartment. Other people rent apartments. I'll need some space to start my new life. A place to paint, enough room to cook. To have people over, have little parties.

I climb the stairs to a vacancy at a nice-looking apartment complex built on a steep hill, which, come to think of it, could slide in heavy rain one year. I need a place where I'll feel safe. More than that, where I'll feel myself so I can begin to heal after a whole year of quiet war with Baker, and after having to leave the man I love. I've tried everything—patience, impatience, kindness, sharpness, always sticking to the truth that I need respect. Nothing goes in for him. It's probably his way of saying he wants things to end.

I slowly walk around inside a tiny, empty, white, eleven-hundred-dollar, one-bedroom apartment with a beige carpet. I try to find something I like about it. It's too expensive. More than our mortgage. Still, I could make it work. I picture myself boxed in here alone at night, alone in the morning. Tears come with a sense that I'll be alone the rest of my life, no one will ever visit me, I'll lose my sanity in these white walls. I'd rather live in my car.

Or, in our sunroom.

I'm glad I didn't tell Baker I'm leaving. I'd have egg on my face when I walk in the door. I'll tell him when I get home that I'm moving into our sunroom, the big cluttered enclosed patio where we sleep in the summer, since it's too cold for Baker in the winter. I don't mind the cold. I have a comforter I bought when I left Isaac that keeps me plenty warm. The sunroom has lots of windows. A beautiful queen-size sleigh bed our neighbors sold us for a hundred dollars. We already had a good bed in the bedroom, but thought, what the heck? Why not have a sunroom bed? I'll make my nest in there, rent-free.

At home Baker looks up when I walk in. "Hello," he says.

"Hello. I'm moving into the sunroom. I looked for a place to rent, but they're too expensive or crappy." I go put my purse down on the bed in the sunroom. The bed's piled with clutter. I hear the front door close. Good. I feel utterly peaceful now. I won't be criticized, belittled or dismissed anymore, I'm sure. He may not even speak to me. I can live with that. He can live his life and I'll live mine.

By eight o'clock at night, I'm tucked into my cozy bed with a perfect table with a lamp, a cup of hot tea, and Jane Austen, a large volume I've never opened.

Tonight's a good night. Such peace. I hear the front door open and close. He's back. Good. I don't want him to do anything rash. He wouldn't, I'm quite sure. He's stoical, not upset by anything except my incompetence, it seems.

I sip my tea. God, I'm happy. It's too bad we couldn't make it as a couple, because in between him needing to put me down, he's delightful, loving, warm and fun. That's what's sad. He's not a dick all the time by any means. But all the goodness we have is punctuated by darts of disrespect I never see coming. It's interesting. No matter how rational I am, I can't rationalize staying for the good times. The bad times are like poison tablets that make the beautiful spring water undrinkable. Baker doesn't understand that. I explained it just that way. He obviously can't change, or he would have. How long will I stay here in the house? Until something better comes along. For now, mission accomplished.

I need to journal these thoughts. Especially that I've done a great thing standing up for myself for a whole year, and now moving out here. Thoughts of standing up to Dad come. I set my book aside, pick up my journal, write:

> Strange, I've stood up to Baker no problem, the moment I made my resolve a year ago. But Dad's a whole other problem. With Dad, I regress every time. I can't object when he quickly gets me when I let my guard down. What's the deal?

My eyelids are so heavy. I haven't felt this relaxed and safe in years. I push the journal aside, slump down to lie flat, turn out the light.

In the morning I'm gleeful at the great new system of me living in the sunroom, exposed to no risk of being put down, since we won't likely be interacting. The air feels fresh and pure. I venture through the house toward the bathroom, startle him in the hall.

He nods formally as we pass one another.

In the bathroom, I notice he's just shaved. That's a good sign. He's not spiraling into depression. I'd have to call his friends to take care of him. When I come out of the bathroom, he's gone. Hopefully to work. Great. I work two to ten tonight. By the time I get home, he'll probably be asleep. We'll hardly cross paths.

At work my supervisor calls me in. As usual, I brace myself for getting fired.

"No, I'm not going to fire you," she says, as usual. She tilts her head of thick, shoulder-length auburn hair.

I smile with a sigh of relief, as always.

"I just want to discuss the clients."

I sit down.

When we're done discussing clients, she pushes her notepad aside. "Listen," she says, "your job is secure. Try that on."

I smile and say confidently, "Nobody's job is secure." I've been fired five times.

"You know what I mean. Your job is secure. I want you to try that on."

Why does part of me resist doing that? Because it's the part whose job it is to keep me on high alert. My supervisor doesn't think it's necessary to be anxious. I'll give it a try. I nod agreement and feel a chilly squeeze against my neck. I leave her office and step down the long empty hall toward the group room to set up, feeling awkward, as if wearing snowshoes.

I try it on—my job is secure. I pass the big windows that look out to the field. To make it stick, I murmur with emotion, "These are *my* walls, *I* work here. This is *my* floor. These are *my* windows. This is *my* job."

A strange calm comes over me. I take a deep breath and sigh. Something's shifted.

Later, after group, I contentedly do my notes in my office, which now feels like a nest which is truly mine. It's hard to believe the fear of being fired is gone.

And I can hardly wait to get home and climb into my new nest-bed.

It's November. Cold out here in the sunroom. I get ready for bed and suddenly remember my parachute. Where is it? I dig in the garage and find it, one I got at a thrift store thinking you never know when you're going to need to trap the heat in your room, the way my roommate Brian did in his flat in the East Bay Area. I wonder how he's getting along? His parachute covered his entire room, which was small. It kept his furnace heat in so he could sit in his cowboy pajamas playing guitar in his otherwise—except for my mattress and books in an adjacent room—empty five-room flat. He was kind, in love with Lila, who was in love with two other guys. I taught him to drive. I'll never forget the night the police stopped us. Brian and I cracked our heads reaching for the contents of his wallet which had splashed onto the gravel. Brian made me feel alive to my spine when he played 'round Midnight by Thelonious Monk. It was the winter I stayed in his back-porch room.

I hang my parachute using thumbtacks in the low ceiling, drape it over chairs next to the electric radiator beside the bed. Bundled up, waiting for heat, I lie back on my bed and kick the parachute to see it billow. Brian brought me back to life after I left Randy, who had been sleeping around. At least Baker doesn't sleep around, I'm pretty sure. All his women friends would be jealous if he did.

My parachute and the electric radiator are no match for Brian's rig—he had a furnace.

In the morning, still bundled up from a night of trying to get warm even with my comforter, I come out to the warm part of the house—the living room and kitchen.

"Hi," Baker says, smiling.

"Hi," I say, with a polite smile.

We say hi and bye these days, which feels too close for comfort. I know how easy it would be to slip back into the old ways for convenience, for fun. To fall back, unconscious, thinking things have changed. I think that's what he wants. Well, of course, he does. I'm not interested. I love being free from insults.

In December, Baker offers me hot popcorn one night. I can't refuse popcorn. "Thanks."

He hands me a quart size yogurt container of buttered popcorn with nutritional yeast and cayenne pepper. "I'm watching Sherlock Holmes, if you're interested," he says.

"No, thanks, I'm good." I don't want to slip.

I go out under my parachute, sensing I need something I can't identify. I lower the "door" of the parachute to bring the warmth from the radiator closer to me. It's not as effective as Brian's.

If only Baker and I had a wood-burning stove out here, I wouldn't need a parachute. Suddenly, I see the flickering flames of a wood-burning stove in the sunroom and feel hope that I'll have a real home here in the sunroom. It's what I need but couldn't name. Other people have them. Why couldn't we? It'd be so beautiful seeing flames dancing behind a glass door, feeling warmth fill the room. I mesmerize myself with this vision for the next three days and nights.

On the weekend I go to the hardware store where they have wood-burning stoves on sale because winter's here. I'm astonished how easy it is to buy one. It's a good thing I'm doing it. The temperature dips into the high twenties some nights. It's almost always in the low thirties. Here's a small wood-burning stove. No glass door, but it's only a hundred dollars.

"How does it work?" I ask the young sales clerk.

He shakes his head, looks to the back of the store and calls out, "Al, can you help her?"

Al comes over and explains it's easy. "You make sure you have a cement or brick pad to set the stove on."

"Our floor's cement."

"Good. Watch your clearances. Cut your hole in the roof or wall for the flue. Use a ceiling or wall thimble. Calculate how high you want your pipe to go to clear the roof line. We carry all the parts."

He said it's easy. Baker could do it. "I'll take this one. I want it to go through the roof." I point to the smallest stove they have.

I pay. They load the stove and several parts into my car.

"Baker," I say at home. "I bought a wood stove. Can you help me bring it in, please?"

He looks up from his book. Searches my eyes. Closes his book. "Okay."

He's being cooperative. That's nice.

Once everything's inside, I show him where I want to put it in the sunroom next to the dryer.

"Marie, I know you don't want to hear this, but that's not going to work."

"Why not?"

"The sunroom's unpermitted with an uninsulated roof. It's a fire hazard to put a stove in here and would draw attention of the fire department."

"But I want it." I can't bear thinking I can't have it.

But he's right. What was I thinking? "What about the living room?" I'm talking to him. I don't care. I need a woodburning stove in the house.

"Can you talk to someone who knows how to install one?"

He's being kind and reasonable.

"You don't know how?"

"I don't. Horticulture's my thing. And soup. Speaking of which, I made a pot. Would you like some?"

I feel heartbroken the stove's not a solution to the cold in the sunroom, or to the longing in my heart. Soup. Why be cold to him? "Yes, thanks. Soup would be nice."

We sit on the couch with our bowls of soup. I wonder how he feels? I left him, moved into the other room two months ago. But he hasn't shown any feelings. "How are you?" I ask.

He smiles. "I've been better."

"You know I didn't move into the sunroom to be cruel."

"I know."

Does he know why I did? I'm not going to ask him like I'm his parent.

It feels good to sit together. He was kind about the wood stove. We always had soup sitting in bed watching Upstairs Downstairs or Sherlock Holmes. I miss those days. I miss Baker, good Baker. "Want to watch a show?" I ask. I'm impulsive. I hope this is a good idea.

But why not? I have my nest in the sunroom.

He smiles. "Shoot. I'll cue the tape."

There's my old table on my side of the bed, with the spiral white glass lamp and my sobriety chips. Nothing's changed. Why would it?

It feels good to be next to him, in the cozy room. How can I be happy in the sunroom, and happy beside him? I think I needed the break badly, to heal from years of damage. Now, I need him. We love each other. I'm sure he gets it now—I need respect. I think he only needed time by himself to understand how damaging it was for me. He'll never apologize. But I don't need him to. I only need him to be respectful from now on.

Halfway through the show, I slump down, sleepy, turn toward him, feel his hand on my shoulder. He's my wood-burning stove.

CHAPTER 30
BUT WE HAVEN'T PRAYED YET

January, 2005. A month later.

January. Every morning there's frost outside on everything. I don't sleep in the sunroom anymore. We don't go into the sunroom at all except to use the dryer, then we run back into the cozy part of the house.

He slipped, dismissed me twice in the past month. I don't care. I love being with him, because we have normal conversations now. I ignored the comments. Things were going so well I didn't want to say anything. Baker's in your hands, God. I can't worry about every little slight that comes my way. I'm in your hands too, God. You show me what to do, if I need to do something.

I take wet clothes from the washing machine in the kitchen. If it were spring or summer I'd hang the clothes on the line, but it's January. I carry the clothes to the dryer in the sunroom.

There's a problem. Boxes and bags now cover the big bed in the sunroom. Baker knows the clutter we already have bothers me. The cleared bed, all made up with the blue and white cotton quilt Martin gave us one Christmas, was the one bright spot of sanity in the sunroom. Otherwise, the sunroom's crowded with stacks of papers, boxes, and bags that cover the furniture and the whole floor except a narrow path from the back door to the living room. Most of it's his stuff. I need to ask him where the new things on the bed came from, where they're going.

In our bedroom, he reads on the bed. I sit on the foot of the bed. "Hi, dear."

"Hi dear."

"Sorry to interrupt, but I need to ask about …"

"I know, the stuff on the sunroom bed," he says in a sour tone without looking up.

Shoot. "How did you know?"

"Because," he says without humor, scowling at me, "you can't give anything a rest. You're like a rat sniffing out anything to complain about whenever I take a minute to rest. I've had enough of it. You have your requirements and I have mine. Give it a rest!"

"I don't know who you are!" I jump up, go to the sunroom, pull everything off the bed to the path on the floor, crawl under the covers to cry.

No tears.

I sit up, sick to my stomach. I won't give it a rest, sorry God. I go back to the bedroom. "Those things that were on the bed need to be put away some place, Baker."

"Yeah, yeah."

"You don't get it, do you?" I ask.

"I get that your pushy ways need to end."

"I won't live in a house where I can't even sit down on the extra bed."

"You didn't have any trouble with it before." He looks back at his book.

"I was barely surviving before! I hated the clutter every day. You knew that. I didn't talk about it because I don't nag."

"News to me." He doesn't look up.

"I came in here to nicely tell you I had a problem with the stuff on the bed."

"You have a problem being alive." He still doesn't look up.

"What do you mean, Baker?"

"I mean, Marie," he looks at me, "first it's my tone, then it's my words, then it's my meaning, and *all* the time it's my stuff!" His open hand asks, well, what do you have to say, Marie?

He's not making sense. He's having a delayed reaction to my having moved to the sun room. He hasn't changed. "I'm going for a drive."

"You do that. But you'd better get back soon."

"You don't give me orders."

"Dinner won't make itself."

Whoa. He's never said that before. "I'm not the cook."

"No? I thought you were because you're acting like my mom. My mistake."

"Why are you talking like this? We've been getting along so well."

He looks at his book.

"Baker, what's going on?"

No response.

I go sit on the sunroom bed.

I don't need to go for a drive, I need to pack.

I hear the front door open and close. Hear his car drive away. Here come the tears.

This is it for us. I gave it my all, God. I don't think he can change. He feels threatened, so he attacks. That's it for us. I hope he finds someone less threatening, who he likes better than he likes me.

I call Jean.

She says I can stay with her.

I stuff clothes into my carry-on bag. Drop my cosmetics into a plastic grocery bag. Fill a brown bag with shoes. Fold the blue and white quilt, tie it into a bundle around my journal and some books. I remember my first bundle, when I left Randy the first time. He had laughed with that girl who kneeled before him with her hands on his thighs. When I objected, he didn't know what the big deal was.

Baker doesn't know what the big deal is either.

Come to think of it, neither does Dad.

I carry my things to the living room.

Baker walks in the door. Good. I don't have to wait around to say good-bye.

He looks defeated, sits on the couch. "You packed."

I sit on the footstool in front of him. Tears flow down my cheeks. "It's nobody's fault." I look him in the eye. "We tried, but …"

What do I say, God? I choke down tears, wipe my face. "I can't make you be the husband I need. I love you, but …" I sob too hard to talk, take a deep breath. "I love you, but I got to go."

His eyes well up.

I stand. Heave a great sigh. His women friends will look after him, hear him cry. He'll be all right.

I turn to my bags.

"Wait," he says.

I look at him fondly. "No."

"But," he says through tears.

I've never seen him cry over me before.

He reaches out and takes my hands. "I know we piss each other off, and you're done, but …."

"No, Baker, you disrespect me."

"Right." He looks embarrassed.

If there were any way through, I would stay. I love him so much. But love's not enough.

He squeezes my hands, looks me in the eye and says, "But we haven't prayed yet."

Damn it.

It's true.

Shit. It was hard to be all ready to go. Now this.

Prayer's powerful sometimes. Not in physical things, as far as I can tell. But it shifts my inner being. Maybe it'll shift his. We've never prayed together.

I can leave any time. It would be good to try prayer, because, if I leave without trying prayer, I'll never know if we could have made it. And what if it works? I don't understand his problem with respect. I don't need to understand it. He needs to get a handle on it. Maybe it's a spiritual malady.

"Okay. Let's pray," I say.

We both wipe our eyes.

"I'll go first," he says, still holding my hands but with a relaxed grip now. "Lord, we thank thee for this moment of clarity, through which I might pass, to quell my desire to speak every thought. So, if it be thy will, we beseech thee to allow the gentle rain of your goodness to quench the desert of Marie's sadness, that flowers may grow where once only existed the parched earth of her marriage to me. May I learn to have only joyful words that please her ..."

I raise an eyebrow. I don't want a sweet façade from him, just respect.

"...and also, if I might implore you, Lord, please teach us to speak from our truest selves. Amen." He squeezes my hands. "Your turn."

"God, thank you for Baker and I, allowing us to choose to be together ..."

"Yes, Lord, marriage is a choice, not a sentence, we thank thee ..."

"It's still my turn," I say. "And if you can hear our prayer, which I know you can because it's loudest in our hearts where you live, please help us learn to be respectful and loving in our words and our silences, our actions and our laughter, our sorrow and our dreams. Let only love be our guide. Amen."

"Amen. Now we hug to let the prayer take effect."

God, I love him.

We hold each other tight, allow the prayer to take effect. The warmth of our chests and the quiet thumps of our hearts seem extra real.

CHAPTER 31
AM I TOO OLD FOR THIS?

March, 2005. Two months later.

I sit in my chair one chilly morning with a nice cup of spice tea, after Baker's gone to work, and reflect on my life. It always feels luxurious to have solitude on the days I don't have to go to work until two o'clock.

Things have changed for the better with Baker and I. It's an odd feeling of peace that I'm having to get used to. When he has a slip and puts me down, I say, "I don't accept that," and that's the end of it. Our prayers helped, and still help whenever one of says let's pray. And spending two months in our separate rooms helped, too, I think. He's never spoken of it, but I think it affected him. The adrenaline in me from walking on eggshells is finally gone. Now, when Baker and I argue, there're no verbal knives. We even had a big fight over my wanting us to clean up the yard and him wanting me to not to push him. We just yelled our feelings and got stuck at an impasse. I despaired and looked over the cliff's edge of our relationship. "Maybe we're done," I said, angry, rigid, miserable.

"Maybe we are," he agreed.

It was shocking how painful it was to see how, just like that, we *could* end things, toss each other aside because of pride. There must be a way through, I thought.

Then I saw the smallest twinkle in his eyes.

We jumped into each other's arms and swore we'll never look over the cliff's edge again. I howled laughing while he did a monologue, playing us both, with our pride and stubbornness, standing at the top of a cliff. "You're done? No, I'm done." "No, I was done first." "I was done before I met you." "I was done before you were born." He makes me laugh every day. I swear he's the funniest man alive.

I get up, add more hot water to my cup of tea and sit back down.

We're both wound way too tight. It's a miracle we manage to get along. Having to split up into separate rooms was rough, but I'm glad we walked through that hell and separated. If we hadn't, I wouldn't have grown a deeper sense of self. I honored my feelings and didn't say I can't. I feel confident I won't be spineless again.

Except with Dad. How is that? At work, I've been given a larger office and promoted to family night counselor in addition to regular groups. I'm not afraid to hold clients accountable, or Baker, so why Dad?

Though I don't usually have to hold clients accountable. One client, an ICU nurse, thanked me for saving his marriage. He told me tearfully that what I do is triage on broken spirits. I was humbled. He and his wife did all the work. I just told them what I saw—two angels buried under the rubble of addiction. The group helped dig them out. But he insists I did something amazing. I did listen to them vent their terror and pain, did re-direct their rage to the disease, encouraged them in their woundedness to trust in love. I did help.

Yet, I'm spineless with Dad.

At least I love my work, at last. I do what I love and I honor my feelings, usually, the way the therapist said I needed to.

Well, now that things are settled at home, it's time to focus on my parents. Thankfully, Martin bought the house right across the street from Mom and Dad to be nearby to help out. Mom's been falling and Dad has a hard time getting her up now days. I'll call them and say I'll come up Saturday morning. Yeah, since Mom's been falling more, I'll stay the night, go home after Mass on Sunday, give Martin a break. It's not easy being around Dad, always on guard against his hands. It's the right thing to do, though. Still, I feel conflicted when I go there, giving comfort to the enemy, so to speak. Some family members are angry that Dad doesn't apologize, that he keeps acting out. I can't stay away. Mom'll turn ninety in a few weeks. Dad's eighty-eight. I can't help feeling he's a child. In fact, they both are. True, she didn't help us out when as teenagers we told her that he always touched us. But it doesn't matter. We all do shitty things. Who am I to judge Mom and Dad? Now they need help and I can't help loving them. What if people cut me out of their lives because of things I've done?

Sure, remorse would help, but what if Dad's literally incapable of remorse? I'll never give up trying to help him mend things with his family, feel remorse, express it.

I take a deep breath and call mom and Dad. "Hi, Dad. What are you doing?"

"Smoking my pipe in my office. We got home not too long ago, myself, Bridgette and Martin from a session with Dr Quinn."

Quinn is the Catholic counselor Dad reluctantly went to see a couple times last year after Dad touched our grown niece. Dad denied doing it, of course. All I can figure is his mom bathing him till he was twelve traumatized him so badly he gets stuck in an altered state and impulsively touches people.

"I don't know that the counseling's doing any good," he mildly complains, "but Martin and Bridgette seem to think it's a good idea, so, I'm willing to go. But I really don't see any point in going eighteen times."

He sounds like a child. "What made you decide to go after all, Dad?"

"Martin came to me a couple weeks ago and said he thought it was time we try seeing Quinn again."

Well done, Martin.

"I was surprised," Dad goes on, "because I thought Martin had buried the hatchet with a handshake and that the solution was for all the girls to only shake hands and not hug me, for everyone to express love with a word or a handshake."

"I see. That does sound like a good solution. But maybe there's more to be discovered. How did the session go?"

"Bridgette said she thought maybe I split into two personalities."

Good for you, Bridgette.

"Dr Quinn didn't seem to think much of that," Dad says.

"What did you think of it?"

"It was the first I'd heard of me possibly splitting. I don't know what to think of it."

I think it's exactly what happens.

"I don't see any point in going back to see him, don't know what more I can say. I already told all I know and I tell the truth, I don't lie. But Martin, well, I won't go into that, but I could tell some stories, but I won't. I think Martin has a vendetta. I think he'd like to see me dead or in jail."

"Well ..." Martin would like to see him heal or go to jail where he can't hurt anyone else. I don't want Dad in jail. Someone would kill him. "...I'm glad you're going to counseling, Dad. You know, years ago I asked my sobriety sponsor why I had to do all this hard work in recovery. She said, you have to go all the way down into the yuck to get to the bedrock and from there you can build a solid foundation." Dad needs to dig deeper, I think.

"Well, the girls have to go down there too! I'm not the only one!"

Wow. He sounds like an eight or six-year-old complaining to his mother. He's not in his right mind. Maybe he never has been. "I think the girls are already doing that, Dad. Well, I hope you keep going to counseling. Can't hurt. And thanks for telling me about it. I guess I'll talk to Mom, now."

"Sure." He chuckles, his usual self again. "I'll hobble off to get her," he says with a self-effacing laugh, sounding stung by the troubles of old age while being extra alive, all in one. "Good talking to you. Goodbye, honey."

"You too, Dad."

Eighty-eight, still able to laugh at himself. Not bad.

Mom gets on the phone and tells me about her hernia surgery she'll have in a month, bladder infection antibiotics, and she now has high blood pressure. Like Dad, she laughs. "Oh, life's indignities!" Almost ninety. "Honey, I'm glad you're coming up to see us Saturday!" She laughs again with a thrill in her voice, a child whirling on life's merry-go-round.

I feel bad about all the people Dad's hurt. But I miss Mom and Dad. I'm not their judge, and they're my parents.

I hang up the phone. My bravado wears off. I love them. That's all that matters.

From day to day, I'm all over the emotional map. By Saturday, driving up to see them, I'm resistant, angry at them both. I've been reading about cognitive dissonance, a double bind, damned if I love them, damned if I don't. So, I'm trying out something I hear at sobriety meetings—wear the world like a loose garment, let it flap in the wind around me. It helps.

When I arrive, Jean, who's staying across the street with Martin, comes out, eyes twinkling. "She wants to go to Penney's." Jean adds a knowing nod.

We laugh, because Mom's outings to Penney's are epic undertakings these days with her having become very slow and unsteady. But raising ten kids, she never shopped for herself. I'm glad she's making up for it now.

Jean briefs me on the hectic day with Mom and Dad so far with confusions over coupons, credit cards, car rental reservations for when Mom and Dad are in Seattle next week. In Jean's patient loving eyes, I'm the fire department to the rescue. Jean tells me how Martin took Mom and Dad shopping for canes yesterday. Mom had refused until our brother Christopher who's an RN told her on the phone a broken hip could mean never coming home from a nursing home.

Mama has her purse on her shoulder but pulls me up short for thinking she's ready to go. "No, it'll be about 5 minutes."

She marches through her preparations for the next forty-five minutes. She's a general commanding her forces—me. I'm happy to fall in with her, knowing she won't be doing much more commanding in her life. I've been impatient with Mom in my life, been clingy, irritated. Today I enjoy being with her and Dad, who's slowly going around on spindly legs getting ready to go to the bank.

"Marie! Find my yellow jacket, will you please?" Mom calls.

"Sure, Mom."

As I look in the closet, I reflect fondly on another time she wrangled me to do her bidding. It was 1964, when I was a high school freshman. She pulled all us kids out of school and put us in a Civil Rights march on State Street. I was livid that she had coerced me to be in public view, where I felt everyone could see my dad had been touching me. When I objected to going, Mom had said to me the organizers were afraid there might be violence, and the presence of children could be a deterrent, and did I want my little sisters and brother to march alone? The old blackmail routine. In the end we marched in the heat in our wool school uniforms. There was no time to change into other clothes. A hundred people spread themselves out over three blocks to make it look like more marchers. Black people wore nice dresses and hats, suits and ties. Long-haired hippies wore flowy tie-dyed and neutral clothes. White and gray-haired senior citizens wore T-shirts with slogans, comfortable pants with elastic waists, and thick-soled sandals. We, the only children, wore our wool uniforms. I marched, mortified, until I saw the main speaker hurry by, a young Black man in a suit, carrying a poster showing a photo of a Black man hanging from a tree. Suddenly I choked up, wept, and was no longer the center of attention in my thoughts. I knew about lynchings, but the young man carrying the poster brought the truth home to me. Someday, it could be him, I thought. I was humbled, felt proud of everyone in the march, including Mom.

"Marie!" She calls from the hall by her bathroom.

Dad's in the hall blocking my view.

"Yes?" I call, looking around him to make eye contact with her.

"Come!" She commands with just a note of impatience. Light-footed as a gazelle and full of love, I avoid Dad. I zip into the kitchen, out the other door, through the living room and arrive to be met by tweezers held up to my face by her hand.

I forgot the routine of plucking her chin hairs whenever I go to see her.

"Did you find the jacket?" she asks, jutting her chin.

"No. It must be in your room."

She's sharper than before in many ways these days. Perhaps because her eyesight is so miserably poor, she has to be on her toes. She's little, embarrassed to have gotten so short. Her body moves a bit rigidly in starts and stops. I don't know what to expect next. It's as though while her specific powers diminish, her life force grows stronger. I'm in awe. Now and then she tries self-pity, but it quickly disappears with her steady astonishment and mirthful embarrassment at both life's degradations and her helplessness to do anything but accept each one. She's such a good role model.

"Good-bye!" Dad calls.

"Bye Dear!" Mom calls.

"Bye Dad!" I nervously listen to him drive away, wondering should he be driving?

As always, Mom carefully does her makeup, puts on a nice jacket, the bright yellow one today. We found it in her room. She tosses her head back just before we leave, as if to toss off a sudden despair of being good enough to go out in public, and buoys herself with a classy air by raising drawn eyebrows and puckering her colored lips. With this rally of emotion, we get out the door.

Now she resumes her private amusement.

"What are you smiling about, Mom?" I ask on the way to the car.

Her eyes brim with mirthful tears. "It's ludicrous! I'm eighty-nine!" She shakes her head as though that says it all. "With failing vision, unpredictable memory, shrinking stature and loss of strength and balance. And all that goes with all of that and with the world!" She laughs.

At least her frailties amuse her no end.

By the time Mom and I pull out of the driveway, Dad drives in, back from the bank. I hesitate to acknowledge him, as we're on our way at last.

"Honk the horn or something," she says.

I stop, put the window down and call out, "Bye Dad."

He comes over, puts out his hand which I hold while he and Mom exchange encouraging words.

"I see you made it!" she exclaims with delight.

"And you look ready to go down town! All but the white gloves," he says.

She waves him off with a grin.

Somehow, it's not a yucky feeling, holding his hand. It's a good feeling. What's happening in me?

They say good-bye. As he walks away, he pauses and calls back to her, "Do you have cash and credit cards?" It means everything to him to provide for her.

"Yes!" she gaily sings.

They're happy.

How do human beings do it? Trudge through decades of hell, and come out singing?

We overshoot Penney's. I know better than to suggest Robinson's right before us. She wants two shirts, two nightgowns, and four pairs of underpants, and only Penney's can handle her order.

We go back, park, and slowly walk across Penney's parking lot.

"Your cane's nice-looking," I say. It'd be better if it touched the ground. It's a touchy subject.

"Thank you. Martin bought them for us."

She and Dad are one unit. What will he do if she dies?

A chill comes with my next thought: what will we do with Dad if she dies? Please don't let that happen, God. I love him but I can't live with him. I'd never sleep. Please don't let Mom go first.

We'll cross that bridge if we come to it, as Mom always says. He may go first. That would be a relief. Sorry, Dad.

In the store, she shops like a hawk, sees what she likes, deliberates over size, remarks on quality of product and brand.

In the dressing room area, waiting outside her stall, I hear to my dismay her sudden gasp in horror as she's wont to do.

"Is my cane out there!?" she cries. She starts out of the stall.

"You stay Mom. I'll go get it."

I hurriedly look, worrying something could happen to her while I'm gone. I realize with some effort she's not a child, she's safe without me. The cane is by the underpants.

The first shirt she wants to try is a nice V-neck. She's clear that the large size she'll try should be the pink. The medium should be the blue, because she thinks the medium will fit, and she doesn't like the pink.

"Marie!" comes her urgent command from inside the dressing room stall.

"Yes, Mom."

"Come in here."

She turns to me, wearing the medium blue, a darling sporty shirt with 3/4 length sleeves and a white panel at the V-neck. She tilts her head to her left and with sad eyes and a despairing tone that breaks my heart asks, "Am I too old for this?"

"Oh no, Mama, that's a darling shirt and you are not too old at all. No. Not at all. It's a rare thing to find a shirt so becoming as this one is." Truly.

As she checks the mirror, I check myself in the mirror. I'm wearing cute fitted low rider bell bottom jeans that teenage girls wear and I'm 54. "If I'm not too old for these jeans Mom, you're not too old for that shirt."

She chuckles, remarks on the quality of the brand, and decides to buy the shirt.

I know I'm losing her and I can't bear it. I fought with her when I was a cynical bitter teenager telling her she was wasting her time organizing demonstrations to protest the Vietnam War. Exasperated with me she said one night in tears, *"Yes, but we've got to try!"*

She never gave up. Life seems so unfair. We're given an allotment of time to do what we must and then time's up, with no consideration for the fact that we love each other, we've grown to love each other more, and now you're separating us, God.

At the checkout counter she holds her credit card signature on the receipt up to me. "Can you read that?"

"Yes, it's clear."

"I do it from memory," she says with a note of pride.

I feel pure joy being with her now.

After our successful mission at Penney's, I suggest I help her make meatloaf for dinner and we ride happily towards Spencer's grocery store. I prize the moments in the car with her. Most of our lives we've been apart. I left home at eighteen. I'm fifty-five.

Suddenly she says with alarm, "I don't feel myself!"

"How so, Mom?"

"I'm not like I was. I was always busy with something."

"That's right." Usually, when I called, she didn't have time to talk.

"Always had something in the works. It's different not being able to see. I know they've got gadgets, all kinds of things to help people see."

"Are you ready to check them out?"

"Not yet. Maybe soon."

She no longer has the activities that made her feel life was meaningful. I feel for her and worry what that'll be like for me when I'm in her shoes. I calm myself thinking it through: if I go blind and can't write or even paint, I'll play harmonica; if I can't do that, I'll make up poems and sing old blues songs. I feel better.

We pause at the produce counters, where she cautions me to get only two tomatoes because you can't tell how good they are by their looks. Then we slowly head toward the meat. She chuckles, leaving me wondering, then says a little smugly, "I don't have to *put* the cane down, it just goes by itself."

I look to see her flick her cane off the ground with a little flick of her wrist, a Fred Astaire flare, smiling into space, lost in her thoughts. I'll never let her go.

She chooses the meat, pricing carefully, feeling in her discerning palm the weights of a few packages.

"What else should go into the meatloaf?" I ask.

"Sausage," she says, a little incredulous I hadn't known that.

But I've only rarely seen her put sausage in.

"And cereal," I say, recalling as a child pouring lots of Rice Krispies over the ground beef at her direction.

"No, no. You don't put cereal in. No. Maybe some onion. An egg, or two eggs, depending on how much meat you use."

This is sacrilege. My entire life I've made meatloaf with Rice Krispies because she made it that way when I was a child. It must have been an economy measure she no longer needs to take.

At the checkout, she asks me on the sly which way her credit card would need to be held for swiping. I show her. She holds it in the ready while the cashier rings her up. I'm proud of Mom, eighty-nine, utterly determined to pull it off. Sadly, the busy clerk ends up swiping the card for her when Mom swipes it too slowly.

We drive toward home.

She watches out her window. "Your father likes to shop bargains, whereas I like to shop Spencer's, because it's small. I've done my share of bargain shopping. I told him, 'I did that for years. Watch every penny. Going to five stores each week because different ones had better prices for different things. I'm not going to do that anymore. I don't have to.'"

"Wow. Good for you, Mom. I remember as a child going to five different stores with you with lists and coupons. No, you don't have to, anymore." How grand to see her be her own person with Dad.

At home she fetches an open bottle of ketchup from a cupboard. "Use this."

"This should probably be refrigerated," I say.

"Oh?"

"Let's see—yep. And it's a year out of date," I say.

"Oh?"

You can't make meatloaf without ketchup.

"Taste it," she says.

My self-preservation caves before her dewy gaze. "Okay," I say, hoping a special protection applies for obeying my mother. I taste it. "I think it's okay."

"Use it. We'll be fine."

Don't argue with her. Taking charge of her own kitchen means a lot. Ketchup's preserved with salt and sugar.

Next, out comes some honey mustard from the same cupboard, by the looks of it a year or two older than the ketchup.

"Why don't you put some of this in too," she says, more as an order than a request.

Once the meatloaf is cooking, Mom lies down in their room while Dad shuts his eyes in his chair, and I trot over to Martin's. Jean greets me. She's moving to the desert soon. Though I'll have my hands full with Mom and Dad, work and Baker, I'll miss Jean.

She gives me some potatoes, because Mom and Dad are out. She gives me a stunning photograph she took, as a birthday present, a desert sunset.

"I printed it from a slide that fell in the street in the rain. It's a long story. The print needed to be scanned and carefully printed to remedy its injuries from the fall," Jean says.

"Wow. It's amazing!" I stare at pink, purple, red and orange light on rock formations. "It's beautiful, Jean. Thanks so much. I'll miss you!"

Later that night at Mom and Dad's, after dinner, we all turn in.

I startle awake several times, with a feeling Dad will come in and touch me. It's strange, because I didn't lose sleep as a teenager. Probably because I had repressed the memory of him coming in when I was twelve. Who knows?

The following morning, I wake to a quiet house. Fortunately, it was a quiet night. Did they die?

I check. No.

I love padding through the carpeted halls getting Mom ready for Mass.

In the car on the way to church, I nervously watch the road from the back seat, because Dad guns it from every stop light. Is he really capable of driving safely this fast? Is it bravado because he can't let Mom down, when he knows he really shouldn't be driving? When he walks, he totters on spindly legs. He'll be eighty-nine in October. It's good Mom doesn't drive anymore. She can't see well enough. I need to check with Dad, see if he feels okay driving.

"So, Dad, do you still like driving?"

"Oh, I wouldn't say that I like it, necessarily."

"But you feel okay about it?"

"I suppose I'm not as sharp as I once was. We are getting older, aren't we, Evelyn?" he says with a chuckle.

Mom laughs. "That we are, honey. That's why it's good we've got *two* pairs of eyes," she assures me over her shoulder.

I chuckle inside, sit back and stay in the relaxed for a crash position the rest of the drive.

CHAPTER 32
A FIERCE INFANT

September, 2005. Six months later.

At home, I stand folding laundry, visiting with Baker.

"Mom's more unsteady. She won't use a wheelchair. Christopher said he'll put handrails everywhere," I tell Baker.

I glance out the window. Night's fallen. Melancholy moves into me with its own little bed, table and chair. It happens again—the frantic and crazy feeling that I'm right here but Mom's looking for me and can't find me, she can't hear me scream for her. "I miss my mom." That's an understatement. I lose my strength to stand, even to sit, and roll over onto my side on the couch, trembling, clutching my sides, sobbing, missing her.

Baker comes over, sits beside me, strokes my hair.

"I don't know why this still happens. I know I was farmed out as a one-year-old," I sob. "I'm sorry."

"Never apologize for tears, dear," he says tenderly.

We may disagree about order in the house and the yard, but he deeply understands trauma.

"Someday you may fully heal. Meanwhile, trust that you need the process of feeling these feelings. You had little rubber legs. Wouldn't eat. You were traumatized as a one-year-old when your mom was gone for six weeks and you got handed off to strangers."

"But it's been over a year since I've had one of these spells. I thought I was healed by nurturing my inner child all these years. And connecting with Mom more and more, now that she's more emotionally present because of her dementia."

"Your mom is getting ready to check out. That would be the most obvious explanation for you're missing her."

I nod. "It would. And I have no conscious concerns about her dying. That's a hint. I'm repressing my feelings about losing her."

"So don't worry about these tears."

The next day I call Madeline, the second oldest, who remembers a lot about our childhood home. "Madeline, do you remember when Mom gave birth to Jean, what life was like at home? I'm asking because I have these crying bouts where it feels like Mom's looking for me and can't find me. She said I was probably farmed out to relatives for a while."

"Oh, I'd say almost for sure you were. There was no way Dad could have taken care of little ones. Let's see. You were one year old. Martin wasn't quite two and a half. Cecilia was still three. Mama almost died. I don't remember a lot. I was six years old. You might not have gotten the attention you needed, even after Mama came home from the hospital," Madeline says with a laugh. "Which is putting it mildly. You may need to do some healing with Mama."

The idea makes me nervous. But what if she's right? "Thanks, Madeline. I'll give that some thought."

We visit and say good-bye. I think about what Madeline said. When I couldn't picture Baker all day because of an object constancy glitch, I took his T-shirt to work for a month the way a baby carries a blanket. It worked. Soon I could picture him during the day, and not panic on the way home. So, there must be something to cure this feeling of being insecure with Mom that comes from her leaving me. Why not? I once read the unconscious is very obliging. The amygdala is part of that. If you can find a way to get through to it, it will sign on for whatever you say. Only, you have to do it with emotion, I found. The amygdala doesn't communicate directly with the logical, calm, front brain, but with the emotional language brain. I'm sure that's why at work, when I instinctively claimed with emotion the hall, the floor, the walls, the job, I never had a fear of getting fired again. My amygdala bought it.

So, I know the power of the right implement to move a boulder out of the way in my unconscious. But what is the right one to establish some missing connection with Mom? What do infants do to get secure?

Gaze into their parents' eyes.

I look at a photograph of Mom and emotionally stare at Mom's eyes. I get sad and scared she doesn't exist. That's so weird.

What if I visit her and lay my head in her lap?

Way too embarrassing.

It's what infants do.

I could never ask her.

It may be the only way.

I've never laid my head in her lap in my life. I could never do it.

Even if it could fix the glitch in my brain?

For weeks I battle the embarrassment of even thinking of asking Mom if

I could put my head in her lap and look into her eyes. Meanwhile, a deeper, quieter self knows it's what I'm going to do. Never mind my frantic pride.

I call her on the phone. "I have a crazy request, Mom. It's nothing bad."

"All right." She sounds nervous.

"I have a strange panic that comes over me sometimes, where it feels as though you're looking for me but can't find me, even though I'm screaming for you. And, I was thinking, if I could lay my head in your lap, look into your eyes, I might be able to make the connection I'm missing in those glitches."

"Well, sure," Mom says.

What a relief. I don't care how embarrassing it is. I'm going to do it.

A few days later, I head north to Mom and Dad's. It's a crazy idea to put my head in her lap. But I'm going to do it. I come upon a slow-moving van. Damn. Stripes. Hand-painted colorful stripes cover the back doors of the van. Dread fills me. I can't look away and there's no passing lane. It's okay. Watch the road. Don't look up.

Finally, a passing lane comes. I go around the van. What a relief.

I arrive at Mom and Dad's, let myself in.

"Hi, Mom," I say in the kitchen.

"Oh, hello there."

She looks nervous, but friendly.

"Where did you want to do this?" she asks. "Your father's in his office."

"Oh, good. Well, let's go in the spare bedroom."

"Sure."

We go into the spare bedroom and close the door.

"Tell me again," she says, "what are we doing?"

I'm mortified.

Don't give up because of shame.

"I'll just lay my head in your lap, Mom, look into your eyes." It feels too intimate, but I have to try.

"All right." She sits on the side of the bed.

I go ahead without thinking so I won't back out, like jumping into the cold ocean. I get up on the bed and awkwardly curl up with my head on her lap. I look up into her eyes.

She looks into mine.

I check to see if I feel something. Not really.

She strokes my forehead with her thumb, smiling, and suddenly I'm tethered to her by a timeless, invisible, warm, liquid magnet. It reaches from her, throughout me, and holds us together.

"I'm glad you asked me to do this," she says, smiling at me.

I'm mute, in bliss, for several seconds.

The phone shatters the quiet.

We ignore it.

In a minute, Dad bursts in and says, with his usual general irritation, "Some guy named Ralph's on the phone for you, Mama."

Frustration rips through me. A fierce infant, I raise my head, glare at him for his intrusion, part of me thunder-struck by the fearlessness of this mute, pint-size self I haven't seen in over fifty years, who now *glares* at the lion who could roar.

Mom sighs with a worried look. "Sorry, honey," she tells me, "I'd better take this call. Ralph's been waiting a while for me to get back to him."

Dad leaves.

"Okay," I say, dazed, disappointed, but glad we did it. I felt connected to Mom in a way I never have. Who knows? It may have worked. And I'm grateful to have met my inner warrior self. She's a brave little thing.

I sit up. Something dawns on me. This is what had *always* happened. Mom didn't *leave* me. Someone, or something, always took her away. I feel compassion for her. It's not all about me. Like everyone, she does the best she can.

I'm getting closer to her. What will I do when she goes?

That night I have a nightmare. I'm a baby in a crib furiously bashing my head against the crib bars, over and over and over. I awake, stunned. I sit up and reflect in the dark. Why was I cracking my head on the crib bars?

I know why. Our family let the baby cry, sometimes for hours in the crib, upstairs, way in the back of the house, away from the rest of the family. I couldn't bear it. I cracked my head on the bars.

I understand something else. The crib bars are stripes. I recall the van with stripes, my little blue dog with stripes, the lampshade with stripes that I had to step on and hide in the trash. I finally know why stripes scare me.

CHAPTER 33
LET'S STAY A MINUTE

January, 2007. One year and four months later.

At work, I set aside a file, look out my office window down to the mostly empty parking lot. I look past the brown field of winter stubble and trash, and up to the white clouds slowly blowing by. I've worked here five years. I'm so grateful I finally became a counselor, after all my years of minimum wage jobs, then working as a law librarian, then making puppets and handbags, and finally trying childcare. I'm fortunate. I've landed where I belong, at last. And though my spells of missing Mom still come, probably because it seems she's not going to be with us much longer—she's losing ground—the spells have lost their frantic quality. Laying my head in Mom's lap had a profound effect on me. Who would have thought? Her dying is no longer unthinkable to me.

My phone rings. It's Bridgette's voice. Bridgette moved in with Mom and Dad last year to help out, which gives us all peace of mind. It's unusual for her to call me at work. Adrenaline surges.

"I'm sorry to call you at work," Bridgette says, "but I thought I should tell you. Her dementia's getting worse. The doctor says she's been having more of those tiny seizures, T.I.A.'s I think they call them."

"They're coming so fast."

"She's worried, seeing cats everywhere. They only have one cat, Lily. So, Cecilia, Christopher, Martin and Jean are all looking into her medications and talking to her doctor. Jean said hallucinations are a side effect of the dementia medication. Can you believe they'd give her that? Just thought I should let you know. She's slipping, changing really fast." Bridgette sounds sadly resigned.

"Thanks for letting me know." Thank goodness I have sisters and brothers helping out. "Poor Mom. I'm glad they're checking her meds. Thanks, Bridgette. I'll come and spend the night Sunday so you can have a night off." I don't have to be at work until two on Monday.

"Thanks," she says.

We say good-bye.

Sunday, I sit with Mom at the table in her sunny yellow kitchen.

"You know, Jean's made some real friends in Yucca Valley," Mom says. "Well, she's capable of the kind of friendship where, you're rowing your own boat and you're permitted to row your own boat, but they're rowing along with you."

Mom sounds about the same as she's been. "I see what you're saying, Mom." They stopped a medication. Maybe that was giving her hallucinations.

"Yah. You're going along and not expecting the world from it."

"Not expecting the world. What a good insight. Thanks, Mom." I reflect on my relationship with Baker, which is wonderful a lot of the time, but other times, he's aloof. Maybe I'm expecting the world. "I guess that applies to marriage too."

"Yah. And I better get rowing my boat or I won't have a marriage!" She laughs. "I've had plenty of time to get ready for church," she says and with a good effort stands up.

I want to be like her when I'm old—a lively, passionate person who's a part of life, not some subdued, cautious onlooker.

At church, Dad's strong arm takes mine and guides me into a pew. I'm on high alert for his other hand, which doesn't get me, this time. Still, he's so controlling. Why?

After we all return from church, I go into the kitchen while Mom hangs up her yellow jacket in the hall closet. I notice bits of brownie in Lily the cat's food bowl, toss them, and give her some cat food.

Mom comes in, puts on an apron. I fry sausage and eggs. Mom makes toast.

"One time," she says in a confederate tone. She pauses to shake her head. "I thought I had lost the last house key. I thought the church might have it."

"Why would the church have it, Mom?"

"Oh, you'd be surprised what the church has. Anyway, I called the church. The gal said, yeah, they had quite a few. Well, *he* had one in his pocket." She glances in the direction of the living room where Dad sits in his chair. "While he was asleep, I took it out of his pocket and drove to the church."

Took it while he was asleep?

"Sure enough, it matched. I think they had two of our house keys. Brother! I was glad to get back home!" Mom rolls her eyes and shakes her head reliving the relief.

"That's funny, Mom."

"Not at the time!" she says. "I paid with worry." She takes a deep breath. "I got back and got the key back in his pocket before he woke up."

"You were brave. You took the key from his pants while he slept?"

"Oh, he wasn't wearing the pants."

"Oh! Good."

She sighs. "I think that's the worst I've done. If you *ever* get in that kind of bind, better to wait till they're asleep." She gives me a twinkling look with a knowing nod.

It's my turn to confide. "I've done something similar in my marriage—shopping. Wait till he's not around before bringing it in, whatever it is. Then, a few days later, tell him."

"Yah!" she says, eyes wide and dancing. She lowers her voice. "Like it's a *casual* thing."

We laugh. She's funnier, freer, more emotionally connected to me it seems than she's ever been. As painful as it is to watch her decline, I feel so lucky to have these days with her. She could go anytime.

Now if I could only figure out a way to get Dad to look at what he does and to reconcile with his kids. Maybe if Mom passes on first, Dad'll be more motivated to make an effort. He'll be more alone, because family come around to help Mom, not him.

I watch Mom dab large globs of butter on the toast and call it good. She is slipping. If I want to ask her about anything, I'd better do it soon.

"Mom, I know Great Grandma came over from Ireland as a girl, got married, and when her daughter, your mother, Grandma, was twelve, Great Grandma committed suicide in an asylum."

"Yah. That's right. It was hard on my mother. She had to help raise her stepmother's children. So, after that, your Grandma believed children shouldn't do work."

"You never did any housework?"

"Mama didn't believe in it. Your father," she goes on, "had to take Grandma the news."

"News that you were pregnant."

I've heard this story before. Grandma didn't believe in having a lot of kids in those days. She had fallen away from the church's teachings that you need to have all the children God blesses you with.

"Yah."

"After the first three," I say.

"That's right."

"Because Grandma didn't approve of you having more than three children."

"That's right."

"That must have been so hard, Mom."

"Yah. I would have liked a relationship with my mother."

"Sorry, Mom."

"Well, I survived."

"So, Grandma's mom killed herself. What about Granma's dad, what was he like?"

"Oh! He was a lady's man! A gambler. Mama always knew what kind of day her father had had by his watch. She was a typist and he'd come by to get her for lunch."

"What did his watch tell her?"

"If he wore it, he hadn't pawned it." She laughs. "She wouldn't have to give him money. She dreaded when he'd call her up to have lunch."

Sweet Grandma, tiny white-haired-with-a-pink-scalp woman who welcomed all ten of us kids once a month on Sunday night, made us burgers with pickled onions, and the best sugar cookies I've ever had. I had no idea her dad was a gambling womanizer.

Poor *Great* Grandma, probably driven mad by her gambling womanizer husband. Is that why she killed herself, if she really did? Some people in asylum's were murdered. Maybe he *put* her in the asylum. Doubt he was together enough to do that. "Did Great Grampa work?"

"Some. You know he made the curtains for the Orpheum Theatre in Seattle."

Theatre curtains. "You're kidding. I remember the Orpheum Theatre in Seattle. That's a huge, beautiful theatre."

"It's gone now. They tore it down to make a hotel."

"That's so sad. So Great Grampa made theatre curtains?"

"Yah. Quite an undertaking."

"I got obsessed with making red theatre curtains. I was bored to tears as a law librarian. Maybe Great Grampa was haunting me!"

"Could be," she says absently, buttering away.

"I ended up making red velvet curtains for a puppet theatre, since I didn't have a real theatre."

Mom smiles and shakes her head, her greasy fingers glistening as she butters the other side of the toast.

Don't embarrass her. We all love butter.

I'm glad I asked Mom about Great Grampa. Mom feeds brownies to the cat, butters toast on both sides, but she's sharp telling old stories. I would never have known Great Grampa made the Orpheum curtains and was a gambler and womanizer. Those are pieces of my own puzzle. It all trickles down.

I sit down with Mom and Dad to eat in the dining room.

Mom gets a big smile as she looks out the window. "Marie," she says, pointing at the window which has a view of their orange tree and roses. "The view out that window, is *exactly* the same view I have from my window at home."

Oh dear. "Mom, that is your window. This is your home."

"Yah," she says dismissively.

"Which is why," I slowly explain, "the view is the same as yours. It is your view, your window."

"Yah, yah. I know. But the view out *that* window, is *exactly* the same as the view out my window at home."

What's made her confused? I look around.

The hand rails. She's used to seeing hand rails in care facilities where she volunteered as an ombudsman for thirty years. Christopher did a beautiful job installing them.

"Now, whose bathroom is that one?" She points to the bathroom by the front hall.

She thinks she's in a nursing home. "It's your bathroom, Mom. Christopher put hand rails around your house. This is your house."

"I know. But *whose* bathroom is it?"

She's stuck. "Mom, it's a bathroom anyone can use."

"Oh?"

"Yes. You could use it. I could, or Dad."

"But whose is it?"

"I'm pretty sure it's the public bathroom for anyone."

When they have to move to get more care for Mom, Dad will probably have to be persuaded, but Mom won't know the difference.

After I help Mom into her nightgown at nine o'clock that night, she walks around finding things to do. I'm exhausted from being on alert all day. I go into the spare room. It has a baby monitor, so whoever's staying over can be sure Mom and Dad are okay in the night. Dad already put his own pajamas on. He's in his bathroom listening to his radio. I put my pajamas on and flop onto the bed, nervous, knowing Mom's up, wandering around. Thank goodness, she's never wandered outside. I don't know where they get their stamina.

Their voices come from the hallway in unusually sharp, loud angry tones. Usually, it's just Dad raising his voice over some irritation. This is both of them. I listen to see if they settle it.

I can't tell what they're arguing about, but it's escalating. I get up to go check on them.

"Well, I want a divorce!" Mom roars at him through the open bathroom door.

Bravo, Mom. I can't wait to write about this. At last, she's standing up to him. I can't help smiling. Her little angel-like figure in her light blue nightgown with her thin, short white hair doesn't look capable of that anger.

"Well, I don't know why you want to divorce me." Dad sounds like a child unfairly accused.

"Mom," I say. "Is everything okay?"

She brightens up when she sees me, reaches out to me as her confederate, takes my arm. I walk her to their room. "These men!" she says, and laughs.

"Did he say something that made you mad?"

"He doesn't know what he's talking about," she grumbles good-naturedly as she climbs into bed.

If he was verbally abusing her, it seems she can take care of herself now.

I cover her up like a child.

In the night, I hear Dad over the monitor. "Evelyn! Stop kicking me!"

I don't want to go in there. I hope they can settle it.

A week later, Cecilia calls me. "Mom fell again. She used to be able to help a little when Martin and Dad got her up. Not this time. They need more help. So, I think it's time for them to move. I've called a few places."

"Can they afford it?"

"For a short time. Then we'll have to sell the house. The Lexington has a small apartment in memory care, so Mom and Dad could both live there, and there are aides trained to help."

I don't feel sad. I feel relieved.

"We need to tell Dad," she says.

Two days later, Cecilia and I sit with Dad in the living room while Mom sleeps. I'm nervous about how he'll react to hearing we think it's time for them to move.

"Dad, I know these past few years have been hard for you," Cecilia says. "We think you and Mom need more help." She tells him about the Lexington and the costs. "It's in Ventura. You'll be closer to some of your children. What do you think, Dad?"

"Whatever you think's best," he says without hesitation.

Cecilia and I look at each other, surprised by his willingness to let go of control.

A week later, Dad, Cecilia, a few other brothers and sisters and I sit in the Lexington lobby. Mom's at home with Bridgette. Dad looks calm. We're still in shock at how easy this is. I thought he'd fight it.

The Lexington host passes around a platter of big warm chocolate chip cookies that make everything all right.

Soon we're all looking at a small one-bedroom unit with no kitchen. It's in the locked memory care section.

"What do you think, Dad?" Cecilia asks. "You can have your own chairs here, your own TV. And helpers are here twenty-four hours a day, in case Mom falls."

He shrugs. "If you think it's best."

He knows Mom needs the care. He doesn't say much. These last few years have been rough on him.

On moving day, Mom looks so pretty in her blue V-neck blouse, blue capris, and yellow jacket. Martin, wearing a nice long sleeve blue plaid shirt, takes her arm in the front hall, walks her out to the porch. She takes hold of the railing. Martin moves forward, but Mom doesn't. She holds the railing tightly.

She knows. I wish I could spare her this fear and pain. She must think we're giving her away to strangers.

We are.

"You want to stay, Mom," Martin says.

"Yah," she says.

"Let's stay a minute," he says.

He's so wise.

"Yah."

She knows she's leaving home. Martin stands still beside her in the sunshine. A breeze lifts Mom's white hair. She takes a shaky step forward.

CHAPTER 34
IT WAS NEVER ABOUT ME

February, 2007. One month later.

At work, Cecilia calls. "The Lexington called. They said they may need to move Mom to a skilled nursing bed in their facility, since she can't help with transferring anymore."

You can't go yet, Mom. I'm not ready. "I thought that might be coming. She can't walk anymore. Though she was chatting up the male aides last week."

"She's probably still doing that!"

We laugh. Mom's a new person with this dementia.

"She's going downhill quickly," I say. "How soon do they want to move her?"

"By the end of the week. Which is good, because we leave for our Cayucos trip the same day."

"Right. Okay."

My brothers and sisters—no spouses or kids, only the siblings—have been going for a week to Cayucos, a small coastal town, in February since 1983. So, it's been a relief to have Mom and Dad settled at the Lexington.

"What about Dad?" I ask.

"He can stay."

"Shoot. He'll be isolated in the little apartment."

"I know. We'll have to figure that out. Just thought I should let you know."

"Thanks, Cecilia."

We hang up.

I look out my office window, admire the lush green grass that grew with this year's early rain. Things are going good for me, personally. I have work I love—counseling—all because I got the obsession to make red theatre curtains that helped me quit being a law librarian. Did Great Grampa, who made the Orpheum Theatre curtains, haunt me with that obsession to nudge me to search for the life I was meant for? I love that thought. His redemption for being a womanizer.

I recall writing the list of five things I love to do some years ago. Visit topped the list. Now, I get paid to visit. I smile at the irony. Just when my life's in order, Mom's is about to end.

I check the time on my "Daring and Beautiful Cow Girls" clock Cecilia gave me for my birthday years ago, when I was doing trail rides to mend a broken heart. I love the galloping cow girl who waves her hat, as her hair blows in the wind. She and the horse look wildly happy. Tears spill down my face at the thought of losing Mom. I have only fifteen minutes until I give the family night lecture. I need to finish preparing. But more than that, I need time with my feelings.

I get up, close my office door, shut out the world.

Back at my desk, I look out the window. A family drags up the stairs, a young man addicted to methamphetamine. His parents are with him. They hold their coats closed against the wind, appear exhausted, at the end of their rope.

Beyond the stairs, the field has grown tall green grasses that move like ocean waves in the wind. They reach all the way to the freeway, hiding a whole layer of garbage that blew into the field all winter. In Spring, nobody cares what's hidden in there.

That's about right, huh, Mom? The breathtaking green. The garbage unseen.

Mom never wanted the trashy side of life to touch her family, so she pretended it didn't. I couldn't blame her for that. I was afraid to push her away. It felt my life depended on her.

I'm not ready to let her go. I've grieved my her my whole life. I don't know what I'll do when she dies.

I think life will be easier when she's gone. It won't be so painful. It's hard watching her lose everything—her vision, reading, driving, memory, now her mind. I feel guilty for not seeing her and Dad more. I'm always feeling anxious, caught in the double-bind of loving them, and wanting to be free of the pain and insanity of loving them. It's hard.

You were always happy to see me, Mom, always up for an outing. More tears come.

My sisters and brothers and I are lucky. Mom could have gotten bitter losing most of her vision, but she got sweeter and funnier. And though I dreaded the slow painstaking steps of driving her to stores, I loved being sixteen again, getting my marching orders from Mom when we were in Spencer's Grocery store. God, I love slipping back in time.

We won't be shopping anymore.

My heart's glued to yours, Mom. You and I float just above that field which hides an entire winter, and we're rocking in the wind. Why do you hypnotize me? You were good at making things look like everyone was getting along, and

I held it against you. I'm sorry, because who knows? Maybe we would have all blown apart without your happy spin on things. And now you're getting ready to blow away. Who will keep your brood together?

The thought of being alone with Dad chills me.

You can't go before Dad, Mom.

She's been an emotional buffer. I've heard of daughters stepping up to look after their dad when their mom died. I won't be she.

Outside my office window, two young parents and their nineteen-year-old daughter, who is two weeks off heroin, climb the stairs. They're a reality check. I think I have problems? I don't know how these parents get through life one day to the next. Mom's almost ninety-two. It's her time, and Dad's difficult, but I'm tough. This youngster coming up the stairs is nineteen. If she dies it'll be a tragedy. And this is the most dangerous window of time. Her tolerance is down with two weeks clean, but her insight is down too, at only two weeks clean. If she impulsively relapses on her usual dose, it'll likely kill her.

The family members whom I counsel don't think they're strong. They have no idea.

I wish the *family* members could come three hours a day, three days a week, same as the patients do, for nurture and healing. They suffer post-traumatic stress disorder from loving someone who has addiction, never knowing day to day, year in and year out, if their loved one is going to live or die. And the parents feel they should have done better? I shake my head. These are precious souls coming up the stairs. They thank me for listening to their horrific stories, and they worry about me having to hear it all. I'm stunned by what I hear, and sometimes I get tears, but usually I don't, I'm a professional. I tell them it's an honor to hear their stories. I thank them for opening up, wonder if I have feelings because I don't fall apart. Tonight, I'm so emotional, the thought of their bravery opens the floodgates.

My fists wipe tears from my face.

Funny. I'm going to teach the patients and their families about Conflict Resolution, how to talk instead of fight, and next week, a lot of them are going to tell me how they tried the tools I taught and how well they worked. Yet they never would have worked with Mom and me. She didn't get it, how things hurt.

I would tell her something important, but it wouldn't go in, it would stick for a second, the way a ping pong ball with static electricity sticks to a sweater and then falls. She wouldn't relate. She changed the subject and talked about people I never heard of. I got so angry when she did that, but could never tell her.

"Who is that?" I had to ask, trying not to sound irritated.

Well of course I didn't know the people, they were from the newspaper.

I'm still mad at Mom.

It took me till my *forties* to get up the nerve to confide in her like a mom about the abortion I had at twenty-seven. I couldn't have used conflict resolution tools even if I had known them back then. Why *did* I tell her?

Magical thinking. I thought, she's my mom, you tell Mom important things. I wasn't thinking.

The faceless sorrow which came each Spring, I had finally connected with the abortion that very day I was at Mom and Dad's house ten years ago. Maybe the inner-child work Cecilia had encouraged me to do had shaved enough general shame away that I was thawing and hadn't noticed, because grief came up on a Sunday at Mom and Dad's house the way a frozen river breaks up in Spring. I finally knew what the grief was connected to, and I remember I got the crazy idea to tell Mom.

I shake my head. It was possibly the worst decision of my life. I'm angry all over again.

But what if she dies and I'm angry with her?

She and I sat outside in the shade of their patio, the dazzling sunlit bank of lantana near us. I told Mom how happy I had felt the day I found out I was pregnant, walking down the sunny street to cook for my elderly charge Etta May, and how I couldn't wait to get home and tell Isaac. And how Isaac had said he wouldn't stay if I had a baby. And how I had panicked at the prospect of being a single mom, having seen Jean's struggle as a single mom. How I was stunned when Isaac wouldn't change his mind. He held firm. He'd leave me if I had the baby.

If only I'd been stronger and had the baby.

I wanted Mom to say "Oh, that must have been hard." Anything like that would have been enough. But why would I think she would say that? I should have known she would brighten up about some article she had just read, which she did. It was an article in the TIMES.

"But where is it?" she mused as she plied through sections of last week's papers, excited for me to see the article.

Luckily, she couldn't remember where she had seen it, or I would have felt obliged to look at it.

"It was about a group in Los Angeles that was helping young mothers keep their babies. A wonderful article."

I was suddenly sick. The disconnect from Mom had never been so clear. How could she think her article would console me? I said I didn't feel well and needed to leave.

I haven't thought of that day for years.

Shoot! Six o'clock! Time to start the lecture. Go.

I grab the stack of handouts and the lecture notes, which I don't use anymore. I've given this particular lecture, one of ten different topics, every ten weeks for seven years.

Hurry. I blank my mind. The soft silence in the long, carpeted hall puts a calming hand on my head.

I turn into the room, smile at a sea of thirty familiar faces, set my things on the small table beside the big white board. I smile at the parents and the young heroin addict. "Hi John. Hi Elizabeth. Hi Brianne."

"Hello," John says. Elizabeth nods. Brianne nods. They all smile, hope for a miracle. They could get one, because the parents are trying new language when they talk with Brianne, bringing the conflict down, shifting to her shoulders her decisions.

David, a stout burly client, scowls at me as he has all week, head tucked into his collar. His presence is electric. He probably won't speak to me for another week or two. I told him his resentment against his mother, for testifying against him for domestic violence, will take him back to using drugs. He was so angry when he first got here, none of the other counselors dared tell him that. He can sulk. I know he's mulling it over, because he's basically honest and knows I'm right. God's darning a hole in his heart. I told him he could let go of his resentment by praying for his mother's happiness. He turned red and raged, saying I was crazy and didn't know what I was talking about. I think he wanted to toss me through the window. I was pretty scared. He's been quiet since.

How come I couldn't tell Mom the truth, when I could tell scary David the truth?

People are tired, hungry, full, anxious, hurting. Some are relieved, even content. They're in recovery, not fighting it.

"Welcome to Family Night," I say with a nod. "I'm Marie, one of the counselors." I don't say I'm the Senior Counselor. It sounds pompous.

I look into their eyes. My eyes heat up and brim. "Each of you is a powerful, precious, courageous child of God, a survivor of the cruel lash of addiction, family members and addicts alike."

Hearing this, almost everyone's eyes redden. It's the truth.

"It's such an honor to get to work with you." I choke up.

I can't give the lecture if I'm crying, Mom. You've cracked my heart wide open tonight. You taught me how to love people. How can I be mad at you?

You're a precious survivor of the cruel lash of life. Ridiculed as a child by your priest who called you a fat pig. Ridiculed by Dad for seventy years. And I wonder why you lived in the newspapers? Who am I to judge you?

I take a deep breath and let out a big sigh. Mom did the best she could.

"We're going to talk about Conflict Resolution. And the first conflict I want to address is the one within ourselves. Negative self-talk is a habit we need to break. It demoralizes us. So, a good rule of thumb is, if you wouldn't say it to a four-year-old, don't say it to yourself. And when you slip, make amends to yourself. In three weeks, you can end negative self-talk."

A few people slowly nod. I'm glad.

"So, for families with addiction, it's *essential* to bring the conflict level down and understand we're all doing the best we can with what we've got at the time."

I saw it spelled out that way on a handout. It's brilliant. But it's hard for some to swallow. Their eyes show pain and power from what they've survived: her daughter over-dosed five times; Zach grew up in juvenile hall for home invasions; Jonas jumped through a plate glass window three stories up but got snagged and someone caught his ankles; she, and she and she and that guy were all raped; Danielle with dazzling eyes was gang raped; Mark found his dad dead; and Ray found his daughter blue and gave her CPR, she survived; and that youngster Tyler saw his two friends get shot dead. About half of the clients were beaten as a child, and more than half were molested. I'm asking a lot from them, but they'll listen, because conflict resolution tools are the truth.

"So. The first step in conflict resolution is to be able to ask yourself, 'Who am I to judge another?' I want you to try that on. We're human, we get mad, we judge, but when you remember to stop judging, that begins to take the power out of the fight, because it's true, we can't judge others, it's not our job. Let's say it out loud. 'Who am I to judge another?'"

They say it.

Who am I to judge you, Mom?

"Thank you. Now, the second step is deciding not to take things personally, because whatever another person does, it's never about you. It's about them. So, let's say that out loud. 'It's not about me.'"

It wasn't about me when Mom happily looked for the TIMES article to ease my abortion grief. It was about her.

"It's not about me," we all say.

I feel better. "Great. Now, what if my husband belittles me, which he rarely does anymore? Isn't that about me? Shouldn't I take that personally?"

I survey the crowd.

Everyone, even David, looks at me. Except not Jonathan. He looks off into another world. His skin is still gray, but he shaved tonight. Progress. Only forty-eight years old, he looks seventy. His daughters won't speak to him. He doesn't think he can do this. Thank God for the old timers who've been here eight or nine weeks. Your daughters will come around, Jonathon, just hang in there, they tell him.

They're all thinking.

Jeanette, Joe's wife wearing a bright red blouse, throws her arm over the back of her husband's chair. Joe looks extra pasty next to the red blouse.

"You have to take it personally, if someone belittles you," Jeanette says.

"It seems that way. But do I?"

"No," says Martha beaming with bright cheeks and long flames of red hair. She's a miracle. *No* one thought she'd stay clean. It took courage telling her the truth that her choices were the problem.

"Thank you, Martha. This is Martha's last Family Night. She transitions to After Care Friday."

A small uproar of appreciation and sadness rises and dies. They're glad, but they'll miss her. I wish you could be here, Mom. You were always proud of my work.

"But where's your family?" Mike asks. He's new.

Martha, gracious, smiles. "My dad's a meth addict and last I heard from my mom was ten years ago."

"Oh, I'm sorry I asked," Mike says.

"It's okay. I'm really okay." She beams, still. "I couldn't have said that ten weeks ago."

Half the room explodes with laughter. They remember she came in with a lot of rage.

"Martha, why don't you have to take it personally when someone disrespects you?" I ask.

"Because it's not about me!" She folds her arms.

"That's a triumphant pose," I say.

"It's true. Whenever someone does a bad behavior, it's about them, not me."

"You really believe it."

"Because it's true. Ever since you taught us that, I've been applying it and it works! My dad'll say something rude, but I don't take it personally. He's using meth, so we're not going to have a rational conversation. I tell myself, what he says is not about me. I just pray for him. He's an addict. A sick person."

"Thank you so much, Martha. Your experience is priceless," I say. "Another useful tool when someone's disrespectful or hurtful, is to distance yourself by pausing to think 'Interesting.' Don't say it out loud, just think it."

Some laugh.

"It's easier not to react with a fight." Could it have worked with Mom's article? "Let's all say 'Interesting.'" No. I was clueless.

"Interesting," most of us say.

"It doesn't work in every situation, it doesn't make us bullet-proof, but it could prevent an escalation."

If I knew then what I know now, I would never have told Mom about my abortion in the first place. I would have paused, thought, interesting, I'm going to get my feelings hurt if I tell her, because she's going to look for some inspirational news article. I wouldn't have told her. I'd have grieved that it wasn't safe to tell Mom, and accepted the fact.

"Good. Remember that. Thinking 'Interesting' can remove you in a useful way sometimes. You're more likely to think things through."

"Now, if someone's disrespectful, we have to speak up. It's not safe to allow ourselves to be disrespected," I say.

David glances my way, but it's not a hostile look. He's beginning to understand.

"You can pause, reflect, and say, 'I need to be treated with respect,' or, 'I don't accept that.' And if you didn't take it personally, because it's only about them, you're calm and free to go enjoy your book, because, why should your day be ruined by someone else's bad behavior? That wouldn't make sense. Someone who's disrespectful will have to make progress, of course, or else you can't stay, right?"

Judging from their faces, some are pushing back on that thought. It goes against age-old family values.

What about Dad? He's disrespectful when he tries to touch me. Do I have to speak up?

I don't live with him.

That's an excuse?

He'll need looking after when Mom's gone. I'll be around him more, I'm pretty sure, since most of the others don't want to be.

I'll cross that bridge when I get to it.

"We can't stay where we're not treated with respect," I say, and pause to let it sink in. "In time you'll learn not to walk into walls, too. What do I mean by that?" I ask.

Mom. Dad.

Martha raises her hand. "Don't expect people to be different than they are."

Martha totally gets it. "Exactly. If you *know* someone's trying to change, it's worth the risk to tell them you require respect. You'll likely get bloodied up emotionally from time to time, but we're tough, and it can be worth it, to save a relationship. My husband and I went through that. It was worth it. Other times, when it's clear they don't want to change right now, we take people as they are, and don't set ourselves up for more verbal abuse. We can distance ourselves. Leave if necessary. Good." I look around. They're listening. "What if it's your parent who verbally abuses you?"

Brian raises his hand. He's almost done here too. He looks relaxed, self-assured in a new black and white plaid button up shirt, instead of one of his usual printed T-shirts.

"Yes, Brian."

"My Mom's never going to change. She's abusive. But I don't take it person-ally anymore. I love her like a sick person. It gives me a lot of peace I never had before. I don't let her go on and on berating me anymore. I take care of myself, leave if I have to, go back when the storm has passed."

I choke up again. I'm not usually like this. It's Mom. I'm losing her. "Thanks so much, Brian. Well done. It's so important to take care of ourselves, because the stress of chronic disrespect can trigger relapse behavior. Why?" I ask.

"Disrespect causes us to lose self-respect," Brian says.

"Exactly. So, they'll have to make progress, or we can't stay, right? In the end, we never stay when we're not treated with respect—we can't."

Which is why I can never live with Dad, it's suddenly crystal clear to me.

I look them over, see a few nods. My words fly against principles of family loyalty ingrained for centuries for many of them, principles which say don't leave if it's only verbal abuse, and don't speak up either. However, swept into the hur-ricane of addiction, the old loyalty rules hold little ground anymore. The clients are open.

"Our happiness is our *own* responsibility, now that we're adults." I look at the group. "We're the stewards of our own well-being." I write that on the board as I talk, proud at last to be able to write one thing while I say another. "Tonight, there are no victims in this room. As children, we were victims. As adults, we're all free, in recovery, to make choices."

Jack raises his hand, smiles. "Isn't that amazing how she writes and talks?" He doesn't mean it.

My guard goes up.

The group agrees, it's amazing.

"So," Jack goes on, "if my wife runs off with the UPS guy, that's not about me?"

His wife Molly smiles, raises her eyebrows as if to say not a bad idea.

They've been having problems. He puts her down with jokes, defends himself, saying he's being funny.

"Are you setting up a joke?" I ask him.

He's setting up a joke. But she can handle herself now.

"No. If she runs off, it's about her. Doesn't say anything about who I am," Jack says.

"Exactly. It *affects* someone who's left behind," I say. "We're human, so we'll be angry, sad. We'll grieve. But no one ever has to take being run out on personally. It's never about us. We can get on with our life."

"Hear that, honey?" Jack says to his wife. "All you have to do is run off and I can get on with my life!"

He's low.

She pulls away from him, smiles at me. "Fine with me, Jack."

I love her conviction.

He pulls her close. "Don't run off."

She shrugs with a smile. "I've been using that thing you taught me," she says to me. "It works. Marriage is a choice, not a sentence."

Which I learned from Baker.

"When I'm disrespected," she continues, "I don't fight. It's not about me. I calmly go sleep in the other room. In the morning, I have a new respectful husband." She looks at him with a glint of pride.

"Progress," Jack says shyly to the group.

"I'm proud of you both," I say. "So, with non-judgmentalness, and not taking things personally, we're ready to commit to a win-win solution in any conflict."

The time's half over. I'd better move on. "Five things to resolve any conflict: first, and most importantly, when you go into conflict resolution, have a commitment to a win-win solution; second, guard how you talk; third, actively listen; fourth validate the others' concerns; and, fifth, if the guns of insecurity do come out, and by this, I mean if you get defensive and want to attack, take a break to settle yourself and talk later. Let's go through this."

God, I love my job. You could hear a pin drop right now. They're going to go home and try this out. And it's going to work.

I'm going to try it out, too, finally, with my thoughts of Mom. Who was I to ever judge her? I took it personally, when it was never about me.

And I'm going to stand up to Dad!

I howl laughing at that one, in my mind.

I need to write about Mom, my abortion, her article and my judging her when I get home tonight. That's a good story.

CHAPTER 35
REMEMBER TO LOOK AT THE SUNNY SKIES
– THE SILVERY MOON!

March, 2007. One month later.

Mom collapsed.

Luckily, the upstairs waiting area of the hospital has lots of daylight, couches and chairs that make the linoleum and steel less cold. Eight brothers and sisters are here. We had gathered to car pool today for our annual week away in Cayucos, when we got the news Mom had collapsed.

"Mom won't be going back to the Lexington, but to a nursing home," Cecilia tells us all after talking with the doctor.

I panic. "But I promised her I'd never let her go to a nursing home."

"Sweety, no one wanted this to happen. It's out of our hands."

I sit on the couch beside Cecilia. She's right. A wall of water rises in me. I weep inconsolably. My body recoils when Cecilia puts her arm around me. She pulls me to her anyway.

Why did I want to resist?

A fairy song within calls me down to a quiet forest pond with lily pads, and I collapse against her. It's only foreign—not bad—the sensation of being held and consoled. When I was little and things went wrong, Mom was glad if nothing was broken. To be held was out of the question. My pain subsides. I wipe my face, sit up. Sorry, Mom. We'll keep a close eye on you in the nursing home. Except we're going away for a week.

Now, our trip's delayed a day. We wait on Mom getting a CT scan. It's nice to be waiting together. And it's nice she was conscious going in. Patricia over-heard Mom gladly telling orderlies in a deep voice, "I'll bake *you* a *pie!*"

The tests show more strokes.

The next day, they move Mom to Calm Shores Nursing Home. We take Dad to see her, and get her settled.

Then we spend time with Dad at the Lexington.

"Tell me again where Evelyn is?" Dad asks.

"She's at that nursing home we just went to, remember?"

"Oh, yeah. Why?"

"She had more strokes, Dad. The doctor wants her there to get more care."

"Oh. Sure, if the doctor says so."

"Your children are all leaving to Cayucos for our annual week away," Cecilia says.

"Oh?"

"Here are our phone numbers. Call us anytime. Okay?" Cecilia hands him a list of our numbers written in large dark print. I wish we weren't leaving, but we arranged it with our employers and can't really change the dates of this Cayucos trip."

"Well, have a good time," Dad says.

It's hard to say good-bye to him. He seems so little.

I car-pool with Cecilia.

"He's so sweet," she says. "He sure was a pain all our lives, but I tell you we couldn't ask for a better Dad right now."

At Cayucos, Dad calls a couple times a day.

"I don't know where your mother is," he says.

Cecilia gently explains.

It's awful, thinking of him all alone. He is like a child. I love him like he's a child, yet I'm not safe being near him. He's never acknowledged what he's done. I haven't gotten close enough for him to try anything lately. No one wants to look after him now. Some of us will, reluctantly. Not in our homes. He's not safe to be around.

If only he would acknowledge what he does, mend his relationships with his children, before it's too late.

A few weeks later, it's arranged at last for Dad to move into Calm Shores with Mom.

Mom can hardly talk now. She smiles. Some things we say seem to go in. Patricia says one night Mom looked at her and said, "It's time the show was over."

I arrive to visit one sunny morning and watch with anguish Mom moan as an aide hoists her with a Hoyer Lift to seat her in a geri-chair, a padded recliner on wheels, so that I can take her outside. I had no idea it would cause her so much pain. I wouldn't have asked them to transfer her. I push her outside into the sunlight. It should be quiet, this sacred moment when I need to say some-thing important to her, but cars roar by, people come and go.

Her eyes are open, but she doesn't seem to see me.

I stroke her strands of unwashed white hair backward. I want to tell her she can go. To ease my pain of seeing her this way? No, so she can relax and know her brood will all be fine. I need to tell her, melodramatic as it seems.

"Mom, I don't know if you can hear me. I hope you can. I need to tell you I don't want to see you suffer anymore. I think you would stay forever to look after all of us. But, it's okay," I choke on the words, "it's okay to go, Mom. Don't worry." She needs to know Dad'll be okay. "We'll take care of Dad. We'll all be okay." I can't believe I'm telling her to die. What if she's afraid to die? I need to help her.

I weep and sing a song I make up to the tune of "Kumbayah:"

"Will you catch me, Lord, when I die?

"Will you catch me, Lord, when I die?

"Yes, I will catch you, when you die.

"I will catch you when you die."

Mom's gaze doesn't change, but I think she heard me. It's all I can do. She knows I love her. I take her back inside, ask them not to use the lift to transfer her. I help the aides get her settled in bed.

Two days later in the morning at work, I get a call from Cecilia. "The nurses said to gather. Mom's going soon."

Did I cause this?

I hand my work over to my boss.

At the nursing home, I join most of my brothers and sisters. Mom lies in her bed, eyes closed, in a coma. Her white hair's brushed back. She's covered by a pink blanket. The nurse shows us Mom's feet, mottled purple and gray on the bottom.

"What does it mean?" I ask.

"Her organs are shutting down."

"Oh." Tears well up. Shock, sadness, relief, and excitement come in together, friends arriving at a party. Something huge is going to happen.

Dad sits in his wheelchair next to his bed, wearing his cozy grey jacket, black sweat-pants, black lace-up shoes and socks.

"How are you, Dad?" I ask.

"Oh, pretty good. And yourself?"

Does he know Mom's dying? "I'm okay. I'm sad about Mom."

We take turns being close to her. Why am I so calm?

"She's close to going, Dad," Patricia says. "Do you want to sit closer?"

Dad doesn't respond. Patricia helps move Dad closer to Mom's bed. He has the appearance of a lean baby, the skin near his eyes is thin, his eyes looking into space, his hair's combed back, blown back by life. His arms rest on his wheelchair arms, his big bony hands droop over his lap. What does he think? Is he capable of taking in the fact that Mom's dying?

Late in the afternoon, long pauses appear between Mom's breaths. In my heart, I root for her to be able to do it, to pass over, slide into the spiritual world.

She hasn't breathed for twenty or thirty seconds. Is she gone?

Mom's eyes open. She takes a breath, and shrugs.

She's with us! It's the shrug she always makes when she wishes she could do more, but she can't. She wishes she could stay! But she can't. She's going *now*. She closes her eyes, takes two more breaths, and no more.

Pain sucks the wind from my lungs, the strength from my legs. I collapse against her bed. I'll never let you go, Mom.

"Are you all right, Marie?" Cecilia asks.

"I'm okay, thanks," I say, straightening back up. Cecilia's words bring me back to think of the others. We hug and weep. Remark on her shrug. Laugh, relieved.

We pull flower petals off an arrangement and sprinkle them on Mom.

"Hey, let's sing, you guys," says Bridgette.

We sing "Sentimental Journey," "Hosea," "The Atchison, Topeka and the Santa Fe" with a lot of na-na-na's for the missing lyrics.

How strange, to stroke Mom's forehead, already translucent and cool, and feel proud of her, relieved for her, and calm in my new decision to never let her go.

We launch into "Amazing Grace" but get interrupted by a nurse.

"We won't call the mortuary just yet," she says, smiling, seeming appreciative of our singing, "But we'll need to do that pretty soon."

"Thanks," some of us say.

"I thought we'd order pizza, have a little party," I say, disappointed.

Why don't I feel sad? I've grieved my mother my whole life, and now she's gone my grieving's over?

We tell each other things Mom said in these final days, and remember her futile efforts to control us as kids.

Suddenly a man in a black suit arrives. "Who's he?" I ask.

"The mortician," Martin says.

"Already?"

"Maybe they want to remove her before residents head down to the dining room," Martin says.

It's dinner time. We beg the mortician for ten more minutes.

People tell Mom again they love her.

The mortician can't move her onto his gurney by himself, that's obvious.

"I'll help you," I say.

The mortician lifts her using the sheet at her shoulders. Martin pulls the sheet at her hips. I put my arms under her legs. I'm shocked at how hot they feel underneath, how they imprint themselves on me. She doesn't feel dead. I'm jolted out of the dream where she's a spirit I won't let go. Why am I helping him take her away? I wish I'd never helped.

I watch her go, zipped into a black bag, taken off by an indifferent young man. Let her go.

Never.

I roll up the pink blanket with petals to take home. We follow her out to the van, wave good-bye as the van drives down the street. We turn to go back inside.

"Look!" Patricia says.

The van has turned around. We hurry back to the street to wave as she goes by the other way.

Back inside, Dad looks exhausted, but not emotional. He didn't cry or say anything about Mom passing. We help him into bed where he smiles, grateful to be tucked in all around, closes his eyes and sleeps.

Tears flowing, I drive home, mesmerized by clouds where I imagine Mom is now. I'll never let you go, Mom. I know they say we have to let people go, but I never will. Why would I? You'll always be with me when I call for you. I can only let you die if you don't make me let you go. I don't even want to write about you're dying, Mom. It'll interrupt being with you.

But a few days later, I'm elected to write Mom's eulogy. I look through my old papers, find the envelope I'm looking for. Written across the back of it by Mom during the Vietnam War are words to console me back then for my sadness about everything. "From Lady of the Sun, Moon, Mountains and the Sea – Remember to look at the sunny skies – the silvery moon!" I've never understood how this came out of her when she was always so practical, reading and writing political articles, letters, flyers. I'll put it at the end of the eulogy.

I reflect as I write. Mom had three lives. Her thirty years of community organizing for Civil Rights, protesting the war, fighting for nursing home patients' rights. Before then, were her earlier years, doing nothing but raising us, her ten children, giving us traditions, starching torn Thanksgiving linens, ironing blouses, darning socks, stretching pennies, always with a positive spin. If she couldn't finish washing the kitchen floor, she laughed and said she gave it a lick and a promise. Her third life was when she lost her ability to read and grew more emotionally present to us all, even as dementia set in, noticing who we are, laughing at her demise, always up for an outing.

At the funeral Mass, I'm happy with my outfit—a black velvet dress with a loose skirt and tall black boots. I'm glad I'm shallow, it'll get me through this. I sit near the front, because I have to go up to read.

I look back and see Dad sitting alone. I can hardly bear it. In the vast church, little groups of families sit a distance from him. I long to be with him, to comfort him, though he doesn't look dismayed. I could help him take it all in—Mom's gone. I can't, though. He might put his strong bony arm around me, put his big hand on my knee. It would tip the balance. He would pull me to him, emotionally overwhelm me. I can't be the daughter who takes over for Mom. Why doesn't someone who feels safe sit with him? No one feels safe. He doesn't molest the boys, but he's cruel to them with an insulting tone.

People must wonder why his ten children don't sit with him. Why does what people think bother me? It never used to.

When the time comes, I read, "First, I know Mama would want me to mention that our family, like many families, was visited at times by interpersonal storms with gale force winds that uprooted many trees and left the landscape changed forever. It was her observation that we all came out of these storms better people. And as she once noted with meaningful intent, 'Sometimes the waters are smooth, and sometimes they're choppy.'"

CHAPTER 36
WHERE'S THE BOOK?

July, 2009. Two years and four months later.

"Once," I shout to my sister Cecilia over the noise of the wind in her convertible one bright sunny morning, "when I was five-years-old, I asked Dad, 'How long does it take to die when your head is cut off?' I thought my question would calm him down because martyrs were his favorite subject. He was in a bad mood and I thought my question would keep him from roaring like a lion."

"That's the kind of thing we worried about all the time! Getting our heads chopped off!" Cecilia yells back.

We burst out howling with laughter at the painful memory of the subject of martyrs.

We gaily sail down the freeway on our way to visit Dad. He's ninety-two years old. Been at Calm Shores nursing home since Mom passed on. He seems to actually enjoy sitting in his wheelchair in the hall across from the nurses' station, wearing his cozy gray puffy jacket, sweatpants, black lace-up shoes and sox, and Indiana Jones hat. Residents wave to him as they pass by. He tips his hat or suddenly splays his fingers to make some of the residents laugh.

"I didn't *want* to be a martyr!" Cecilia yells. "I worried about having my fingernails torn out!"

"I know!"

We laugh the whole way about how badly we had hoped as little children not to have to be burned alive.

"It was graphic!" she shouts. "The images of being boiled in oil, burned at the stake."

"Left naked out on a frozen lake," I add.

We scream.

"We were so little!" she says. "But remember how he used to grill us on catechism? He made it fun. I loved him asking us questions about life, making us think," she says.

"Me too."

"It's so good to laugh," she shouts. "I think it gets us ready to see him.

Dad's still so hard to deal with. You have to really watch his hands—he's quick! Remember, when we had to call Child Protective Services after we confronted him? And the clerk asked how old are the children?"

"We told them most of us are in our thirties and forties."

We howl.

"We're in our fifties and sixties, for crying out loud," I say, "you'd think we'd all be used to Dad by now!"

"You don't get used to feeling unsafe!" she yells. "We're lucky both our brothers are supportive."

We exit the freeway, stop at a light. The loud freeway wind is suddenly gone. I look at Cecilia. "I can't help feeling sad that none of us siblings can have Dad at home. He seems so vulnerable, like a little boy, most of the time. But he's not safe for us, is he?" I know he's not.

"That's right. He's quick as ever and more stubborn. And just as strong. You wouldn't think he would be, at ninety-two, but he is. He got me a few weeks ago."

"Darn it. And he makes inappropriate remarks now. He didn't used to, that I recall," I say.

"Really?"

"He asked if I was wearing anything under my white jeans."

Cecilia groans. "Did you say anything?"

"Are you kidding? He still scares me."

"Me too!"

The light changes and she starts the long drive down the thoroughfare.

"He can still roar like a lion," I say. "I teach my clients assertiveness, yet knowing all the assertiveness skills in the world still wouldn't help me." I shake my head in awe of my fear of Dad. "I'm fifty-nine years old. I've grown a lot! I've had therapy, been to self-help groups. It all helps, but for some reason I still freeze when Dad acts out."

Cecilia nods. "Me too. I know what you mean. We've both grown a lot. Still."

"We have grown! Especially since I began learning to take care of my inner child, and about neurotic attachments. Even without a real connection with Dad, I'm in a real relationship with Baker. We're both wound too tight, but we work it out. We're both very assertive. I'm not afraid to be assertive. That's not my problem."

Cecilia nods. "I hear you."

I look out to the fields planted in strawberries that stretch for miles. "I'm so hard-wired to be afraid of Dad, I need something besides assertiveness skills. I don't know what I need. There's got to be a way I can disconnect the wires inside my brain that prevent me from standing up to Dad."

"Just reach inside with a pair of pliers?"

We laugh.

Inside Calm Shores, we find Dad beside his bed wearing a thin gray shirt too small for him.

"Hi Dad," Cecilia says, rubbing his hands. "Your hands are cold."

"Yes, they are. You wouldn't have something I could put on, would you?"

"We'll find your jacket," she says. "It's July, but the air conditioning makes it cold in here."

I look in his closet. "They always put his jacket on him. There's nothing here but a few thin pieces of clothing belonging to someone else." I look under the bed, in the bathroom, on his roommate Bill's side of the room. "I don't see it."

Cecilia flags the aide in the hall. "We can't find his grey jacket. It's a fluffy warm jacket."

"Yeah," she says, "we looked everywhere. It went to the laundry because he spilled food on it, and they say they don't have it."

Cecilia takes a deep breath and sighs. "Okay. Thanks. It's hard to keep track of things here. Marie, let's put a couple of T-shirts on him, and another shirt."

"Good idea." I look in his drawers for T-shirts. "And I know you have to get to work. I'll buy him another jacket this afternoon."

A bright red, down jacket. That's what I want for Dad. It'll keep him warm no matter what. I see the jacket in my mind's eye and know I'm doomed because it's July. No store has winter jackets in July.

In the afternoon, I go to three department stores and walk what seems like miles. No winter jackets anywhere.

I begin to wonder why go to such lengths for a man who molested my sisters and I? I feel like a traitor. I'd rather look after Dad than my younger sisters. I didn't know it at the time, but he went into my little sisters' rooms when we were all teenagers, put his hands on their breasts to say good night. He only woke me up once doing that when I was twelve. And here I am feverishly needing a red down jacket to keep *him* warm. I've been torn for years, keeping him at a distance in my heart, on the one hand, and feeling deep compassion for him, on the other. He's always seemed like a young tyrant, roaring like a lion, or a young boy, unable to bear criticism or contradiction, always going into hiding. Mom once called him the eleventh child. Am I a traitor? Is something wrong with me? I'm driven to find this red jacket. I don't feel in control of myself. But it feels wrong after all he's done.

I drive to the sporting goods store. Nothing. Maybe it's a sign he doesn't deserve it.

I'm not superstitious.

I drive to Ross and park in the lot. I can't go inside. I need to settle this conflict once and for all. I need to talk to someone. I dial Marietta, my youngest sister. "Hi. I need to run something by you."

"Sure."

She's so sweet, angelic and kind. "I feel guilty, like a traitor, taking care of Dad. I'm driving all around obsessed with getting him a red down jacket because his warm grey one's gone missing. I think of how he molested you and Patricia and Jean. I didn't know it was happening, but I should have wondered, asked you, tried to protect you. And now I'm helping him."

"Listen, Marie, don't feel like a traitor. I'm glad he doesn't have to fend on his own. I'm glad you have the stomach for it!" She laughs. "So don't worry about it. A red jacket? You probably tried Ross."

"I'm in their parking lot, about to go in. I tried everywhere else."

"Yeah, warm jackets are out of season. Seriously, thanks for doing this. I love him. He's just hard to be around."

What a relief. "Thanks, Marietta. I feel better."

He is hard to be around. It's been almost fifty years of him finding ways to touch me. My stomach churns whenever I see him. It's not easy to love him. I'm not in total denial. Except about finding a red down jacket in July. There's no point looking inside Ross. But I'm here.

I go into the store, glance over at the jackets rack. It's empty, except for a few sweatshirts, and a dazzling red winter jacket. I walk up to it, touch it. The size is large. It's down. I slowly take it off the rack, hold it to myself. I imagine God says, you're not bad for loving your dad, and here's that jacket you need. The tension of having felt so conflicted snaps. Tears are coming. I need to pay, get to the car, have a good cry. I hold things in. They all want to come out.

Back in the car, I shed some tears of relief. I think of Dad. He must be very conflicted. If I hold things in when I'm conflicted, imagine what he holds in. He needs to open up. I cut the tags off the jacket.

I'll take Dad the jacket and see if he'll open up to me.

I drive forty minutes back to Calm Shores. I find Dad still wearing the layers of three T-shirts and two button up shirts, using his feet to propel himself in his wheelchair across the lobby.

"Hi, Dad."

"Oh. Marie! There you are. I was hoping to find something." His face muscles tighten and his eyes close.

I hear his quiet, hearty laugh.

"I can't remember what I was looking for!" he says through his laugh.

How can I be mad at him?

Do I want to have a serious talk with him right now? Probably not a good time. "You're not usually out here in the lobby. Were you looking for your gray jacket?"

"No, I don't think so, though that would be good. I'm awfully cold."

"The air conditioning in here makes it chilly. Your gray jacket got lost, but I found a new red one for you. Here. Let's put this on you."

He holds up a bony arm, like a child. "Oh, this is warm," he says as his arm goes into the sleeve. He puts his other arm in.

I'm dreaming thinking he's capable of a serious conversation about what feelings he's holding in.

I stuff the jacket down behind him, and zip it up in front. What a beautiful jacket.

"Let's go add the jacket to your property list."

"Sure."

Dad pats the fluffy red arms of his jacket.

"I'm so glad it fits you," I say.

"Fits like a glove!"

He looks so happy. He never complains about being here. Him being so easy to please makes everything else bearable.

"Do we have to give it back?" he asks, suddenly serious, just like a child.

"No, Dad. This is your new jacket. Your gray one got lost. This red one is yours to keep."

He grins. "Well, thank you!"

As I move to get behind him, his hand reaches up toward my chest. I jump away. Close call. Shake it off.

It won't shake off. The air around me is imprinted with menace.

We update his list at the nurses' station.

I want to go home. "Do you want to lie down before dinner?"

"Oh, that'd be grand."

When he's in bed with his heavy blanket on, I crank the bed up so he can drink some ice water, which he loves. I'll be home soon enough.

He takes a sip. "This is delicious!" He drinks some more, hands back the cup. "What's new in your world?" He sounds revived.

My world. It's pretty much you, Dad. "What's new in my world? I'm still writing my book." And you're in it.

"Oh? What's it about?"

"My life. I've had a few adventures that helped me grow. You know, living in the barn on Bear Creek Road." Don't tell him about panhandling with two black eyes. "Spending a night in the San Francisco bus station. Relationships I've had." Writing Joe's name in my stomach with a razor blade to prove I loved him. Confronting you, Dad, in an intervention. "Good times, hard times."

"You've been at that a while, haven't you?"

"I have. Years, actually."

I look down at my hands in my lap. The writing's taking so long. I keep writing outlines to put the early chapters into. Whenever I begin to write about what Dad does with his hands, a little group of censors in my mind say, *You can't write that about your father!* And I bounce back to other chapters.

I'm still trying to get at how it all turns out.

"Well, that's all well and good, to be writing, but," he gives me a meaningful look with a note of scolding impatience, "where's the *book?*" Like, come on, let's quit dilly dallying and get this thing written.

I'm confused between feeling hurt for being scolded for not having produced a book in all these years, and feeling excitement for being spurred on by Dad, of all people. He must know he's in the story.

CHAPTER 37
THE EMPTY CHAIR

November, 2009 Four months later.

For continuing education hours, I sign up for a special group therapy training for drug and alcohol counselors, given by a well-known instructor. The night of the training, when I get out of my car, the thrilling cold November air flows down the back of my neck until I pull the collar of my jacket tight. I take a deep, bracing breath. I love the cold! I must have a past life at the North Pole.

We could have past lives, I think. Time seems so elastic whenever I read a little about physics. We could have future lives we've already lived too, and probably parallel lives too. Wild. And I know we go to heaven. All the near-death stories I've read say so. They all say they're no longer afraid of dying. That all we need to do is love and not be afraid. That is so grand.

Inside the warm classroom, I take a seat at one of the long tables. The instructor begins. She walks back and forth discussing techniques of motivational interviewing. She knows the material inside and out. We students scribble notes for an hour and a half.

After a short break, the instructor says, "Please circle your chairs up here in the front of the room for some empty chair exercises."

This should be fun.

"You're going to take turns being the client. We need two chairs inside the circle."

People bring two extra chairs.

"Set them facing each other, a few feet apart. That's it. Thank you. Now, this is an effective Gestalt technique which helps clients gain insight in the here-and-now to their relationships with others. Who wants to go first?"

I'd rather think about past lives. My relationships with others are about as good as they can be. I don't think I need more insights. Dad molests me, still, I love him in his blindness to what he does. Baker tries my soul with his friendships with women, but his warmth to me rivets me to a sweetness I love. What insights do I need?

Several take their turns. They tell co-workers or family members in the empty chair how they feel about one conflict or another. We get to hear what the person in the empty chair has to say, as imagined by the one playing the client. But each time as the conversation goes back and forth and arrives at an amicable outcome, my stomach tightens. There won't be an amicable outcome when it's my turn.

"Who's next? Have you gone yet?" The instructor looks at me.

"I haven't." Get it over with. Just think, soon you'll be back outside in the frosty air and sailing toward home.

I stand up, take the client chair in the middle of the circle.

"Who are you putting in the empty chair?"

"My dad."

"All right. Go ahead and begin."

I blow out a deep breath and look straight ahead at the empty chair where I picture a slightly younger Dad sitting, so he'd be strong enough to actually sit there and not fall over without armrests. He's ninety-three years old now.

"Dad, I'm mad at you." That's a good start. I never say I'm mad at him, though I must be, on some level. "You hurt me. You've always touched my breasts whenever you got a chance. It made my life hard. I want you to stop."

I look at the instructor.

"Good," she says. "What's he saying to you?"

I look back at the chair.

"He's calling me a slut, a whore and a liar."

The instructor looks surprised, and frowns. It seems she doesn't know what to say.

"I have an idea," I say. "My dad's in a nursing home. I'm going to pretend he's already passed on, and do it again."

"All right," the instructor says tentatively.

"Dad, you molested me my whole life. It made my life really hard. I've been anxious, had no self-esteem, hated myself."

I stare at the empty chair, picture Dad as a spirit. It's as though he's really here. "He's saying, 'Please forgive me. I'm so proud of you for standing up to me. I'm sorry I hurt you and wasn't able to stop hurting you. You're so brave, Marie. I love you so much.'" I choke up. I'm done.

I get up and take my seat in the circle.

Thanks Dad.

Outside after class, I walk feeling full of life's sweetness. All the stress of loving Dad while he still hurts me is lifted. Life's deeper than I knew. My mind's speechless as I walk in the frosty cold to my car. He doesn't want to do what he does.

Now, how will I get through to him?

CHAPTER 38
THE TROUBLE WITH SEMIS

February, 2010. 3 months later.

Sitting up in bed on a cold winter morning, in the cozy glow of holiday lights strung over the big window at the foot of the bed, Baker and I sip coffee and write two pages each in our journals.

Before he reads, Baker pretends to spray mist to prepare his voice. I laugh. The book from which we learned to journal said don't share your journal writings, tear them up. We can't bear to tear them up and we always share them.

After he reads his, I read mine.

When I'm done, Baker says, "Lot of Mom stuff."

"It's been almost three years, but I still can't accept that I hurried Mom along to die, to save myself from seeing her in pain. I don't know why this is coming up now."

"You're ready."

He's wise.

I move to get out of bed.

Baker pulls me back.

"Wait, wait, wait just a gosh darn minute."

He puts his arm around me.

My tears well up, overflow. I take a deep breath, let out a big sigh.

"You're a wonderful daughter," he says. "You love your mother. You helped her."

"Why does it hurt so much?"

"It hurts because she's gone."

"No, she's not. I'll never let her go."

He smiles, wipes my tears.

Once again, the crazy battle within about How could I have hurried Mom along, dissolves. It transforms into something sweet. "I thought maybe she needed permission to go, and I gave her permission. That was all."

He nods. "That's all you did."

We sit up.

"But how did she feel when her own daughter told her to go ahead and die?" I ask.

"Dear, she was ecstatic. I know because when it's my time, I hope to *God* you pray Please take my messy noisy husband so I can have some peace, for God's sake!"

I laugh. I'm glad we stuck it out together. We still hit our rough patches, but always come through them better than before. Thank God we're clean and sober.

I dress for work. We make our lunches. He walks me out to my car.

"I'm off at five. I'm going to see my dad after work tonight."

"Of course, you are."

"I know you don't approve, because of what he does, but he's still my dad." I visit Dad a few times a week. "It's true, I have to make myself go, but I always feel better when I leave to come home. Dad's so grateful after I help him to bed, get him tucked in. I'm always glad I went."

"You're a good daughter."

"Thanks. Do you ever get scared of passing semi-trucks?"

"No."

"Me neither, until lately," I say.

"Dear, you're scared of me coming around the corner from the hall. Of *course*, you're scared of semi-trucks."

"No, I've *never* been afraid of passing big trucks."

"You'll be fine."

He squeegees my windows.

I get into my shiny red Corolla, my fifth car since I met Baker. I bought it the night the *second* windshield wiper blew off my Supra, which I loved for the power. That poor car was ready for the boneyard when I bought it. I close the car door.

I'm content. Ready to visit Dad tonight. Happy this car's not like my old cars. It's pretty, all the windows go up and down, there're no fumes coming in from the tail pipe. And I'm glad Mom's not mad at me for telling her she could die. Life's good. Maybe there won't be any semi-trucks today.

I roll down the window. "Thanks, dear. Love you."

"Love you too," he says.

We kiss. I start the car.

"Eat!" I say. He doesn't eat enough.

"Okay." He grins.

"And watch for snakes!" I say.

I startle at the loud rattlesnake sound he makes with his mouth.

"Well, ma'am, grappling with rattlesnakes is all in a day's work for a horticulturalist. But don't worry. I have a snake grabber. And don't forget I have good snake karma. Haven't killed one yet. Why would I kill them? They're just being snakes."

"That's right," I say.

Snakes are just being snakes. And Dad's just being Dad.

Driving down the road, I soak in the life of the giant trees, the oaks and eucalyptus along the country highway, imagine that these old trees know I'm thinking about them. The trees *must* know I'm here, because, you couldn't have that much life in you as these trees have and not sense someone's thinking about you.

Suddenly it feels as though God's warm spirit flows through the trees, the air, everything, including me. A deep peace comes from soaking up the consciousness of the trees.

I'm speechless, riveted by love for everyone I see in the parade of commuters going the other direction on a short stretch of town road—a tired looking, shaggy-bearded man, a large dark-haired woman with perfect eyebrows, an old guy in a red baseball cap. I see myself in each one. There I am. There I am. There I am. We're each a child of God.

People's faces are so worn. We all try so frigging hard. How could God judge anyone?

God couldn't. Judging is a petty human failing, I'm sure of it.

The pace picks up as traffic flows onto the 126 freeway. I need to entertain myself. Listen to George Elliott's Silas Marner? No. Pretend Bonnie Raitt suddenly got laryngitis at a concert and I get up on stage and sing her songs so well that the band lets me do an entire set? No... I'll imagine that driving home tomorrow night when I have the late shift.

I probably don't need to entertain myself, but to think about Dad. I always thought somehow when he's *old* he'll stop reaching to touch me. But he's the same as he's always been. And now he comes right out with comments about my figure, or my under-clothes, which he never used to do.

And I don't forget about him. He doesn't wear off between visits, the way he did when I only saw him once every two weeks, because back then Mom and Dad were two hours away. Back then, whenever he grazed my breast when I helped him get out of the car at church, or when he tried to steer me to my chair, I absorbed it like a few volts of electric shock, rolled my eyes and thought *I'm going home soon.* I forgot about it. And I was okay.

Yeah, I absorbed it better when they lived two hours away.

I get on the freeway.

Now, it's usually only he and I when I visit, and when I leave him, he's all alone at the nursing home. I feel for him. There're no protective barriers of space, time, or Mom. I usually dread going to see him. Baker says, then don't go. But when I think yeah, don't go, I feel so sad I could die, because nobody else hardly goes to see him. Shoot. I was happy this morning, and now I'm on pins and needles again. Why? I'm not conflicted about looking after him. He needs me. But it all goes in, still. Even though I felt so much peace after the empty chair exercise. It was as though God gave me a glimpse of truth to hold on to, but didn't take my human reality away.

Damn it. Semi-truck ahead on my right, and it's too late to drop back and get behind it. I have to pass.

Driving past big trucks never bothered me before. Mom took the fear out of me when I was barely learning to drive. She told me to take a freeway on-ramp.

"Mom, I can't do that! I don't know how to drive the freeway!" I cried.

"Go! Take the ramp!" she commanded.

I did, headed down the ramp. "Mom, how do I get on?!"

"Step on it!" was all she said.

From the corner of my eye, I could see her smile with excitement.

She always had confidence in me.

I never had fear driving after that. But now, for at least a month, I've been close to having panic attacks when passing semi-trucks. It gets worse each time, as though I'm losing my mind.

I pull alongside the truck, avoid looking at it, but feel it's massive steel presence. I'm getting light-headed. It seems we're inches apart. Blood's leaving my head, my face is getting cold. I shouldn't be driving, but it's too late to pull off the freeway. I have to pass. Here goes. I grip the wheel, begin to see stars. Damn it! I'm going to pass out if I don't do something. Sit up straighter! Damn. Starting to see white. What am I afraid of?

The truck could come over and crush me. That's not rational.

The unconscious uses symbols to alert us to deeper problems.

The semi-truck is a symbol.

It's Dad.

Dad's always coming into my lane and crushing me. I need to get away from the truck.

Step on it!

As I speed past the truck, the stars that I see mix with colors of cars. Warmth returns to my head. I zoom past, take the next off ramp, park on a side street to calm down. The truck was Dad. Nearly passing out on the freeway was awful. I can never do that again. Yeah. Dad's been coming over like a big semi-truck my whole life. It doesn't matter how much I love him, the shocks from his hands and words don't go away. They build up inside me.

What am I supposed to do?

Tears well up.

I have to stop him.

I have to speak up.

In the empty chair exercise he said he was proud of me for standing up to him. I thought that was about the intervention. I need to stand up to him again.

That's what my unconscious is using the trucks to tell me: Stand up to Dad.

I have to. I will.

CHAPTER 39
I'M YOUR DAUGHTER

February, 2010. That evening.

That evening, I park the Corolla outside Calm Shores and walk slowly toward the tall glass doors. It's dusk. The day's old but I'm brand new since that panic attack beside the semi-truck this morning. I'm ready to speak up. I don't care if Dad roars. I won't let one more inappropriate word or move by Dad go unchecked.

The sidewalk feels extra hard underfoot. The few stars I can see sparkle with hope for me. The lobby lights pierce the twilight with an especially warm welcome. Everything has meaning. I'm not guarded inside with eyes that are glazed-over hoping for the best because I'm helpless. That's how I've been, really, all my life. Glazed over. Hoping for the best.

If Dad's inappropriate, I'll speak up.

I enter the lobby. How vivid the couches and silk plants all appear. Very solid. I always thought I could glide through my life like a spirit, letting things roll off me, the way Mom seemed to.

But they weren't rolling off, were they, Mom?

I'm not ready to go see him just yet. I want to feel myself be myself for a minute in the middle of this big soft sofa in the giant lobby.

I sit, sink in and seem to float through a veil into a safe feeling of childhood. A soft voice comes from down the long linoleum hall, then audience laughter from someone's television. These quiet sounds of evening thrill me. Life feels good.

He's going to be surprised, isn't he? I hope he's not too hurt when I speak up and object. He has no idea how I've changed in just one day, so that'll be shocking to him. It's amazing to think terror of a freeway semi-truck unlocked my will. There's no way to warn him. It's not like I can tell him, 'Dad you've always been inappropriate, and from now on I'm standing up to you.' No. That would be petty. And he doesn't need warning. He's fine. And maybe he'll grow through the experience of my confronting him, when I do. Or maybe not. But I'll grow and survive. I almost fainted passing a semi-truck today.

No. I can't let one more thing go in, Dad. No more hurt will fit.

Wow. The crystals of the lobby's big chandelier make me miss Mom. Tears! It feels like Thanksgiving and I'm small. She takes the dusty crystals off our chandelier in the dining room and I, kneeling on a dining room chair, plunge my hands into warm suds in the stainless-steel bowl we make cakes in. The bowl sits on the dark wood dining room table. I wash thick dust off the crystals.

That's how she tethered me. I was always anxious. She almost died, and I was farmed out at fourteen months. And Dad was a roaring lion, before he became a semi-truck.

I never knew something was wrong with Dad. He was fun, and then out of the blue he roared at us little kids like a lion. I startled, froze in fear. He went into the library and shut the door—his private space where no one was allowed to go except for spankings. No wonder I could never speak up to him, object to his hands. I was a drop-tied elephant—trained since I was two to believe I'd die if I stood up to him.

Molly, with fluffy gray hair and one leg, wheels herself through the lobby. I am so lost in childhood. She seems like one of my siblings heading off to bed.

"Hi Molly," I say.

"Hi. You here to see your dad?" she asks.

"Yep." A little shock comes as I remember him.

"He's down the hall," she says, and smiles down at the floor, a world away. "I think he's been up all day."

She thinks I don't take care of him, and doesn't want to say it. I steel against the little prick of sorrow and shame that comes from thinking of him up all day in his chair.

But I can't take him home and save him. And I won't tell her why.

"He'll be ready to lie down," I say and get up, walk over to her, see him way down the hall, a bent figure sitting in his red jacket, small because he's so far away.

As I look at him, I'm afraid to stand up to him, though I will do it.

"Did you play bingo?" I ask.

"Yeah. I got my goodies," she says, shaking a plastic bag, smiling. "Well, have a nice visit."

"Thanks, Molly. Good night."

Molly glides away in her wheel chair. Her only leg grabs the linoleum like a swimmer's arm grabs water. She's strong and warm, despite her condition, and being stuck here. Humans find meaning where we decide to. I hope I can be like her.

I turn toward Dad. Even bent way over, he looks pretty sharp in his brown hat and bright red winter jacket. The gray sweats don't go, but he insists on black lace-up shoes. No one can touch or change that part of him.

I walk towards him.

I don't get far. At the intersection with the side hall, small Jane reaches up to me from her chair. Her hair appears extra snowy next to her light blue nightgown.

"Hi, Jane," I say, taking her hand. "You look so pretty."

She laughs and bursts into tears.

"Tough night?" I say.

She nods, and smiles through her tears. She's unable to speak, so I don't ask what's wrong. It's probably the usual, what we all go up and down about—hurt feelings, sorrow, regrets.

I kiss her and say, "I'm going to see my dad."

She whoops and laughs, nods down the hall at the man in the red jacket, waves me on. I check her eyes, smile, see signs she likes him. She isn't afraid of him. I bet he makes her laugh.

I'm not proud that I troll for good things about Dad. It says my love's conditional. Everyone's worthy of love. But finding good things makes it easier to love him.

Jane gazes into my eyes, I into hers. I see centuries of mute love and human pain in her deep blue lakes.

"Thanks for being my dad's friend," I say.

She grins, nods.

I kiss her cheek, she mine, before I turn and walk in his direction again.

I could help Dad, if I could get him to talk. He says he never had an unhappy day in his life. That's his anthem. But I doubt that's true. I could help him get at all of it. I'm good at that.

But it would be unethical to try to counsel him.

Which really doesn't make sense in this circumstance. He can't have long to live, and nobody's working with him. Well, he hasn't asked for help, but he wouldn't. But I could bring help to him—myself. I'm a counselor.

Except, no, I can't. I have to accept him as he is. I'm family and he hasn't asked.

He'll take his secrets to the grave, but I will keep loving him. Obviously, God does, because no one sells a red down jacket in July.

I wonder, as usual, why my sisters and brothers can get mad at him but I never have. I can't. Something's wrong with me. Some chip in my brain is missing. Oh well. I'm happy. The quiet TV voices coming from the rooms are more interesting than usual. The linoleum is extra shiny.

Seven-thirty. Most people are in bed. I can help him get in bed and since he's been sitting up in his wheelchair all day, he'll be so grateful that I'll feel like a hero and not feel so sad for him. Shallow, but true.

Will I have to stand up to him tonight? We'll see.

"Hi Dad," I say, from a little way off.

"What? Who's that?" He turns his head sideways to look up. He grins.

I'm glad I came. "It's Marie."

"Little Marie?"

"Yep. But I'm sixty."

He laughs. He takes my hand. I'm on guard. Yep, here comes his unshaved face up to kiss me. Sorry Dad. Can't do it. I have limits. I kiss the top of his head. He tilts his head and shrugs. His faint smile of resignation stings. He's all right though.

"How be you?" he asks.

"I'm good. Let me get a chair and I'll sit with you."

I wheel one of the nurses' station chairs over beside him and sit down. He looks okay, not pink with a fever the way he often is. He gets respiratory infections and we think this is it, he's going to die. With antibiotics, he always bounces back.

We sit as though on the bank of a river, watching wheelchair boats go by. I like being here in the calm, quiet hall.

"How are *you*?" I ask.

"Oh fine, fine. Couldn't be better!"

He never complains.

"Really, Dad?" I say, because I'm thinking, he's all busted up—can't walk, hardly sees, spills more food than he eats. If I can get him to be authentic, there's nothing wrong with that, and it might help.

"Well, maybe I have seen better days," he says in a sober tone.

There's the truth, and what's that sound? He's actually crying. Wow. I didn't mean to make him cry. Still, good job, Marie. In my whole life I have never once seen him cry. Not even when Mom died. This is progress. His defenses are breaking down.

Wait a minute.

He's not crying. He's laughing so hard he's crying and making wheezy sounds. I wait to hear what's so funny.

He takes a sober pause and says, "Yah, maybe I've seen better days," and breaks up laughing again.

I can't help but chuckle, because, it's true, and I'm heading where he is in a couple more decades.

Dad stops laughing again. "Nothing's *wrong*," he says with wide-eyed sincerity, waving a hand as if to say he means it.

I nod.

And his face crumples again. "I just wasn't always like *this!*" He barely gets the words out before he softly howls, pointing all his fingers at himself.

I laugh, seeing myself and all my siblings in the same boat, in the same hallway, someday, with wiry tufts of white hair, tears streaming, laughing.

He mops his tears and coughs loudly.

"I'll get you some water." I get up, refreshed by the laughter.

God, thank you for my mirthful Dad. He has made light of himself all my life.

"Hi, Bill," I say to Dad's roommate, who watches the Lakers on TV from his wheel chair. I pick up off the floor the clip end of Bill's alarm string. The alarm only works if it's clipped to him when he stands up. I clip it back onto the shoulder of his pajamas, which are so faded and crisped by the hot dryers they're almost white. I notice his shoulder's warm. He has a fever. I hope he'll be okay. He's a kind man, a nice roommate for Dad.

"Well, *thank* you," he says.

"You're welcome," I say. I doubt he knows what I clipped on him is the alarm that calls the nurses whenever he gets up to try to walk on his own. "You're warm. Are you all right?"

"Yes, *yes!*" he says.

He's annoyed or passionate, I can't tell which.

"Are you here to see your dad?" he asks.

"Yes," I say, pouring a cup of water from the pitcher by Dad's bed. "He needs some water."

"Poor soul," Bill says.

"Oh, he's okay."

"Really?" he asks.

"Yeah, I think he's okay," I say.

"Well, I worry about him. But the main thing is *you're* all right," Bill says.

"I am. Do you want me to turn the *sound* on your TV?"

"What's that?" he asks.

"Do you want the *sound* turned on the game?" I say loudly.

"*Oh!* That, no. I don't hear. Unless you're calling me late for supper!" Bill laughs riotously at his joke.

"You're funny, Bill."

"What's that?"

"You're funny!" I shout.

"Well, thank you. And you have a nice evening."

"Thank you. You too."

I go back out into the hall. "Here, Dad. Water."

"Oh. Thank you." He drinks in small, barely perceptible sips.

What a pleasant evening. I don't know if I've ever had so much fun alone with my dad. He can be a fun man. Especially at family gatherings, but those don't happen much anymore, and no one really wants to come and be with him, since Mom died. She was a buffer. On his own, he's too much work. He can be nice and congenial and then suddenly be mean or lewd. I can't really let my guard down.

I'd probably stay away more too, if I could get angry with him. But I can't get angry.

And I can't bear thinking of him being alone so much. Cecilia comes once a week. And Christopher pops in a couple times a week. Others, maybe once a month. After all those years he spent travelling, working, raising us, putting us all through Catholic school, it breaks my heart all over again to think of him being here alone, the way he was when he was on the road.

It's just a challenge, that's all. Him switching. Good dad, bad dad.

Because if he could do better, he would do better. I'm sure of it. So how can I hold it against him?

Dad hands me the empty cup and I take it back in his room. Bill's head is slumped down so I check to see if he's still breathing. He is. I go back out in the hall and sit down.

"I needed that laugh," I say. "I haven't laughed like that in a long time."

"Me neither. Me neither."

Dad's got that mirthful look that makes me believe deep down life really is good, we just don't always know it. Life's bigger than we are, somehow, and someday, when I die, my life's going to be like a dream, part nightmare, part bliss. Somehow it has to all be okay in the end. I think God works that out.

"Life's something," I say.

"Yes, it is," Dad says, looking into the glassy linoleum with smiling eyes. "You never know what it's going to bring you. You can wait and wonder but you'll never, *ever,* guess. Not in a million years."

"No, you never know. Luckily, I don't mind surprises. Do you like surprises?"

I ask.

"Like them?" he asks. "Oh," Dad raises his eyebrows and smiles faintly. His eyes stare wide into middle space. He's gone somewhere far away. "No. I don't like surprises," he says.

Now his brow knits in worry. He nervously taps the arm of his chair which makes me nervous because the hand that's tapping is the hand that's between us. It's a nervous tapping and—

Shit! His hand jumps down toward my thigh—

I grab for his hand in mid-air. Got it!

My heart thumps. I guide his hand back to the arm of his chair, stand up and move away from him. I'm suddenly weary, glance down the hall toward the tall glass doors, wish I were home.

Do I confront him? Did he do anything wrong? He won't understand if I say something about his hand coming at my leg.

"I'm going to have to get home pretty quick," I say. It *was* a nice visit.

I can't say anything to him about a hand in mid-air. It didn't land. He didn't do anything wrong.

Dad glances up. "Oh? So soon?"

"Yep. I can help you get in bed before I go."

That's usually safe. In order to stand up, he needs his hands. I only help him pivot by pulling the back of his waistband.

"That would be grand." He nods. His feet turn his chair and propel him into his room.

When he's backed up beside his bed facing me, he waves a questioning finger at me. His sweet smile is gone. His eyes and mouth are slack, now.

Here it comes.

"What's that you're wearing, under your blouse?" he asks.

His question makes me feel sick. My instincts scramble to not let the hurtful words in, but the words are already in. I remember the semi-truck. It's Dad.

Say something.

It won't do him any good.

It doesn't matter if it'll do him any good. Speak up. It'll save you.

"*That's* not okay, Dad."

"What?" He looks confused.

"It's not okay to ask what I'm wearing under my blouse. I'm your *daughter*."

Well done. I like the I'm your daughter part. Good thing his roommate Bill is all but deaf. I'd be embarrassed if he were listening.

"Whatever you say," Dad says with a disgusted shake of his head.

I'm not going near him now that he's upset. He might grab my wrist and not let go. I've never just left him in his chair. But I have to leave. Someone else will have to help him.

"I got to go," I say. That's the truth.

"Go then!!!" he roars like a lion.

I startle.

He glares off to the side, avoids my eyes.

My neck and cheeks burn up. I'm not paralyzed by his roar. No. I'm angry! How dare he roar at *me!*

I'm mad at Dad? What a strange feeling. It's grand!

I get it. He doesn't need me. He's *fine*. It's all some game to him. He gets to do whatever he wants. Meanwhile, I'm stuck with feelings of shame my whole life. I'm so fucking stupid to take care of him.

Except, I don't think he'll remember this tomorrow. And I won't be able to abandon him. Still, I'm not helping him to bed. The aide will find him. I'm leaving. I stood up to him! He roared! I survived!

Say good-bye. To leave with no good-bye is cruel. I'm angry, not cruel. "Good-bye," I say.

No comment. No look.

I'm angry he won't look at me. I want to scream. I make do with a glare at the side of his head. I leave, hurry down the hall, watch the reflection of light in the shiny linoleum. Angry! I smile. I'm happy I stood up to Dad!

I wave good-bye to Jane, walk straight through the lobby, out into the starry night, ecstatic. I'm going home, to my house, to take care of myself. Merriment floods in. I burst out laughing. I'm mad at Dad! I stood up to him! I said, 'I'm your daughter.' Good for you, Marie. Well done. I was direct and respectful. He roared and nothing bad happened!

"I'm *mad*," I say, starting the car, feeling outraged that he would roar at me, sweet me. I feel powerful. I speed away.

I'd better slow down.

I join the stream of traffic on the boulevard, inspect each detail of the incident with Dad, satisfied. Fresh anger comes each time I replay his voice roaring, *"Go then!"*

I've *never* been mad at Dad. Is that possible? Never up close. I've been angry from afar. God, this feels good.

Hm. I'm halfway home. How long do I stay mad?

Oh.

A day? Try a day.

I never thought I could be happy and mad at the same time, but I am.

The next morning, I wake from a grand sleep. The day unfolds effortlessly. Every time I think of Dad, I think, yep, I'm still mad.

At five o'clock in the afternoon, done with work, I get ready to pull out of the parking lot. Turn left to go see Dad? Or right to go home? I don't *want* to go see him. I'm still mad at him.

But it's cruel to leave him all alone.

He'll survive. He may need to feel the sting of my not showing up, or he may not. But *I* don't want to stuff my feelings ever again. I turn right toward home.

On the way to the freeway, the trees and buildings seem to glide by me. I feel wild and also still within. It's a good decision to take care of myself. The semi-truck panic taught me how important it is to not let fear paralyze me. I refuse to visit Dad for fear he'll be upset with me if I don't. I'll never throw myself under the bus because of fear again.

Dad's been really difficult to deal with my whole life.

A muffled quiet mood walks in. It asks, "What's been hard?" as though it's not obvious.

I float into another world where things are sunny but silent. My blank, quiet mind wonders what has been so hard. I turn the car toward the blue haze of mountains, then toward the stop light for the freeway on-ramp to head home. It's a long stop light. Good. I have things to think about.

What's been hard? The answer comes by way of a deep, warm well of sorrow which sends tears up to my eyes before I understand what the answer is.

Suddenly, I see. It's that I'm his daughter.

I continue to wait for the light to change.

In my mind, I look down from a sunny balcony, with those blue mountains behind me. On the sunlit ground below me, girls hug their dads without fear. They smile, happy. They fall into their dads' arms, safe, protected. I'm not afraid for them.

Alone on the balcony, I see clearly now what's been so hard: I could never safely hug my dad.

Tears trickle down my cheeks.

What a relief to know after all these years, being touched was hard, being afraid of him getting near me was hard, but never being able to relax into his arms was the hardest thing of all, the biggest loss for me.

I take a deep breath and sigh. I feel sane.

The crazy-making emotional plate-spinning I've done since I can remember, trying to be okay with Dad being the way he is, while not even understanding the real loss, makes sense now. I feel calm with tender compassion for myself. I've felt strong, tough, scared, resigned, ashamed, guilty, even mad, but I've never felt compassion for myself, for my loss. I never knew what it was until now.

The light changes. I get on the freeway and drive in silent observation of everything—sunlight glinting on the mostly white and silver cars, green fields of strawberries below the over-pass, orange haze over the western part of the ocean you only get a glimpse of here with the southern exposure to the sea. Life around me happens without sound. All these years I've wanted to believe unbearable stress was nothing, of no importance. I was wrong. It was huge.

I'm going home to our neck of the woods where the weather's been hot today, according to the forecast, although it's December. I'll put my pajamas on, make a frosty seltzer fruit juice drink, sit in front of a fan and pretend I'm on a sloping lawn with a blanket on my lap, recovering at a sanitarium.

Two days later, I get in my car after work. Left? Or right? It's been three days since I've seen Dad. I can feel angry if I try, but my anger's dissolving the way onions dissolve in soup—you know the onion's there, but it's part of the soup now, there's no taking it out, and who would want to? It's a great thing to get angry when Dad booms at me. I love my life.

I think three days is long enough. It's been grand being mad at Dad, but I'm done. I'll have a three-day rule for being mad at him, because this was the first but won't be the last time I get mad at him. I'm sure he doesn't even know why I haven't been showing up. And in the universe of hurts and bruises, that's okay, because he's tough. I took care of myself. God looks after him. But I don't want to completely abandon him, just because he has bad behavior.

I'll go see him. I wonder if he'll even remember I stood up to him.

I find him sitting beside his bed, cozy in his red jacket, though it's eighty-five degrees outside. "Hi, Dad."

"Marie? Is that you?" he asks, reaching for me, his hands trembling.

Poor thing. I feel bad he had to be alone, but I don't feel bad for staying away to take care of myself. "Yes, Dad." I take his hands. "It's Marie. Your hands are warm. How are you feeling?"

"Great. Just great, now that you're here. Pull up a chair."

He missed me.

He has a fever.

I didn't cause that.

He's on his path.
I'm on mine.

CHAPTER 40
THE DOLLY WITH THE PURPLE GOWN

March, 2010. Two weeks later.

It's Saturday morning, two weeks since I stood up to Dad. I feel good. He hasn't acted out since, and the antibiotics took away his fever. I'm going to meet Cecilia at Rite-Aid where we'll car pool to see Dad. She's always fun to visit with. I'm not going to wear a giant T-shirt. I'm going to wear my nice yellow one. Ever since I told him that big truth which had been lying in wait all his and my life—*I'm your daughter*—something in me is slowly breaking, in a good way, like the seal on a water bottle snapping in slow motion. It's the lock I put on Dad to keep me out, because of my profession as a counselor. The lock broke when I said, "I'm your daughter." Now I know I have to try to help him, because I think he doesn't have peace with himself, or with his family, and I can help him with that, because I'm good at it, and because I'm his daughter, first, a counselor second. I'm going to try to help him gain access to himself, because if he dies and I didn't even try, I could never forgive myself.

At the Rite-Aid parking lot, I get out of my Corolla and wave at Cecilia. She stands next to her shiny beige convertible, smiles and waves in her pale lime green cashmere sweater, like it's easy to be her, but it's not. She gets pulled in fifty directions and has the same demons I have.

Once a week, Cecilia comes from thirty minutes north, I come from twenty minutes east, and we travel together forty minutes west to visit Dad at Calm Shores. We hug next to her car.

"I'm so glad to see you!" she says. "Strength in numbers."

We laugh.

"Yes! And I've made a decision," I say.

"A decision!"

We grin as we climb into her car.

"You know, I've always wanted to get Dad to apologize to his children before he dies."

"Of course," she says backing up to leave.

"But I've always held back, because it's crossing a line as a counselor."

"Yes." She pulls onto the cross-streets.

"Well, today I don't care about crossing a line. I just don't care. It's a stupid rule in this circumstance. I want to ask Dad about his childhood again. Will you help me?" I ask.

"Sure," she says. Her curiosity shows in her eyebrows.

"I want to try one more time to help him get inside his psyche. We know his mom bathed him until he was twelve. He says he never had an unhappy day as a child and his parents were saints."

"Well, that tells you right there something's wrong."

"Yes!"

"And this might be a good time to try," she says, "because he hasn't been sick for almost two weeks. *God* he's tough, isn't he? I mean, just when it seems an infection's got the better of him and the antibiotics aren't helping, the second round of antibiotics kicks in! He's ninety-*two!* Tough as nails. At least our parents gave us good genes!" She laughs. "Sure, I'll help you talk to him."

"It's so helpful that you relate," I say.

"Thanks. That goes both ways. Well, I have news, and this may bear on what you're saying," she says.

"What?"

"He hurt one of the aides last night. I didn't want to tell you on the phone."

"Oh dear. He's deteriorating."

"Apparently the aide wasn't one whom he knew, and when she pulled his covers off of him, he grabbed her hand and bent her fingers back and wouldn't let go. Nothing broken. But she was scared and crying."

"I feel bad trying to help someone who hurts an aide. By the way, thanks for fielding all the problem calls, like, he's off hospice, he's back on hospice, needs new meds to help his anxiety at night when he calls for Mom. Now this. Thanks."

"You're welcome. So, I need to meet with the nurses," she says.

"Okay. You know, he doesn't like *anyone* whom he doesn't know pulling his covers off."

"No. Nobody would like that. But he almost broke her hand and wouldn't let go. What do you suppose that's about?" she asks.

"His mom bathed him till he was twelve. Did she pull his covers off too?" I ask.

"Right," she says.

"Grandma didn't have good boundaries, always talking about our little bosoms when we were small. Making us take our underpants off for naps. But what about Grampa? Maybe he pulled Dad's covers off as a boy." I watch the miles of strawberry fields go by. "Grampa ran his hand up my thigh when I was twenty-five and asked me for sex because Grandma had died and he was lonely. He didn't seem to think twice about it."

"Yes."

"And Patricia came home from one of those summer weeks we stayed at Grandma and Grampa's house," I say, "mute for at least three weeks. Nobody had a clue something bad might have happened to her. We just tried to get her to talk, like it was a game or something. A five-year-old doesn't go mute for three weeks for no reason." A sudden sadness fills me up. I haven't thought of Patricia going mute in years. She can't eat food with white seeds. If Grampa put himself in her mouth, he might have reassured her he's just giving her his seed. Something happened so she couldn't talk. "It's like your therapist said, if you come home, your windows are broken and your things are missing, you know a burglar's been there, though you didn't see the burglar. Patricia had a burglar at Grandma and Grampa's."

Cecilia nods. Shakes her head. "So. What do you think we should say to Dad about hurting the aide?" Cecilia asks.

"Let's see if he remembers," I say. "A river of frozen feelings might be break-ing up in him, frozen for over ninety years. He exploded at me two weeks ago when I got mad at him and stood up to him."

"No. You got *mad* at *Dad?*" she says.

"Yep. He asked what I was wearing under my blouse and I said *that's* not okay, Dad. I'm your *daughter.*" I look at her with a grin.

"You just *said* that?" she says.

"Yep. I especially like the 'I'm your daughter' part," I say, sitting a little taller.

"Oh yes, I like that too. What happened after you said that?"

"He said, 'Whatever you say.' I knew there was no use trying to talk, and he might grab at me if I helped him to bed. So, I said, 'I got to go.' Then he roared, '*Go then!*'"

"What did you do?"

"I left! I wasn't mad till he boomed, '*Go then!*' But when he did that, some-thing unlocked inside me and I got mad. Stayed mad for three days. You know, I've never been mad at him."

"How are you now?" she says.

"Fine. I feel empowered, in case he does it again. Or rather, when he does it again."

"Yeah. I get mad, but I don't *tell* him. God forbid, right?" We laugh. "I just cajole him. Wow. Good for you."

"Thanks," I say.

"So, you've seen him since then?" she says.

"Yes. Several times."

"And how is he?"

"If he remembers that I got mad at him, he hasn't let on, but in two weeks he hasn't tried to touch me or made lewd comments even once."

"Wow." She gives me a puzzled frown.

"Yeah." I nod at her with raised eyebrows.

"Do you think he's cured?" she asks slowly, with a wide-eyed look, her lips curling in a funny smile.

We howl.

"Twenty years of strict boundaries not letting him see his grandchildren didn't cure him," I say. "Me getting mad once sure isn't going to do it. No, he's not cured. But *I* am."

"Really?"

"Yes. I'm cured because he doesn't scare me anymore." I lean my head into the wind.

"He doesn't?"

"Nope. The fear's gone. I had to pass a semi-truck," I say, "and to make a long story short, I was having these panic attacks passing trucks for a month, and finally one day I all but fainted passing a giant truck, I was so scared, and *puzzled*. Because trucks never were a problem for me. So, I asked myself, what do these panic attacks mean? And boom. Just as I was seeing white there was the answer. Dad. He was the semi. I'm telling you I haven't been the same since. I decided after that, no matter what, I have to object whenever he's inappropriate. Not scared of semi's anymore either."

"Wow. *Marie*."

"Yeah."

"And he hasn't done anything since?"

"Nope. He's scared of me." I belly laugh at my joke.

"No, Marie, maybe he is."

"Are you kidding? No way. He's not afraid of me. I'm a flea on his psyche, a pest. Not a threat," I say.

"No," Cecilia says.

I watch the fields. Dad scared of me? I didn't think I mattered enough for him to really care one way or the other if I got mad. But she thinks it mattered to him.

The Dolly with the Purple Gown   279

"You think it mattered to him?"

"Yes."

That was emphatic.

"Well. I guess time will tell," I say. "I just thought it was coincidence, him not acting out these past two weeks. Maybe he is scared of me."

"Like you say, time will tell. Well, about the aide," she says.

I rub my brow, sick for the aide and for what may be coming for Dad—a move to a crowded, noisy ward for people who act out badly.

"They're going to try a new medication, first. But, if he doesn't respond to it, you know, if he does it again, they'll have to move him to South."

The wing for people with behavior problems.

"He seems to do it when they go to change him," Cecilia says and shrugs.

"I wonder if they just pull the covers away without letting him *know*," I say, irritated. "I think he gets scared when someone grabs his covers."

"Well, they have to change him."

"I know but they have to *tell* him before they touch him. That's just how he is. And you should only pull the covers up from the feet, not down from the chest."

"They must know that, right?"

"I don't think so. An older aide taught me that when I was nineteen. So, yeah, when I get Dad up out of bed, I don't have any trouble, but I *talk* to him before I touch his blankets. That's just common sense. But it's easy to forget. He did get my hand *once*, and I was scared he'd break it, but that was a year ago and I'm sure I must have grabbed his blanket, you know, without saying something first, and scared him."

"Yeah," Cecilia says, "there's something about that."

"Anyway, when that happened, when I thought he might break my hand, he looked at me terrified and fierce, like he'd rather die than let go of those covers. Come to think of it, he told me the night I got mad at him, he doesn't like surprises. We'd been talking in the hall, getting along. In fact, that was when he changed. I asked if he liked surprises. He got a distant look in his eyes. He said he doesn't like surprises. He got nervous and started tapping his hand, then went to grab my thigh. I had to intercept his hand and stand up."

"Well. Like you said, we know Grandma bathed him till he was twelve. God knows what else might have happened," Cecilia says, shaking her head. "You know?"

"I agree. Because he switches, into somebody else, it seems."

"He does."

We ride in silence.

"Almost there," Cecilia says. "I love that we ride together. It really helps to talk about it all."

I nod. I can't talk more. I'll cry thinking of them drugging Dad in South.

We find Dad in his red jacket and brown hat in the hall, with his wheel chair breaks locked on. That's illegal, but it's better than putting him in South.

"Hi Dad!" Cecilia says. She's like a song bird. He's really glad to see us, by the way he grabs our hands. A little scary. "How *are* you?" she asks warmly, smiling.

"Oh, am I glad to see you two!" he says, sounding anxious and relieved, like a child who was lost and has just been found. He trembles with relief.

"I bet you are," Cecilia says, so tenderly. He probably doesn't understand. They probably yelled at him to let go of the aide, and maybe restrained him. Who knows? After he was already scared. "I'm just going to talk to the nurses, Dad. Marie will stay with you."

"Oh, don't go. Either of you."

"I'll be right back." Cecilia smiles at me, I nod. She goes to the nurse's station.

"You want to go outside, Dad? The sun's out. It's not too cold," I say.

"Oh, that'd be nice."

"Come on." I unlock the chair.

"Yeah, I don't know what was wrong," he says, pointing at the foot rests of his wheel chair. "I couldn't go, but you've got things going now so that's good. How are you, Little Marie?"

"I'm good. It's good to see you. Rough night?"

"Yes!" he says with conviction.

I push the square automatic door opener, and as the door opens, push him outside into the sun, just beyond the shade of the broad entry breeze-way. I pull up two patio chairs and take a seat. I have to ask him what happened.

"So, sun feel good?" I ask.

He nods, grinning at the cement.

"I have to ask you something."

He raises his eyebrows, gazing downward still, and nods like a child in trouble.

"Do you remember grabbing an aide last night?"

He nods.

"You hurt her hand."

He nods.

"Do you remember why?"

He shakes his head no.

"You really hurt her."

"I did?"

"Yes. You don't remember why you grabbed her hand?"

"No."

Ah. Here's Cecilia. "He remembers grabbing her hand but doesn't remember why," I say as Cecilia sits in the other chair.

Cecilia nods. "Dad, how are you?"

"Pretty good." He nods at the pavement.

"Joanne and Ella said you had a pretty rough night. You hurt one of the aides. Marie says you don't remember why you grabbed her hand."

He shakes his head.

"But you remember you did?" Cecilia says.

He nods.

"Well, they think you might have anxiety. You're not sleeping well, Joanne says. So, they want to give you a new medication that will help you feel calmer," she says.

"Oh?" he says.

"Is that all right with you?" she asks.

"Sure. Sure. Whatever you think is best," he says.

"Okay," she says.

Cecilia and I nod at each other.

"So, do you think you hurt her on purpose, Dad?" I ask.

He shrugs and slightly turns his palms out as if to say, maybe so.

"But you don't know why you grabbed her?" Cecilia asks.

Dad mumbles something toward the ground.

"What's that, Dad?" I ask in a quiet voice, leaning close.

"Maybe she grabbed me."

"Oh. I see. Okay. Okay. Well, Dad, even if the aide grabs you, you need to not hurt them, okay? You really hurt her. You're a lot stronger than the aides."

Dad looks up for the first time. He shakes his head no.

"The aides are strong," Cecilia says.

Dad nods.

"Okay. We'll talk to them and make sure they all know *not* to take your covers off without telling you first."

"That would be good," Dad says, and nods.

"Okay. Well, everybody can try to do things better," Cecilia says.

He smiles and nods.

"Is that sun too hot on you Dad?" she asks.

"A little." He smiles.

It's an understatement. Beads of sweat on his head show through his thin strands of silver hair. We move the chairs so everyone's in the shade and sit back down.

He's so sweet and so scared. And lewd and mean. It's now or never.

"I have an idea," I say. "Let's everyone say what they're favorite toy was as a child."

"Oh, that'll be fun," Cecilia says. "Mine was a panda bear. What about you Marie?"

"My blue stuffed dog, with white stripes and black ears."

We both look to Dad, but he doesn't seem interested in what we're saying. This was a stupid idea. He looks far away, which more and more these days he seems to do. Oh well. It's probably too late to get him to go within. But at least I'm finally not afraid of him. And not afraid to try.

"What about you, Dad? What was your favorite toy as a child?" I ask.

His eyes smile but he's far away. I don't think he's with us. They probably gave him meds to calm down last night. Maybe they're making him space out even more than usual.

"My dolly," he says.

Cecilia and I look at each other.

He had a dolly? What kind of dolls were boys given in 1920? I thought his favorite toy would be a gun or a truck or a train engine.

"You had a dolly, Dad?" Cecilia says.

"Yes." He nods with a big smile.

Cecilia and I nod at each other and shrug.

"What kind of doll?" I ask.

"Was it a soldier doll?" Cecilia asks.

Dad grins and quickly shakes his head no, like she's silly. "No," he says.

"Was it a baby doll?" I ask. Maybe boys played with baby dolls back then.

"No," he says.

We're losing him, plainly. In just the last month he's gotten less and less responsive. There's not much time left.

"What did your dolly look like?" I ask.

"Oh," he says. "She had long dark hair fixed in a bun." He forms an imaginary bun with his hands. "And she wore a purple gown." His hand draws in space before him the lines of a gown, his gaze fixed in middle space. "With a white," he moves his fingers in delicate circles, "lace collar."

He looks far away and happy.

"She sounds beautiful," I say.

He nods.

Dad's always been a man's man, making fun of effeminate men and girl's things, watching football and boxing. He was a boxer.

"Wow. She must have been beautiful, with a purple gown," Cecilia says.

"With a white lace collar," he says, outlining the lace with his fingers again, like she's right here with him.

It's hard to believe it was his, not his sister's.

"Dad, was it Aunt Jane's doll and you got to play with it?" I ask.

He shakes his head no with a grim smile. "No. Mine."

Amazing. "How old were you, do you remember?"

He suddenly looks away, irritated by something. He looks down. "I was four," he says.

He knows that for a fact.

"Did you and Aunt Jane play dolls?" Cecilia asks.

He presses his lips grimly and shakes his head no. "Jane can go to the moon." Whoa.

"You'd like to send Aunt Jane to the moon," Cecilia says.

He nods.

"You and Jane didn't get along," I say.

He shakes his head no, smiling.

I never knew they didn't get along.

"Interesting," says Cecilia. "Big sisters *can* be a problem."

Dad nods.

So far so good. I want more information though, to see what his childhood was really like. "How about let's say our favorite games when we were little. What was yours, Cecilia?" I ask.

"Mine was jumping rope. I got pretty good at it. What about you, Marie? What was your favorite game?"

"Freeze tag. In the summer. In the street," I watch Dad's face. He smiles to himself. "I loved getting to play with the big kids, watching it get dark. What about you Dad? What was your favorite game?"

Dad grins. His eyes look full of mischief. "Catching mice. And killing them."

Oh, dear. "Really?" I ask.

He nods. "Catch 'em. Kill 'em." He has a gleeful look.

He could be a sociopath. "How did you kill them?" I ask.

"Poke 'em. Till they're dead." He smiles, but seems a little embarrassed.

"Oh," I say. I make a face at Cecilia, who shrugs, wide-eyed.

Dad nods again, like it's basically a satisfying memory.

It doesn't go with the dolly, in my mind.

Grandma could have damaged his brain with those routine Lysol douches Grampa told me she used for birth control every Wednesday and Saturday. She probably didn't know she was pregnant with Dad.

"It sounds like you were a good mouse catcher," Cecilia says.

He nods appreciatively. Beads of sweat trickle down his temple.

"It's pretty hot out here—shall we sit in the lobby?" I ask.

"Sure," says Cecilia. "Will that be all right with you, Dad?"

"That'd be nice." He nods.

We settle into one of the lobby's three sitting areas.

"So, what was your favorite thing about school?" Cecilia asks, shrugging with a smile at me. I nod.

"Boxing," he says.

"Oh. Boxing at school," I say. "Well, that explains why you always liked to watch the Friday night fights. Were you good at it? I mean was there a boxing team?"

He nods slowly with a sly smile. "I'd *knock* 'em down."

"Wow. Good for you. Were the boxing gloves different back then?" I ask.

"No gloves."

"Oh."

I wait for him to go on, but he's not talking, darn it.

Oh, just ask the big one. Time's running out. "What was your mom like?"

He laughs nervously, shakes his head no. "Don't ask *her!*"

Whoa.

"Don't ask your mom what she's like?"

"Don't go *near that* one," he says softly, hanging his head, losing his smile.

Wow. Cecilia and I raise our eyebrows at each other.

Well. That's something. At least that's a little different than the old anthem, "My parents were saints and I never had an unhappy day in my life." He obviously doesn't want to talk about her. At least his response is real.

CHAPTER 41
THE THING HE'S SNAGGED ON

March, 2010. The same afternoon.

After I say good-bye to Cecilia at Rite-Aid, I drive home with my mind swirling. I need to think. If Dad's a sociopath, would he have spoken so fondly of his dolly? Yet there were the mice. And he didn't cry when Mom died. He never showed emotion.

Except the night after Mom's funeral. He called Cecilia and cried, missing his children.

Wind buffets the car. I love the wind.

Why didn't he put his foot down sooner with Grandma bathing him?

The same reason I didn't put my foot down sooner with him—intimidated. And for years, I didn't even know for sure something was wrong with the way he touched me. I thought something was wrong with me, that I was too sensitive. He probably didn't know something was wrong in the early years of his mom bathing him. Getting molested can be like air, if you don't know there is such a thing, you don't know you're breathing it.

The highway ends in the two-lane road through the small town of Casitas Springs. Sadly, the wind stops there.

A thought exhilarates me as though it were the wind—I'm going to block Dad's old exit route! The one where he disconnects and hides inside himself. Of course! He disconnects from everyone because on some level his shame's over-whelming. Being bathed by your mother till you're twelve will definitely create a shame-based person.

I picture her bathing him, a youngster, under a bare forty-watt bulb in an old depression era bathroom, till he was twelve. And did she bathe with him? I'll never know.

Dad lost his own psychological ground around women, because of his mom. So, he *has* to ridicule, control, always dominate with his words, or hands in order to not be over-whelmed by the pain in his psyche. Of course. His mom wore the pants in the family.

People have free will, but they don't always have a choice in their actions, especially if they're not conscious of what's going on inside them There're reasons for what Dad does, but he doesn't know those reasons. Because he wouldn't do that behavior if he were in his right mind. He loves me. Like he loved his dolly. He's not a sociopath. They can't love people.

I'm going to try again. This time I won't question him about things in a casual tone, the way a child tries to casually hide something bigger than herself. I'll be normal, tell him it makes me sad that his children hardly see him, and tell him I think he can fix that. Yeah. Simple. He obviously trusts me now. I'll go back tomorrow.

At home, happy with my new resolve, I sit down on the wool rug in the living room with Baker, help him fold the clothes. I love the wool rug. It reminds me of my childhood. I tell him everything I found on my archeological dig with Cecilia. The dolly. The mice. Dad almost breaking the aide's hand. "Probably because the aide grabbed his covers. It makes perfect sense."

Baker nods. He understands that part about the covers.

"Remember, his mom bathed him till he was twelve," I say. "I think my dad's scared—like he's a child—of being molested. And get this, he enjoyed killing mice. That's a sign he could be a sociopath. Except he loves me. And the dolly. He looked so *happy* talking about his dolly."

"Pretty amazing, Dear," he says. "At least *finally* at the age of twelve he grabs his mother's wrist and says *listen* you old bag—"

I laugh. "Baker, stop!"

"Why?" He's full of mirth.

"You're so irreverent."

"You betcha baby. Well, he put his foot down, anyway, right?"

"Yeah. Mom said so."

"Poor fuck."

"Exactly. They didn't have therapy in those days," I say. "They didn't understand all of this."

"Well how come I didn't become a molester?" he asks.

"I don't know. Did you torture mice?"

"Of course not."

"Maybe he got brain damaged from Grandma's Lysol birth control," I say. "Every Wednesday and Saturday, Grampa said."

"That could mess someone up," he says.

"He had to have gotten the compulsion to touch us from his mom. He's always been strange. Like, he can't ever have anyone disagree with him."

"Well, that's a family trait."

"Hush. He's never cried, that I know of. Not even when Mom died. Seventy years together. No tears. When he didn't cry when she died, I thought, oh, he's in denial. But it's been three years. He still hasn't cried. He calls for her at night. It's so sad. And, he has no concept that his molesting affected us. That's not normal. You know?"

"What are you saying?"

"Maybe he's a partial sociopath. He knows how to be kind, but can't actually connect. He plays the part he's supposed to. Apart from rage and laughter, I don't think I've seen a real emotion in him. I mean, he left his home to move to a nursing home and wasn't angry or sad. He was nervous, and suspicious of strangers, but not depressed or irritated, that I could see. How do you leave your own home forever and not be upset? He really is sick, I think. I just think it's so sad. He's going to die and not have connected with his own children."

"What, are you going to try to be his counselor?"

God he's smart. "No. Of course not. But, as a friend, as a daughter, I can tell him what I'm thinking, what I see. What do I have to lose? No, of course I can't be his counselor."

I draw my fingers through the soft wool of the rug and stretch them into the air. Of course, I'm going to be his counselor, because, even if he would agree to see a counselor, no one else could get at it, the thing he's snagged on, the way I can. I'm sure of it. He's beginning to trust me.

Though, I may have waited too long.

"Dear, you already are his counselor. And it's okay. That rule that you can't counsel family members is bullshit anyway. Counsel me any time you need to."

"Okay, Dear." I'm grateful for his blessing.

We kiss.

"I'm going to go play my guitar," I say.

He pulls me up off the floor.

I need some quiet time with myself. In our walk-through closet where my guitar playing is least likely to bother the neighbors, I slip on a cute skirt and boots—why not? It's who I am when I play. It feels good to be myself. I'm a lot more myself since I stood up to Dad. I pick up my glossy electric guitar from its stand next to the coats, sling the strap over my head. I'm speechless, calm. I plug things in, thinking, I'm going to lose my dad someday soon. Tears warm my eyes. I listen for the small pop as I turn on the amp. I tune the guitar, begin a G minor blues progression, a rocking cradle for my soul. From inside the music, I take a silent breathtaking look at life. I'm in love with it all. Dad, Baker, hurts and bruises, short fuses, painstaking love.

I begin an instrumental intro to Ball and Chain.

No one's immune from life's lessons.

The minor chords resonate in my throat as I hum. Dad's not conscious of having hurt people. But as a result of what he does, people don't want to be around him. I'm going to help Dad connect with himself, so he can wake up, see what he's done, connect with his children. I'm not afraid of his roar anymore.

Baker comes around the corner. "Wow. Cute outfit."

"Thanks, Dear."

Chapter 42
A Mountain of Pride

March, 2010. The next evening.

I park the car in the dark under the stars in front of old Calm Shores again. "This is it," I say to the steering wheel. I'm going to help Dad connect with his children. There's no putting it off, but, dang, I hate these butterflies in my stomach. I should have come earlier. It's bed time now. I always talk big. Where's my zest now?

Can't I skip this part of life, God, and just live my own life?

What am I afraid of? What can go wrong? He'll roar? So?

He's my dad. It seems wrong to confront him.

Is it wrong to be honest? No. After all these years of saying nothing, to finally act as though things matter, as though people's lives and feelings matter, is that wrong? No.

Is it wrong to continue smiling as though a life-long thousand-car train wreck weren't still in progress? Yes.

My thoughts stop while I open the car door, step out into the night.

Talk about living my own life, this *is* my own life. I shut the car door with a small flourish. Like a slow-motion sequence in a movie, I slowly cross the front patio and go in through the tall glass doors. This is who I am.

There he is in his red jacket outside his room, bent way over. He probably wants to go to bed, but I'll ask him if we can talk in the dining room first. More peaceful, private.

"Hi, Dad." His life's about to change, for better or worse. I'm going to say what I see, the way I would with any client.

"Marie?"

God, I love him. I don't care that I never feel safe around him. I don't fucking care about that anymore.

"Yeah, it's me, Dad."

"How are you?" he asks. He looks up at me with a question in his eye, which is different than the one he asked. He's psychic, or he picked something up in my walk, my tone. What are you up to, Marie, he's asking with his look, I'm sure of it. There must have been a new note in the melody of my voice.

"I'm really good," I say.

He's like a child and I'm sorry I let him sit alone, didn't come to see him sooner. My butterflies are gone.

"Pull up a chair," he says with a grim note, looking at my feet.

"You know, I wanted to talk to you about something," I say.

He looks out across the hall. "Oh?"

Right now, his hall feels to me like Meursault's indifferent universe, before he was executed, in Camus' *The Stranger.*

"It's nothing bad." Is that true?

He smiles into space and nods, like he's heard that before.

I say, "It's really not anything bad. It's something good, actually." It is. "Let's go in the dining room," I say.

"Sure."

I unlock his chair. "I'll push you," I say.

He nods and holds his feet out in front of him.

As we go, I feel alive, like life is running all around and through us, even bouncing off the linoleum floor. Dad and his dolly, the mice he killed and my talk with Baker—it all makes me sure I'm supposed to try to get through to him.

I'm just going to start with telling him that if he would just apologize to everyone, they would happily come to see him and he would feel better. I'll call it like I see it. Approach him as a truly sick person, who, maybe with encouragement and love, could change. Why didn't I think of it before?

I was afraid of him before.

We round the corner into the brightly lit empty dining hall where hip hop music blares. Darn. I was hoping for classical music in an empty soft lit dining hall. No. The big moment has to come with bright lights and upbeat music. Oh well. Where do we sit for this kind of talk?

We park in the middle. I pull up a chair from one of the eight big tables and sit in front of him. "So, I'll just tell you what it is I'm thinking. Um, I know it's mainly me who you see, of all your kids."

"That's right. Where are the others?" He sounds as though he thinks he could do better than me, as though I'm a pest or a poor substitute for the others

A twinge of hurt pricks me. Oh well. Focus. "Well, that's just it. You know, they're still hurt."

"Oh?"

"Well, yeah." Funny, the hip hop music sounds far away, now. It seems we're in a quiet private place. Still, I move close to his ear so what I say doesn't have to come out too loud "You touch our breasts sometimes, Dad, and it's not all right. And you never apologize."

He slowly looks down to the right with a nervous smile. He's thinking about what I said.

Don't mince words. "You know, you need to apologize to people in order for them to want to come around."

Dad shakes his head no, eyes wide, still smiling at the floor.

"You don't want to apologize?"

He shakes his head no.

Well, he's not roaring, not calling me a slut or arguing. This is progress. Now he's looking toward the door to the hall. He wants to go to his room.

Talk fast. "It's not awful to apologize. It makes you feel better. Everyone feels better." I'm glad for the hip hop music now. It makes it hard for anyone who might be around to hear us. "And your kids would come to see you, I'm sure of it. Well, I'm pretty sure. They love you, Dad. They love you so much. But—"

Now, I'd better use a confederate tone to tell him this part. "You know, they're mad at you. You can't blame them. Heck, I'm mad too, sometimes, and it's not easy to come and see you." I wait for his response.

He nods, shrugs like a child who doesn't want to talk.

But he's not denying that he molested us. This is strange and good. Think Marie. Say what you see. He looks remorseful. But it would be hard to apologize, since no one's here.

Letters. "You look remorseful. I know, Dad, why don't you write each of your kids a letter. You dictate and I'll write. Short, simple letters of apology. Here." I get a piece of folded paper and a pen from my purse. "You say the words, I'll write. I'll re-write them later, on regular paper. Okay?"

"All right. If you say so." He shrugs.

"Good. Good plan." Wow. It's working. "Okay you talk. How about Sarah first."

"Oh no!" He grins and shakes his head with nervous wide eyes. "Not her."

"Not Sarah?" I can't help smiling. "Are you afraid of Sarah?"

He nods at the floor.

A kitchen aide comes out, turns off the radio, goes back in the kitchen. It's quiet.

"How come not Sarah?" I softly ask.

No answer. He makes a grimace and shakes his head no.

"Do you want to say something to any of your children?"

He shakes his head no.

I'll be badgering him if I keep on.

"Okay," I say. "Maybe some other day."

He nods. Still no words.

I tried. Maybe it is too late. It could be he's really like a child inside now.

"You want to go to your room?"

He nods.

"Okay," I say, put my piece of paper and pen away.

I don't know how much of this he understands. It was a good try, but it's too late. Too much time has passed. He can't really function. I need to let it go. It's time to leave him in peace.

I stand up, push my chair back up to the table. I feel like a jerk pressuring him to write letters of apology when he can't function that well. I begin to push Dad back to his room.

"Marie," he says.

"Yes?" I stop. Give him time. It takes him time to think. He's not like he used to be, quick, sharp.

"I know I've hurt you," he says. Dad glances back at me and looks back at the floor, nods. "I shouldn't have."

His words quench a thirst I've had for decades. I come around to where he can see me. "Thanks, Dad. That means a lot to me."

He raises his eyebrows, nods. I want to hug him, but he's not safe for me. I squeeze his bony shoulder through his red jacket. It feels so inadequate, but it's what we have, in fact it's who we are, and that somehow makes the awkward gesture so beautiful it brings tears to my eyes.

So. He's not a child. He's taking it all in.

Over and over his words—I know I've hurt you. I shouldn't have—rain gently down from my mind into my heart as I push him back down the hall to his room. I help him stand up and sit down on the bed, take his shoes off and swing his legs up onto the mattress, tuck his ten-pound Our Lady of Guadalupe blanket around and under his feet and up under his chin. I swear he has a fever.

At peace now, I feel the divine, like an atmosphere that can never be avoided, cradle us. I can't help wonder if this will be the fever to finally take him.

"You feel warm. Would you like some ice water?" I ask.

"Sure."

I don't want him to get sick and bounce back again. It's too painful watching him live out his days without his family nearby. I pour ice water from the frosty turquoise plastic pitcher, roll the bed up, help him pull the blanket away from his face, hand him the cup and sit in the wheelchair facing him.

"You're a good daughter, Marie."

"Thanks, Dad." I need to ask him. "Dad."

"Yes."

"I'm just wondering."

"Fire away."

He's not afraid of me anymore. "How come you don't apologize to the others?"

He looks ahead into space, seems to ponder for a minute. "Pride," he says grimly. "A mountain of it. I drag it around with me everywhere I go." He nods like he can see it all in front of him, plain as day.

He actually let me see inside him. The lion opened wide. I'm a little dizzy, I'm so grateful, honored, humbled. "Thanks for telling me, Dad."

What a cruel burden he carries. Pride covers up old anger, which covers up old fear, which covers up old loss. What loss? Grieving the original loss is what heals us. What's the original loss beneath Dad's pride? Must be Grandma bathing him.

I have to tell the others what he said. It feels as though he were just now born.

He looks tired, and small.

"You want to go to sleep, Dad?"

He smiles, nods, closes his eyes.

I put his bed back down, turn off the bedside light, pull his covers up, kiss his forehead. He's definitely warm. "You feel warm."

"Oh?"

"I'll tell the nurse."

"All right," he says softly, sounding almost asleep.

"Good night," I say.

"I love you. Always have. Always will," he says.

"I love you too."

He smiles.

"I'll see you tomorrow, Dad."

"That'll be nice."

He won't be here long now, I think. I tuck his covers snug around his feet.

"Thank you. You're a good daughter."

"You're not mad at me for being honest. Thanks, Dad. You're a good dad."

He smiles.

It's over. There's nothing more I can do. I'm exhausted.

I love him, but I hope he goes soon. It's hard seeing him like this, hard not knowing how long he'll hold on, hard saying no to the things I want to do. I'm ready for my own life. But it's your time, God. We're all on our path.

I stop at the nurse station. "My dad seems to have a fever again, not too high."

"Thank you. We'll check on him and call the doctor."

"Thanks." I walk down the long hall. With antibiotics, he'll bounce back. It seems better to naturally let him go, but, maybe I'm wrong. Thankfully, it's not my call.

CHAPTER 43
YOU KNEW THIS WAS THE NIGHT

May, 2010. Two months later.

The phone rings. I jump out of the shower, grab a towel and run to answer it. Dad's been sick for two weeks this time. He could go any time.

"He's back on hospice," says Cecilia.

"That makes sense."

"I don't know, this could be it," she says. "Christopher's with him this morning. I was wondering if you could see him tonight. I'm tied up and Marietta's got a new grandchild coming any minute."

"No problem. I was going anyway. I've been going almost every day, because he's sick."

"Thank you. As long as he sees one of us, I think he's okay. He's on the second round of antibiotics. I don't think they'll go to round three."

I find Dad disheveled, sitting up in bed, eyes wide. He looks different from yesterday. His face seems stretched across his skull. His bony knees are bent stiffly near his chest. His fingers quickly pinch ineffectually at his sheet, which is near the foot of the bed.

"Hi Dad!" Funny, how dark purple his fingers always are, from bumps against hard things, I think. One arm is outside of his white T-shirt. By the looks of his cotton pajamas, he's dry.

"Marie? Oh, thank goodness you're here," he says, his voice worried, froggy from his chest cold. One arm starts to flutter my way and I take it by the elbow, not the hand.

"How are you feeling?" He's so changed from even a month ago. Small, and light in a T-shirt and diaper. Each round of sickness takes a toll, but I've never seen him like this. "You've been pretty sick," I say. He looks so determined and so helpless. The thought of him being this sick without family around breaks my heart. "Let me help you get that sheet up here and get your arm back in your T-shirt."

"Well, fine, but you see, what needs help is *this*," he wheezes a laugh. "Thank goodness you're here. You see, *it* can't do it."

Something about the sheet. "I'll pull it up for you." I feel his head. He's hot.

"Well, it's got to, this, this right here. There were one, two, three, four, five, six of them and they've *got* to find their way, or, well, it'll be dark. I don't need to spell it out. You fix it."

I hazard a guess. "And if we straighten the sheet, they'll be okay?"

"We don't know," he says, staring grimly at the sheet.

"Okay. Let's start there anyway."

He's hot and dry. I think he's dehydrated.

"I knew you would have an answer," he says.

"I'm going to put your bed down, first, to pull you up in bed, get you situated. Then we'll sit your bed up, so I can cover you properly and you can drink some water."

"Oh, that would be heavenly," he says, his arms shaking as I push one away from me, and pull the other away from the crumpled little top sheet.

Six of whom, I wonder.

"Let's fix your shirt." I pull the cotton T-shirt fabric down over his elbow and bend his arm until his wrist pulls through the sleeve. "There. Now let me just fluff these pillows."

"That'll be nice. You know what to do."

He's so appreciative. "I'm going to roll you back now."

He sings in a high shaky voice a few words from "Old Man River." I cradle his hot back with one arm and his bent legs with the other. I want to move him up higher in the bed. I could hurt my back, but he's so light, I'll chance it. I move him up higher in the bed. It worked. I roll him back on his pillows and slowly push his bent legs straight. He's bony and stiff now. It seems he changed overnight.

I pull the sheet up, and straighten it at his feet.

Maybe this *is* it.

"There, now let me roll your bed up. First the knees," I say, pushing the button that elevates his legs. "Now your head." I push the button that raises his head.

He sighs deeply and seems to finally relax.

"Thank you!" he says.

"You're welcome. I'm going for ice for your water."

"Oh! Wonderful!"

I scoop ice from the dining room machine. Tears fill my eyes. How can I want it to be over? How blessed is this to get ice for him now? He's so grateful.

Back in his room I pour a glass. "Here's some ice water, Dad."

I put the straw to his trembling lips, hold the cup. He drinks.

"No extreme measures," he says with the straw still in his mouth, his wide eyes trained on the cup rim as he drinks some more.

"Okay, Dad."

"No antibiotics. Let nature take its course," he says.

My tears well up again. Wow. He's really ready. I am so ready for him to go, but it hurts to hear him say it.

"Okay," I say. "I don't want to lose you," I say.

He glances up and keeps drinking, then pauses with the straw in his mouth and shrugs with raised eyebrows, as if to say, 'Well, it can't be helped.' He drinks more.

"Let the others know they should all come and gather around my bed," he says, his voice stronger.

Now he sounds melodramatic. I smile. His tone reminds me of the way he could make us laugh with humorous melodramatic acts, such as, I don't mind suffering in silence, as long as everyone knows I'm suffering. That's my favorite. He always said that and made us laugh when we were kids.

He sucks the last of the water. "More," he commands.

He appears to have revived before my very eyes. It's inexcusable the facility let him get so dehydrated. They do a great job here, and he's hard to deal with, and they can't catch everything, but this shouldn't have happened. I'll tell them he needs ice water every hour.

"Sure. Here you go," I say, pouring more water and holding the cup for him.

He drinks. "Let the others know," he says solemnly with the straw in his mouth, "what they should bring. Nothing fancy, just the usual. Don't make a big fuss."

"You mean at your funeral."

He makes a matter-of-fact nod. The second glass is empty.

He's not dying.

"And tell them to get whatever they want for themselves, something of this, or that, you know, but nothing for me."

"Okay, Dad," I say, pulling on the straw in his mouth. But he clamps down on it. I let go.

"I'll be sure to tell them, Dad. More water?"

He nods, but then he takes the straw out. "I mean, yes, please," and returns the straw to his mouth.

I pour another glass.

As he drinks, he looks like an infant.

His body's like a fine music box whose wood grain's so parched it drinks a pint of oil. The wood grain is who I've always known. Someone fun and unpredictable, mean and boundaryless, kind and funny. A music box that's locked tight. I see the outside wood, but mostly don't get to hear what's really within him. He's all but dying, and treating it like a farce, which is nice in a way, I mean he doesn't take himself too seriously, but it would be nice to be allowed inside. Which, I guess I was allowed inside, a few weeks ago, when he told me he was sorry and had a mountain of pride.

He didn't say why he had the mountain of pride.

I'm sure he doesn't know why he has it. But I bet he *could* know. If I reference things for him, something could break lose within. Yep.

But he's not well. I need to let him be.

But I want to see who he is. How can a man be locked up so tight he doesn't even cry when his wife of seventy years dies, and he won't make peace with his children when he's dying?

Tread carefully. "Dad, it was really nice hearing about your dolly with the purple gown."

He pulls the straw out to speak. "White lace collar."

He thought the world of that dolly. Good. He's there. Maybe he'll get talking about what things were really like. "And her dark hair in a bun," I prompt.

He nods. I'm getting nowhere.

"It was nice to get to know you a little better when you told Cecilia and me about your dolly. Your dolly seemed to mean a lot to you."

He nods, from far away, as he drinks, but says nothing.

I have an urge to randomly mention everything that seems loaded with emotion, like boxing, catching mice, Grandma bathing him. But, obviously, I'm the one with the problem, not him. He's not the one needing to talk. And he's sick, and I had my chance. So, of course, there does come a time in life when looking back—going back over it all—is over, Marie. Accept that. Let him be.

"Would you like to sleep?"

"I would." He lets the straw fall into the empty glass. I put the glass on the bedside table, pull the light blanket up on him.

"Okay. I'll put your head back a little and turn off the light.

He sighs, closes his eyes, smiles, and says, "Thank you. You don't know the good you do."

My eyes well up. "Thanks Dad. That's a nice thing to say." I feel guilty for being such a meddler. "I meddle a lot. I'm pretty pushy sometimes."

"You never are," he says sleepily.

How sweet. "Thanks, Dad."

He's like a baby these days. Awake for a little while, and then he sleeps.

I'm done. For real this time. No more digging.

The next evening after work, exhausted and cranky from not eating right, because I'm always on the go, I get a fast-food fish burger and eat on my way to Calm Shores to see Dad. I'm emotionally drained. That's what's wrong. And I feel bad, but the truth is I hope Dad passes on soon. He'll be in a better place, and I can get on with my life. What a terrible way to think. But it's true. I want to write so badly, but there's no time. All I can do is dash off thoughts in my journal. I wonder how he is tonight. There's no way he got out of bed today.

When I get to Calm Shores, Dad's not in his room. I get frantic thinking someone took him somewhere, maybe the hospital. He's always in the hall or his room. I wanted him to die, but not without me.

I go to the nurse at the desk. "My dad's not in his room."

"No. He was up and around, feeling better today. He spent a lot of time in the lobby. I'll call his aide."

Up and around? "Thanks," I say, a little disappointed to hear he's bounced back.

In a few minutes his aide hurries down the hall from the other side of the facility.

"She's looking for her father, Mr. Wells," the nurse says.

"Oh. I think he went to the dining room."

Why did they let him go on his own? "Thanks. I'll look for him there." I hurry down the long hall of polished linoleum, recalling how fragile he was the day before. Why don't they hover around him? Don't they know how fragile he is? Well apparently, he wasn't fragile today.

What's wrong with me? I'm unhappy with everything tonight.

Anyway, everyone who lives here is fragile, Marie.

Well, evidently, he isn't, if he took himself down to the dining room long after dinner. Why did he? He's never done that before.

I get to the dining room. All the tables are cleared, and the dining room's empty except there's someone at the far side of the room. I go nearer. It's Dad, in his wheelchair, only partly visible, because most of him is bent way under a table. I walk near, lean down, and see him repeatedly snatch at something under the table, but I see nothing there.

Amazing, he's up and about after being so sick yesterday.

But he's never done anything like this before. Dementia's setting in. I'll get him out of there, take him back to his room. Don't startle him.

"Hi Dad," I say. I pull up a chair and sit down close to him in his wheelchair.

"Marie? Is that you?"

"Yes. What are you doing?" I ask.

"I can't, I can't quite get her."

"I see. Can I help you?" I lean down to be able to see under the table.

"Yeah. She's right there." He snatches at the dark space on the far side of the underside of the table.

I bend way down to look closer, but see nothing. "Who's there, Dad?"

"My dolly."

"Oh!" Oh dear. What have I done? "I'm sorry. I don't see her there."

His hand darts forcefully up under the table. "She's right there."

I shouldn't have talked so much about his dolly. It wasn't good for him with the dementia coming on.

"Dad, this is the dining room. I don't think she's here under the table." I'll bring him back to the moment. "Come on, I'll help you get out of there. Would you like to go lie down on your bed?"

Most of him is under the table. He usually moves his feet to push his wheelchair to comply when I ask him to come away from somewhere, but he's not moving his feet this time.

Instead, he holds his hand still in mid-air close to the bottom side of the table top, like he's deciding something in the dim light.

Suddenly, I hear a strange, loud sound come from Dad's lungs. He goes silent, takes a breath, wails loudly and bursts into loud frantic sobs.

I catch my breath as a lifetime of savage sorrow breaks the dam inside him and floods our world. How can I comfort him? My hand hovers near his back, but I'm afraid if I touch him, the touch will interrupt him. I don't want to interrupt him. But that's not fair. Cecilia comforted me when Mom was dying. She put her arm around me. It helped. It was good for me to let her comfort me.

I rest my hand on his back while he cries so hard it seems he can't speak. Tears are good, they need to be spent. But how long do I let him cry?

Until he's done.

Does he need me, the way a child needs a parent to help them stop crying?

"Let me help you come out from there, Dad."

He moves backward with his feet, but only two inches. He stays under the table, begins to murmur something through his sobs.

"What is it, Dad?"

"They should never have done that to a four-year-old boy!" he cries.

I feel sick. "What did they do Dad?"

He sobs.

"Dad, what did they do?" I say, softly touching his shoulder.

He weeps, trembles, catches his breath to talk. "They took my dolly away."

He wails softly.

Tears flood my eyes. She was everything to him. "I'm so sorry." What do I say? "Did your big sister take her?"

He shakes his head no, sobbing. "Mom." He takes a deep breath. "And Dad."

"I'm so sorry."

My neck aches from leaning under the table. I don't know how he's managing it.

He nods, takes a deep breath. "Well, they picked the night," he says through his tears, his voice weak, still under the table, still sobbing. His hand punctuates the air as he speaks to mark exactly how it happened. "Everyone was there. Mom." He nods. "Dad, my sister."

I imagine Dad, four years old, in Grandma and Grampa's living room, roses in the carpet, and an old-fashioned radio.

"Come here, Eddie," Dad says in an eerie, high-pitched coaxing woman's voice. He's mimicking his mother's voice. "Come here. You knew this was the night. Give her to me."

He sobs.

"Eddie, you remember," he says in his mother's voice, "this is the night. Give me your dolly."

He softly wails.

How sad they did that to him.

"Dad, I'm so sorry they took your dolly away."

He shakes his head, as if in disbelief of what happened. He doesn't shrug this time with his usual palms up, what-can-you-do expression. He nods, seems to let the truth go in. He takes a deep breath, and quietly sobs, nodding.

He slowly comes out from under the table, using his feet to back up. He raises his head the best he can after being so bent over.

This was what he needed. Not writing letters to his kids. No. He needed the memory of the night he had to give his dolly away. It may have been repressed all these years. This could be the base of his mountain of pride, along with getting bathed by his mom all those years, the trauma that twisted all his relationships.

He looks exhausted.

"Would you like to go lie down, Dad?"

"Very much."

I push him back to his room, help him to bed, cover him up. He closes his eyes.

I sit in his wheelchair beside him, while he, smaller than ever, sleeps. And yet I'm the one who's at rest, at last. He let me see his most vulnerable self. We're connected, at last.

Watching him sleep, I ache to help him heal the wound left by them taking his dolly.

Why don't I make him a dolly with a purple gown, a white lace collar and brown hair in a bun? I'll find a doll with dark hair, sew the dress by hand. She must have had a satin dress the way his eyes light up talking about it. Finding a tiny lace collar will be tricky. I have to hurry. He could be gone soon.

CHAPTER 44
WHERE ARE THE OTHERS?

June, 2010. A few nights later.

Baker watches as I empty onto the wool living room rug the contents of a Beverly Fabrics bags: purple satin fabric, purple thread, and a small bag from an antique store with a vintage baby dress. "And here's the doll." I pull a new doll with long dark curls out of a department store bag.

"You're going to make him a doll with a purple gown," says Baker.

"And white lace collar," I say, reaching into the small antique store bag and pulling out a baby dress with a lace collar. "It's just something I want to do. It's for me."

"No, it's for him," Baker says. "You can't help it, dear."

Nothing can get in my way. I don't know why I'm obsessed. I'm going to make a purple gown by copying the plaid dress the doll's wearing, add the collar, et voila.

Baker says a few more things, but I don't hear him. I'm getting my scissors and a good needle.

Don't be scared. Just measure and cut with enough room for a seam. Leave it open in the back so it's easy to slip on, and put a button, two buttons to hold it. It's not like he's going to play with her. I just want him to have her.

The floodgates open as I begin. Baker's gone in the other room watching ball.

"I just want Dad to have her before he dies," I murmur, looking at my supplies from behind a veil of water. I cut off a piece of purple fabric for a sleeve, twice as big as it seems it should be, so there's enough for gathers. I see how it goes. I don't have to measure. "How long does it take to die when your head is cut off, Dad?" I murmur, sobbing, remembering asking him that when I was five. "Oh, instantly," I see and hear him say. I see his shiny white cuffs. His happy face at the dinner table.

I can't see through the flood of tears pouring out. How can that much water be in our eyes? My dad is going to die. I always worried about Mom dying, never you, Dad. Sorry. I thought it would be a relief. I never thought it would hurt like this.

I hold the fabric to the doll's chest, eyeball it, then cut the semi-circle for the neck. It was so hard, living with you, Dad. I hold the fabric against the doll, wipe my eyes with my sleeve so I can see, look where the arms go, and cut, my hands shaking. The electric jolts of your hands on me left me electrified my whole life, but I don't care now. Now I have you at last, you who you really are. But now you're leaving.

Tears pulse steadily as I work and talk in whispers, lovingly running the tips of my fingers over the purple satin. I see in the fabric the painful truth of my life and of his. My heart bursts with love for us both. Every sob digs deeper until all the old pain is scooped out of me it seems. I take three deep breaths and sigh deeply three times. I already miss the dad I lost over fifty years ago, who I got back, and am losing again. I never thought this would happen.

Well. It has happened. I have gotten him back. My lion, tame now.

I sew. My forehead's hot. I brush my hair back with my wrist. A little dramatic, but why not? Yes, why not?

Because my life's not dramatic, it's real and I can push my hair back if I want and I don't need some inner critic's commentary about being a little dramatic. Whoever is making fun of me pushing my hair, I say please go sit down and be quiet. Have some tea.

Oh dear! I cut the fabric too small! I thought I cut it big enough. It doesn't close in the back. Darn it!

That's okay. Sew an extra flap, I hear Mama say with a smile. It won't show anyhow. Problem solved.

Two hours later the dress is finished, white lace collar and all. I slip it onto the doll, get bobby pins from the bathroom, put her hair in a bun. I don't know if the sleeves were supposed to be long but that's how I made them. She's ready. I hope he likes her.

The next evening, getting ready to go see Dad, I drop the doll wearing the purple gown with white lace collar into the department store bag.

The phone rings.

"Well, the fever's back. But they're not giving him antibiotics, this time," Cecilia says. "He's on hospice and he's comfortable."

"Okay." Tears well up. "Thanks. I'm on my way there now." Everyone knows he can't get better without antibiotics.

At Calm Shores, I walk down the hall toward Dad's room. The nurse smiles at me from the nurses' station across from his room. "He ate some dinner and seems to be getting better," she says brightly.

Something in her tone says this is what we all need to believe, so nature can take its course, because otherwise, we'll get in the way.

"Good news," I say.

I go into Dad's room. He's in bed. "Hi Dad!"

"Well, hi, Marie. Where are the others?" he says sleepily.

I'm conflicted about no antibiotics, though not enough to speak up. Dad himself said no antibiotics, but that was when he wasn't dying, only planning his funeral.

"Your other children?"

"Yah, I thought there'd be more of you coming."

"Oh. Well, I think they'll be along. I'm not sure when. They know you're not well. I think they had to make arrangements."

"Oh. Sure, sure." He has that wincing tone of disappointment.

"I brought something for you." I hope no one comes in. I'm embarrassed because suddenly the doll seems absurd. It means way too much to me. What if it means nothing to him?

"Oh?"

"Here."

I pull the doll out of the bag and hand her to him. I look for a light of recognition in his eyes. There is none. He has no expression.

"I made her for you, since they took your dolly with a purple gown away from you."

"Oh?"

He looks at the doll, doesn't seem to know what I'm talking about.

"Well, all right," he says, handing her back.

"I'll just put her here beside you," I say, tears welling up as I lay the doll beside him.

"Okay."

What did you expect?

I'm insane. Not because I did it, but because it meant so much to me to do it. I live in a fantasy world where everything means so much when it actually doesn't. It doesn't mean anything—get it?

"She probably looks different than the one you had," I say. I'm a trespasser in his private world.

"Do you know when the others might be coming?" he asks.

He's tired of me. I'm not who he needs to see. He always sees me. His dolly's in another world. The door to that world closed. Why do I feel so hurt? He's very sick and wants his other children. Grow up. Of course, he wants the others.

The doll seems to crowd him. Did I think a doll like this could somehow fix what happened that horrible night?

"I don't know where the others are, but I'll give them a call and let them know you'd like to see them," I say.

"Well, suit yourself."

That's old irritated Dad, not new sweet Dad I've gotten to know. "So, you don't have to have the doll here on your bed," I say. He might feel embarrassed, a man with a doll.

"Yeah, put it over there, if you wouldn't mind." Old Dad.

"Okay." I blink back tears, put her on the nightstand with the other things that hold little interest for him these days—the CD player, dog books, religious books.

Well, obviously making the doll was for me. Something I had to go through. His eyes close.

"Goodnight, Dad. I'll tell the others you'd like to see them."

"Thank you," he says.

I kiss his forehead. He smiles, warm with fever.

That night I tell all my siblings Dad wants to see them. They'll make plans to come.

Chapter 45
I'm Not a Quitter

June 2010

The next day I can't wait to see Dad. I'm over the doll hurt. I can't bear to go to work knowing he's sick and alone, so I take the day off and get there before lunch. He's in bed sleeping.

"Hi Dad," I say, all my hurt feelings gone. I glance around. The doll is gone!

He opens sparkling eyes and his face lights up as though it's been years since he's seen me. I feel his fever on his forehead.

"Little Marie, good to see you."

"Good to see you, Dad. Good news—most of your kids are coming to see you on Sunday."

"That's wonderful."

"Madeline won't be able to travel down. Her back's giving her trouble."

"I see."

"How's your dad?" Bill, his roommate, asks.

"Oh, he's got a fever. I need to get him something for it."

"Poor old soul," says Bill. "How old is your Dad?"

"He'll be ninety-four in October."

The doll's on Bill's night stand. I feel relieved.

"Well, we're not going to live forever, that's for darn sure!" Bill says.

"Nope, we're not." I smile at Dad.

Dad smiles too, closes his eyes.

"*We… have … to …die!* That's all there is to it. I'm ready to go right now!" Bill adds.

Dad's still smiling, so I guess the dying monologue is okay.

"I've had a good life," Bill says. "I don't have any regrets. Well, maybe a few. But what can you do? Live your life the best you can and then you're gone! That's that. It's *over!*" he says pounding the arm of his wheel chair for emphasis.

Dad grins.

"Do you believe in heaven?" I ask Bill, wondering if Dad still does. After all the years of talking about Jesus and the martyrs and heaven, Dad seems to have nothing to say about it all anymore.

"Heaven? No. No. I don't think so. When you're gone, you're gone," Bill says.

"I believe in heaven," I say. "And a loving God who takes you there."

"You do?" Bill asks.

"I do. Do you believe there's a God?" I ask.

"Oh sure, sure, there's probably something."

"I think so," I say. "I think God is loving and it doesn't make sense to have us go through life and all its hardship just to let us die and that's it. I believe in heaven." I believe that, but I'm spelling it out in case it'll help Dad not be worried about dying.

"Well, you could be right," Bill says. "You could be right."

Dad smiles, eyes still closed.

"Is that what you believe, Dad?"

"Pretty much," he murmurs, barely audible.

"What'd he say?" asks Bill.

"He says he pretty much believes the same thing about heaven."

"Well, it'd be nice." Bill chuckles softly. "How old is your Dad?"

"Ninety-three."

"Ninety-three! God *bless* him! And how old am I?"

"Ninety."

"*Ninety!?* And he's Ninety-three? The poor soul. But that's the way life is. You go along day after day, and then you get sick, and *you bounce back!*" He shakes his head in disgust. "But then the day comes," he says on a brighter note, "and it comes for all of us. You don't bounce back, and things start going wrong. First one organ, then another, and another. Until—well, *finally,* you die! But why can't I just *lay down and not wake up*? Just die in my sleep."

"That's what you'd like?"

"Hell yes! I'm *old.* I'm ready. How old am I?"

"Well let's see, you were born in …"

"Nineteen twenty."

"Okay. And this is 2010. So that'd be …"

"A hundred! Am I a hundred?"

"Not quite. You're ninety."

"That'd be quite an accomplishment. Live to a hundred. Are there very many people that are a hundred?"

"Not too many. Most of us go before a hundred," I say.

"How old is your dad?" Bill asks.

"Ninety-three."

"Well, he's on his way to a hundred," Bill says with a note of admiration.

An aide brings Dad his lunch. It's steaming hot.

"Your Dad going to eat?" Bill asks.

"I think he'll eat a little bit."

The aide and I pull Dad up in bed, raise the foot and the head.

"Would you like some milk, Dad?" I ask, knowing it will make phlegm, but that it's about the only nourishment he'll take. He nods and with shaking lips takes two sips of his milk.

"Do you want to try a bit of chicken?" I ask.

"Yes," he murmurs, so softly I barely hear.

I feed him a bite and then realize it was too big. He looks up at me to get my attention.

"It should be a very small amount," he instructs, and smiles.

"Would you like to try another bite?" I ask.

"Not at the moment. But don't stop asking me." I strain to hear his faint murmur.

"Okay." I survey the tray. Ground broccoli. Rice. Prune juice.

"I could use some ice water," he says.

I pour some. He drinks a few ounces.

"Would you like to try some pureed chicken?"

He nods.

"I'll be right back," I say, and find the aide who returns in less than five minutes with a big bowl of piping hot pureed chicken.

I feed him a bite, but he flinches.

"Hot," he says.

"I'm so sorry." What was I thinking? I should have tried it.

He smiles. "Make sure the next one is not too hot."

I like being instructed by my dad for the last few times ever, like I'm a child.

"He's eating that, is he?" Bill says tenderly.

"Yes."

"God *bless* him!"

An aide comes to take Bill to the dining room.

"Have a good day!" He sings gleefully with a salute as she wheels him out the door.

"You too!" I say.

I offer Dad more chicken. He shakes his head no.

"Would you like some chocolate?"

"Oh!" he says with delight, probably for my benefit.

I give him a morsel of a Three Musketeers someone left on his bedside table.

"Jean wanted to bring you a chocolate cake for a belated Father's Day present, but wasn't sure if you could eat it. I told her bring it anyway. She's bringing it Saturday."

"You said a very wise thing," he whispers.

"Would you like another bite of chocolate?"

"Not now," he says so lightly I struggle to hear.

"Ok. Water?"

He nods.

He sips, and pauses to look up at me. "Don't give up on me," he says. "I'm not a quitter."

"I won't give up on you," I say, feeling remorse, because I have given up on him.

He needs to say don't give up on him, and I need to promise I won't, but we're both lying. I can't believe he wants to bounce back again. I can't believe I'm letting him go. I can hardly bear it, but it's what I'm doing.

Maybe it was a mistake not to give him another round of antibiotics. It wasn't really my call. I didn't argue. I'm not arguing now. He said no antibiotics.

"You are not a quitter, Dad," I say. That's what matters to him, that I know he's not a quitter.

He smiles, closes his eyes.

CHAPTER 46
I LOVE YOU, I LOVE YOU, I LOVE YOU

June 27, 2010

The next day, Dad's immobile again, able to just murmur and cough up phlegm. I undertake the arduous task of scooping phlegm from his mouth, cleaning inside his cheeks.

"Thank you. I feel better," he says.

The aide feeds him some of a nutritional drink. I put his bed down a bit so he can rest again.

His eyes close.

"You're a little better today. It'll take a little time, but you'll bounce back," I say, trying to encourage him, because he said he's not a quitter. "And you have three days to do it, because remember, Jean's bringing you a chocolate cake on Saturday. She found a great recipe that calls for chocolate chips!"

But he seems to be deep asleep, now.

I sit in silence beside him for half an hour, grateful to be with him.

Suddenly, his eyes open wide.

He raises his head with strength that seems to come out of nowhere.

He could be dying right now. Adrenaline shoots through me.

"Dad?"

He points, wide-eyed to the space before him, jabbing the air to draw my attention to what he sees.

I study the space toward the foot of the bed, like I'm going to see it too, whatever it is, but I see nothing. "What is it?" I ask.

"A ship! A ship is coming!" he says.

I struggle to think of something to say. "Wow," I say lamely, wanting to hold his head for him which must be heavy on his scrawny neck, but afraid to make his vision disappear by touching him.

I want it to go on and on, but he relaxes back into his pillow and again I feel useless. I'm sure it was his ship coming for him. But it's too personal to speak of that, it seems. All I can think of is how he had wanted to be a merchant seaman as a young man, but he became a Catholic convert and had ten children instead.

"You always wanted to be a merchant seaman, didn't you?" I say, lamely again, because I can't keep quiet and can't bring myself to say what I really think—it's his ship coming for him.

He takes that in a moment, and nods.

Saturday comes. Everyone, except Madeline, has come. Dad's dying. We all have pieces of the richest chocolate cake I've ever tasted. All except Dad. He's in a coma. I want a moment alone with him to say good-bye without people around, but it's embarrassing to say so. Instead, I say, "How about anyone who wants to spend a few minutes alone with Dad, go ahead." Several do.

I take my turn, stroke his head. "I love you so much. Thank you for loving me. Don't worry about anything and don't worry about me. I'll miss you." I choke back tears.

I leave the room and feel glad. There's nothing else to do. Only live my life, enjoy my siblings. I let him go.

We siblings are pretty raucous, laughing in the night around his bed, and at peace. The strain of sixty years comes out in jokes and muffled howls of laughter. I think he probably appreciates it all.

Some of us sleep on the mats in the physical therapy room. I'm exhausted but can't break the surface tension of new doubts. Did I do the wrong thing? He didn't want antibiotics, but then he said don't give up on him. Should I have argued for another round of antibiotics? I doze, irritated with the feeling I'll never get things right.

Well. I'm dehydrated. Maybe that's all it is.

The next day we gather in his room. His roommate agrees to sit in the hall so we can have the space. But Dad's his roommate. Bill should get to stay. But I'm not in charge.

Dad will die today, in about four hours, the nurse said a few hours ago. She could tell by the mottling of his feet.

Nine of his children are gathered around his bed. We chat quietly. Someone brought the little Saint Therese relic—a bit of hair and sliver of bone on satin under a small circle of glass facing out from a gold enclosure on a gold stand. It's on the bedside table. I don't know if it's real, or if relics of saints really have power of themselves, but it gives everything meaning: when we were children, Dad blessed us with the relic with all the reverence and solemnity of a pope. Those blessings are what I feel now.

I watch Dad struggle for each breath. How can God let us suffer for days without food or water? Dad is skeletal, almost overnight. Why is it so hard to die? His breaths have grown far apart. He's going soon.

I'm too exhausted to feel sad or scared. I want to sing "I've Been Loving you a Little too Long to Stop Now," because I want to tell Dad that, I've been loving him a little too long to stop now. But I'm embarrassed to say I want to sing.

Martin moistens Dad's lips with a little sponge. He takes the relic and blesses Dad the way Dad used to bless us, touching the clinking glass to Dad's forehead, chest, one shoulder and then the other. Everyone is softened, it seems.

"Marie, why don't you sing?" Sarah asks.

God bless her. "Thank you. I would love to sing."

"But wait until Patricia gets back."

Patricia's husband wanted them to go to Mass. How can I wait? What if he dies before I can sing?

But here comes Patricia!

Martin puts the relic in Dad's hand. Dad clutches it.

I close my eyes and sing, "I've Been Loving You a Little too Long to Stop Now."

At the end of the first verse, Patricia says, *"Look!"*

I look. Dad has opened his eyes! His mouth forms words without sound: "I love you, I love you, I love you."

He sighs, closes his eyes, and is gone.

❀

Epilogue

It's September and I have once again performed the ritual of shopping for brown leather round-toe shoes to mark the Fall, though I've never found the right ones. I've found ankle boots with round toes and brown shoes with long toes, but no brown shoes with round toes.

My oldest sadness—missing childhood—usually off to the side, a bother to no one, beckons me now to tether myself to the past. I go to the past by longing harder. People say be in the now, but I feel utter despair at the thought of *always* being present—you mean never go visit myself who lives in the past?

A little girl in a brand-new navy-blue uniform, a part of me so split off she needs an invitation to come to the present, has come from my longing. She comes every Fall, but she'll always live in the past. As the wind picks up and night falls, she walks me down a rainy street toward a big house with yellow lights in the windows. She's going to make her father happy by taking off his shoes and rubbing his stocking feet. She'll peel potatoes and whip powdered milk with water in a giant aluminum pan with a pour spout, without making lumps, the best she can, a hopeless endeavor, though a valiant effort, with her mother nearby in a secret life, wearing an apron, silent in her own thoughts and fears, distractedly acknowledging the girl's efforts when the girl persists in showing her mother the milk. The mother is otherwise impervious to the ebb— and mostly flow—of the girl's relentless anxieties.

I was but one of the many sets of waves in the tide that pushed and pulled on my mother who was pregnant almost half my young life and deathly sick when I was fourteen months old. I was handed off for weeks, to which relative in those frantic days of survival no one recalls. The only clear thing is the girl in navy blue is *not* moving away from the wind-blown rain-soaked street or the house with yellow lights in the windows, where her devoted mother smiles down on her, and her tame lion sleeps in his chair, with a migraine.

Dear Reader,

I'm glad you've joined me in my world of books. I hope you enjoyed LION TAMER MEMOIR: How It All Turned Out: The Love that Healed Trauma (Man in the Red Jacket, Mountain of Pride, Dolly with the Purple Gown). Please leave a review on vendor sites. Nothing sells books more than good word of mouth, and I would be so, so grateful for any words you might be willing to leave!

If you enjoyed following along with Marie (myself), you may want to read the prequel, LION TAMER MEMOIR: How It All Began (Here I Am, Steel, Not the Kind of Girl You Marry).

The prequel opens on a dinner table scene. "'How long does it take to die when your head is cut off?'" I ask Dad at the dinner table. I'm five years old. I hope he likes my question. Martyrs are his favorite subject." How does Marie try to win her father's affection when, later on, he roars like a lion? What happens when he begins traveling as a salesman and is gone for months at a time? The steel cylinder that protects her heart, which you already read about in How It All Turned Out, grows one night when she wakes to her father's hands. Her early love affairs, alcohol and self-harm become salves for overwhelming emotions. When she accidentally sets her bed on fire at nineteen living in her own rented room, her oil paints set up, a bottle of whiskey on the dresser, she makes a decision.

Another book follows that prequel: LION TAMER MEMOIR: The Inevitable Cauldron (Van Gogh's Cadillac, Angel's Storm, Bear Creek Road). In it, through many attempts to have a "real life," Marie grows, at a cost. But she still has a hole within where a connection with her father belongs.

The fourth and last book is LION TAMER MEMOIR: The Elusive Sense of Self (Bend This Pain into Meaning, The Yellow Sponge, Tightwire). In it, Marie begins the climb from the quicksand of childhood conditioning to the solid ground of self-nurture and nurturing others. It ends where LION TAMER MEMOIR: How It All Tuned Out begins, on her way to a therapist office, ready to do whatever it takes to end the mortal dread of abandoning herself again and again.

I hope you enjoy all the LION TAMER MEMOIR books (these next three are scheduled to be released in 2023). Watch for them on my website:theresemarieduncan.com

And look for them at your favorite vendors.

Meanwhile, let's all curl up and enjoy a good book!

Best wishes,

Therese Marie Duncan

Made in the USA
Monee, IL
03 January 2023

20140483R00198